INFORMATION AND INFORMATION STABILITY OF RANDOM VARIABLES AND PROCESSES

HOLDEN–DAY SERIES IN TIME SERIES ANALYSIS

Gwilym M. Jenkins
Emanuel Parzen
Editors

by M. S. Pinsker

Laboratory for Information Transmission Systems

Academy of Sciences, USSR

INFORMATION AND INFORMATION STABILITY OF RANDOM VARIABLES AND PROCESSES

translated and edited by Amiel Feinstein

HOLDEN–DAY, INC. *San Francisco, London, Amsterdam* 1964

Originally published as INFORMATSIYA I INFORMATSIONNAYA USTIOCHIVOST' SLUCHAINYKH VELICHIN I PROTSESSOV by the Academy of Science, USSR, Moscow, 1960.

Library of Congress Catalog Card Number: 64-14623

Printed in the United States of America

Translator's Preface

This translation has benefited substantially from the author's friendly cooperation not only in giving prompt attention to various queries from the translator, but also in sending several pages of corrections and minor revisions in the text, for which I express my sincere thanks. These changes served to eliminate essentially all outstanding differences of opinion between author and translator; a minor remaining one is taken up in the Remarks to Chapter 3.

A number of basic results which are used here either appear solely in Russian journals, or else are scattered about in various English language publications, often with a lesser degree of generality than is required. For this reason, all of the necessary proofs have been included in the Remarks following various chapters, which also contain some further comments which seemed pertinent.

Amiel Feinstein
Sunnyvale, Calif.

Author's Preface

The theory of information is a comparatively young but rapidly developing science. Following the appearance of the fundamental work of C.E. Shannon and W. Weaver [36] there have appeared a large number of papers devoted to various areas of this theory. In particular, a significant number of works has been devoted to: (1) studying the properties of the basic concepts of the theory of information; (2) proving basic theorems; and (3) calculating information. Among the many such works we should call attention to the articles and books of C.E. Shannon [34, 35, 36], B. McMillan [21], A.I. Khinchin [15, 16], A.N. Kolmogorov, I.M. Gelfand, A.M. Yaglom [8, 9, 18, 19] and R.L. Dobrushin [3].

The present work is directly related to this series of papers. However, almost all of these investigations consider the case of discrete time and discrete state spaces. At the same time, situations are frequently encountered in applications, for example in radiotechnica, in which both time and the state space are continuous. Of particular importance is the case of gaussian processes. Under actual conditions the noise which limits the rate of transmission of information is, as a rule, well described by such processes.

Our intention here is to give a mathematical basis for the application of the ideas of information theory to such situations, and also to obtain effective solutions for a number of informational problems.

The methods of this book which relate to the study of stationary random processes, as well as the results obtained, may be of interest for the theory of stationary random processes, independent of their value for the theory of information.

In Parts I and II we try to give a systematic account, with adequate mathematical rigor, of the properties of the information density, information and information rate of random variables and processes. Much of Parts I and II is given over to the study of criteria for information stability, which play a large role in the proofs of the basic theorems of information theory.

Almost half of this book, namely Part III, is devoted to calculating the information, information rate, and also the higher moments of the information density of gaussian random variables and processes. Necessary and sufficient conditions are established for information stability and for the convergence of the distribution of the information density to a normal distribution.

Throughout the entire book it is shown that the concepts of information density, information, information rate, information stability, etc., are special cases of the more general concepts of entropy density, entropy, entropy rate, and entropy stability, etc.

Various properties of the entropy density, entropy, entropy rate and entropy stability of random variables and processes are stated.

For gaussian random variables and processes certain very general formulae are obtained which enable one to find, in a number of cases, the distribution of the entropy density, to compute the entropy, entropy rate and the second moment of the entropy density, and also to establish the entropy stability and the convergence of the distribution of the entropy density to a normal distribution. These results can be used to solve problems of mathematical statistics concerning random processes, in particular the problem of recovering a signal in the presence of noise.

We assume of the reader a rather good introduction in the areas of measure theory and the theory of stationary random processes (for example, to the extent of the books [4, 12, 39]). Due to the large number of formulas which are worked out, this book may also be useful to specialists who do not posses all of the mathematical prerequisites.

I consider it my pleasant duty to express my sincere appreciation to A.N. Kolmogorov for drawing my attention to the questions considered here, and to A.A. Kharkevich and I.A. Ovseevich for their assistance in the writing of this book.

M. S. Pinsker

Table of Contents

PART II INFORMATION RATE AND INFORMATION STABILITY OF RANDOM VARIABLES

Chapter 7 Information Rate of Stationary Random Processes: General Case

Chapter 8 Information Stability of Stationary Random Processes

PART III INFORMATION, INFORMATION RATE, AND INFORMATION STABILITY OF GAUSSIAN RANDOM VARIABLES AND PROCESSES

Chapter 9 Information and Information Stability of Gaussian Random Variables

PART I

Information and information stability of random variables

In Part I we discuss the properties of information density, information, conditional information, and information stability of random variables. The concepts of entropy density, entropy, and entropy stability of a pair of distributions are introduced and certain of their properties are formulated. The relation between the information density and information of a random variable, and the entropy density and entropy of one distribution with respect to another is also established.

Most of the results presented here are contained in the papers of C.E.Shannon [36], A.N.Kolmogorov, I.M.Gelfand, A.M.Yaglom [8, 18], A.Y.Khinchin [16], and R.L.Dobrushin [3]. Proofs of results which are to be found in the work of Dobrushin will be omitted.*

* These proofs are included in the remarks following Chapters 2 and 3.–Tr.

Chapter 1 Probability spaces

For the most part, this chapter contains, with certain complements, a discussion of the definitions and properties of various basic concepts of probability theory. Our treatment is similar to that of [3].

1.1. PROBABILITY SPACES

The pair (Ω, S_ω) consisting of a set Ω and a σ-algebra S_ω of subsets of Ω is called a **measurable space**. Any finite system $\{E_i\}$ of disjoint sets E_i which belong to S_ω, and whose union is the whole space Ω, will be called a **partition** of the measurable space (Ω, S_ω) or simply a partition of Ω. If each member of a given partition is **entirely contained** in some member of a second partition, the first partition is said to be a **subpartition** of the second.

Let $\tilde{\omega} = f(\omega)$ be a function defined on the measurable space (Ω, S_ω), with values in the measurable space $(\tilde{\Omega}, S_{\tilde{\omega}})$. For any set $\tilde{E} \in \tilde{\Omega}$ we denote by $\tilde{E}^{-1} = f^{-1}(\tilde{E})$ the set of points $\omega \in \Omega$ for which $f(\omega) = \tilde{\omega} \in \tilde{E}$. If for every $\tilde{E} \in S_{\tilde{\omega}}$, the set $f^{-1}(\tilde{E}) \in S_\omega$, we will call $f(\omega)$ **a measurable function**. The set $\tilde{E}^{-1} = f^{-1}(\tilde{E}) \in S_\omega$ will be called the **inverse image**, or **cylinder set** in the space Ω, corresponding to the set $\tilde{E}$.

A measurable space (Ω, S_ω), together with a probability measure P defined on the σ-algebra S_ω will be called a **probability space** (Ω, S_ω, P). A σ-subalgebra S'_ω of the σ-algebra S_ω is **everywhere dense** in S_ω with respect to P, if for every $E \in S_\omega$ there is an $E' \in S'_\omega$ such that

$$P\{E \Delta E'\} = 0, \qquad \text{where} \qquad E\Delta E' = (E - E')(E' - E). \qquad (1.1.1)$$

Let $\{E_i\}$ $i = 1, \ldots, n$ be a partition of Ω. We choose sets $E'_i \in S'_\omega$ such that $P\{E_i \Delta E'_i\} = 0$, and set

$$E''_i = E'_i - \bigcup_{k=1}^{i-1} E'_k, \quad 1 \leqslant i < n; \qquad E''_n = \Omega - \bigcup_{k=1}^{n-1} E'_k.$$

Clearly $\{E''_i\}$ is a partition of Ω, and $P\{E_i \Delta E''_i\} = 0$, i.e., for any partition $\{E_i\}$, $E_i \in S_\omega$, there is a partition $\{E''_i\}$, $E''_i \in S'_\omega$ such that $P\{E_i \Delta E''_i\} = 0$.

1.2. RANDOM VARIABLES

A measurable function $\xi(\omega)$, defined on a probability space (Ω, S_ω, P) and taking values in a measurable space (X, S_x), is called a **random variable**. The **probability distribution** $P_\xi(\cdot)$ of the random variable ξ is defined by

$$P_\xi(E) = P\{\xi(\omega) \in E\} = P\{\omega \in E^{-1}\}, \quad E \in S_x. \tag{1.2.1}$$

If (X, S_x) and (Y, S_y) are two measurable spaces, their **product** $(X \times Y, S_x \times S_y)$ consists of the space $X \times Y$ of all pairs (x, y), $x \in X$, $y \in Y$ and the σ-algebra $S_x \times S_y$, generated by all sets $E \times F$ of pairs (x, y) with $x \in E$, $y \in F$ and $E \in S_x$, $F \in S_y$.

A pair ξ, η of random variables may be regarded as a single random variable (ξ, η) with values in the product space $X \times Y$. The distribution $P_{(\xi\eta)}(\cdot) = P_{\xi\eta}(\cdot)$ of (ξ, η) is called the **joint distribution** of the random variables ξ and η. By the **product** of the distributions $P_\xi(\cdot)$ and $P_\eta(\cdot)$, denoted by $P_{\xi\times\eta}(\cdot)$, is meant the distribution defined on $S_x \times S_y$ such that

$$P_{\xi\times\eta}(E \times F) = P_\xi(E) P_\eta(F) \tag{1.2.2}$$

for $E \in S_x$ and $F \in S_y$. If the joint distribution $P_{\xi\eta}(\cdot)$ coincides with the product distribution $P_{\xi\times\eta}(\cdot)$, the random variables ξ and η are said to be **independent**.

Similarly, a sequence $\xi_1, \xi_2, \ldots$ of random variables, with values in (X_1, S_{x_1}), (X_2, S_{x_2}), ... respectively, may be regarded as a **single** random variable $(\xi_1, \xi_2, \ldots) = \{\xi_i\} = \xi$ with values in the measurable space $X_1 \times X_2 \times \ldots = \mathop{\times}\limits_{i=1}^{\infty} X_i = X$ consisting of sequences $(x_1, x_2, \ldots)$, together with the σ-algebra $S_{x_1} \times S_{x_2} \times \ldots = \mathop{\times}\limits_{i=1}^{\infty} S_{x_i} = S_x$ generated by sets of the form $E = \mathop{\times}\limits_{i=1}^{\infty} E_i$, $E_i \in S_{x_i}$ where only a finite number of the E_i are different from X_i.

Finally, any collection of random variables $\xi_\tau, \tau \epsilon N$ (where N may be any arbitrary set, for example the real line) may be regarded as a single random variable with values in the space $X = \underset{\tau \epsilon N}{\times} X_\tau$ consisting of all $x = \{x_\tau\}$, $x_\tau \epsilon X_\tau$, together with the σ-algebra $S_x = \underset{\tau \epsilon N}{\times} S_{x_\tau}$ generated by all sets of the form $E = \underset{\tau \epsilon N}{\times} E_\tau$, $E_\tau \epsilon S_{x_\tau}$, where only a finite number of the E_τ are different from X_τ.

Let ξ be a random variable with values in the measurable space (X, S_x), and let $y = f(x), x \epsilon X$ be a measurable function with values in the measurable space (Y, S_y). Then the composite function $\eta = f(\xi) = f[\xi(\omega)]$ will be measurable with respect to the space (Ω, S_ω), and is therefore a random variable, which from now on will be called a **measurable function** of the random variable ξ. A random variable η which is a measurable function $\eta = f(\xi)$ of the random variable ξ is **everywhere dense** in ξ, if the σ-algebra consisting of cylinder sets $E = f^{-1}(F) \epsilon S_x$ is everywhere dense in S_x with respect to the measure $P_\xi(\cdot)$. A random variable η is **subordinate** to the random variable ξ, if ξ is everywhere dense in the random variable (ξ, η). A random variable η which is a measurable function $\eta = f(\xi)$ of a random variable ξ is obviously subordinate to ξ.

We exhibit some examples of functions of random variables.
(1) If $\xi = \{\xi_\tau\}$, then each random variable ξ_τ is a function of the random variable ξ.
(2) If $S_y = S_x$ and $\eta = \xi$ with probability one, then both η and ξ are everywhere dense in (η, ξ); in other words, ξ and η are subordinate to each other.
(3) Let η be a measurable function of ξ and $\zeta = (\xi, \eta)$; then ξ is everywhere dense in ζ, or equivalently, ξ and ζ are subordinate to each other.
(4) Let $\xi_i, i = 1, 2, \ldots$ be random variables taking values in the measurable spaces (X_i, S_{x_i}), where X_i is the real line, and S_{x_i} is the σ-algebra of the Borel sets; i.e., the ξ_i are one-dimensional random variables. If $\xi_1, \xi_2, \ldots$ converges with probability one, it is well known that there exists a family Ψ of one-dimensional random variables such that with probability one

$$\xi_\infty(\omega) = \lim_{n \to \infty} \xi_n(\omega), \ \xi_\infty \epsilon \Psi \tag{1.2.3}$$

and any two members of Ψ are equal with probability one. The random variable $\xi = (\xi_1, \xi_2, \ldots)$ is everywhere dense in the random variable $\xi' = (\xi_\infty, \xi_1, \xi_2, \ldots)$. More generally, if $\xi_1, \xi_2, \ldots$ converges in probability, i.e.,

$$\lim_{n \to \infty} P\{|\xi^n - \xi_{n+m}| > \epsilon\} = 0, m > 0, \epsilon > 0, \tag{1.2.4}$$

uniformly in $m > 0$, then there exists a family Ψ of one-dimensional random variables such that for any $\xi_\infty \epsilon \Psi$ the random variables $\xi_1, \xi_2, \ldots$ converge in probability to ξ_∞, and any two members of Ψ are equal with probability one. The random variable $\xi = (\xi_1, \xi_2, \ldots)$ is everywhere dense in $\xi' = (\xi_\infty, \xi_1, \xi_2, \ldots)$.

We remark that a particular instance of convergence in probability is convergence in mean square, defined by

$$\lim_{n \to \infty} \mathbf{E}(\xi_n - \xi_{n+m})^2 = 0 \tag{1.2.5}$$

uniformly in $m > 0$.

(5) If $\xi = \{\xi_t\}$, $t \epsilon N$ and $\xi' = \{\xi'_\tau\}$, $\tau \epsilon K$, where N and K are arbitrary sets, and if for every $\tau \epsilon K$ the random variable ξ is everywhere dense in $\xi^\tau = (\xi, \xi_\tau)$, then ξ is everywhere dense in (ξ, ξ').

The proofs of the assertions made in the preceding examples are simple and straightforward, and hence will be omitted.

1.3. THE VARIATION OF DISTRIBUTIONS

Let $P_1\{\cdot\}$ and $P_2\{\cdot\}$ be two probability measures defined on the measurable space (Ω, S_ω). The measure P_1 is said to be **absolutely continuous** with respect to the measure P_2, if $P_2\{E\} = 0$ for some $E \epsilon S_\omega$ implies that $P_1\{E\} = 0$. It then follows from the Radon-Nikodym theorem [38] that P_1 may be expressed as an integral with respect to P_2,

$$P_1\{E\} = \int_E a(\omega) P_2\{d\omega\}, \tag{1.3.1}$$

which holds for every $E \epsilon S_\omega$. The function $a(\omega)$ is called the **density** (or **derivative**) of P_1 with respect to P_2 and is denoted by

$$a(\omega) = \frac{P_1\{d\omega\}}{P_2\{d\omega\}}. \tag{1.3.2}$$

The measure P_1 is said to be **singular** with respect to P_2 if there exists a set $C \epsilon S_\omega$ such that $P_1\{C\} = 1$ and $P_2\{C\} = 0$.

In the general case there exists a set $C \epsilon S_\omega$ such that for every $E \epsilon S_\omega$ we have

$$P_1\{E\} = \int_E a(\omega) P_2\{d\omega\} + P_1\{EC\} \quad \text{and} \quad P_2\{C\} = 0. \tag{1.3.3}$$

The set $\Omega - C$ is called the **set of absolute continuity of** P_1 **with respect to** P_2.

The **variation** of a probability measure P_1 with respect to the probability measure P_2 is defined as

$$V(P_1, P_2) = V(P_2, P_1) = \sup \sum_i |P_1\{E_i\} - P_2\{E_i\}|, \tag{1.3.4}$$

where the supremum is taken over all partitions $E = \{E_i\}$ of Ω. We show that

$$V(P_1, P_2) = \int_\Omega |a(\omega) - 1| P_2\{d\omega\} + P_1\{C\} \tag{1.3.5}$$

where $a(\omega)$ and C are defined as in (1.3.3).

Let $\{E_i\}$ be any partition of Ω, and consider the subpartition consisting of the sets $\overline{K}_i = E_i C$, $K_{i1} = E_i N_1$, $K_{i2} = E_i N_2$, where $N_1, N_2 \subseteq (\Omega - C)$ are defined by the conditions $a(\omega) \geqslant 1$ and $a(\omega) < 1$ respectively. Since it is clear that $\sum_i |P_1\{E_i\} - P_2\{E_i\}|$ can only increase under subpartitioning, it follows that

$$V(P_1, P_2) = \sup \left(\sum_{i,j} |P_1\{K_{ij}\} - P_2\{K_{ij}\}| + \sum_i |P_1\{\overline{K}_i\} - P_2\{\overline{K}_i\}|\right). \tag{1.3.6}$$

Furthermore, since $\overline{K}_i \subseteq C$,

$$P_2\{\overline{K}_i\} \leqslant P_2\{C\} = 0 \text{ and } \sum_i |P_1\{\overline{K}_i\} - P_2\{\overline{K}_i\}| = \sum_i P_1\{\overline{K}_i\} = P_1\{C\}. \tag{1.3.7}$$

According to (1.3.3), we have

$$|P_1\{K_{ij}\} - P_2\{K_{ij}\}| = \left|\int_{K_{ij}} a(\omega) P_2\{d\omega\} - P_2\{K_{ij}\}\right| = \left|\int_{K_{ij}} (a(\omega) - 1) P_2\{d\omega\}\right|$$

and since $a(\omega) - 1$ has a fixed sign on each set K_{ij}, it follows that

$$|P_1\{K_{ij}\} - P_2\{K_{ij}\}| = \int_{K_{ij}} |a(\omega) - 1| P_2\{d\omega\}$$

and

$$\sum_{i,j} |P_1\{K_{ij}\} - P_2\{K_{ij}\}| = \sum_{i,j} \int_{K_{ij}} |a(\omega) - 1| P_2\{d\omega\} = \int_{\Omega - C} |a(\omega) - 1| P_2\{d\omega\}. \tag{1.3.8}$$

A comparison of (1.3.6), (1.3.7) and (1.3.8) proves (1.3.5).

TRANSLATOR'S REMARKS TO CHAPTER 1

The concepts of "everywhere dense" and "subordinate" for random variables have been defined by conditions on certain σ-algebras in the value spaces of the random variables. It is both simple and convenient to map these conditions back into the probability space Ω on which the random variables are defined. Let us denote by $\beta(\{\xi_\tau\})$ the smallest σ-algebra in Ω with respect to which every member of a given family $\{\xi_\tau\}$ of random variables is measurable. Then the random variable η is subordinate to the random variable ξ if and only if $\beta(\xi)$ is everywhere dense in $\beta(\eta)$. The proof of this assertion is a straightforward application of standard facts concerning measurable transformations. We notice that the concept "η is everywhere dense in ξ," which is simply the union of "η is a function of ξ" and "ξ is subordinate to η," appears rather superfluous; however, the author uses it to good purpose as a stepping stone in proving a number of important results.

Using the necessary and sufficient condition just stated, the assertions following (1.2.3) and (1.2.4) are an immediate consequence of the following:

(1) If $\xi = (\xi_1, \xi_2, \ldots)$, then $\beta(\xi) = \beta(\xi_1, \xi_2, \ldots)$. This is **not** merely a matter of notation, as ξ is **not** a short notation for the family $\{\xi_1\}$; but it is easy enough to show.

(2) If a sequence of random variables which are measurable with respect to some σ-algebra $\mathscr{F} \in S_\omega$ converges to a random variable ξ either in probability or pointwise almost everywhere, then $\mathscr{F}$ is everywhere dense in $\beta(\xi)$. This is a completely standard result in measure theory (e.g., Halmos [12], Sections 21, 22).

In this connection we may mention the following result (cf. Doob [4], p. 603): If η is subordinate to $\xi = (\xi_1, \ldots, \xi_n)$, where η, $\xi_1, \ldots, \xi_n$ are real valued random variables, then η is a measurable function of ξ. It is not hard to show that this result also holds if ξ is made up of any infinite family of real random variables.

Chapter 2 Information

This chapter is mainly concerned with defining the concept of information and examining some of its properties. We shall follow the treatment given in [3], supplying more details only in the case of certain properties of information which are not adequately discussed there.

2.1. DEFINITION AND VARIOUS EXPRESSIONS FOR THE INFORMATION

Let ξ and η be random variables with values in the measurable spaces (X, S_x) and (Y, S_y) respectively. By the **information** of one of these variables with respect to the other is meant the value [3, 8, 18, 36]

$$I(\xi, \eta) = \sup_{i,j} \Sigma P_{\xi\eta}(E_i \times F_j) \log \frac{P_{\xi\eta}(E_i \times F_j)^*}{P_\xi(E_i)P_\eta(F_j)}, \tag{2.1.1}$$

where the supremum is taken over all partitions $\{E_i\}$ of X and $\{F_j\}$ of Y. The quantity $I(\xi, \xi) = H(\xi)$ is called the **entropy** of the random variable ξ.

The sets $E_i \times F_j$ in (2.1.1) form a special type of partition of $X \times Y$, i.e., a **partition by means of rectangles.** The following theorem of R.L.Dobrushin shows that this restriction is not necessary.

THEOREM 2.1.1. Let $\mathscr{L}$ be an algebra contained in $S_x \times S_y$ which generates the σ-algebra $S_x \times S_y$, and let R be a family of

---

*The logarithm will always be taken to the base e.

partitions of $X \times Y$ *consisting of sets belonging to* $\mathscr{L}$. *Then, if every partition consisting of sets from* $\mathscr{L}$ *has a subpartition which belongs to* R, *we have:*

$$I(\xi, \eta) = \sup_R \sum_i P_{\xi\eta}(E_i) \log \frac{P_{\xi\eta}(E_i)}{P_{\xi \times \eta}(E_i)}. \tag{2.1.2}$$

The conditions of the theorem are obviously satisfied if R consists of every partition of $X \times Y$, i.e.,

$$I(\xi, \eta) = \sup \sum_i P_{\xi\eta}(E_i) \log \frac{P_{\xi\eta}(E_i)}{P_{\xi \times \eta}(E_i)}. \tag{2.1.3}$$

If ξ and η are one-dimensional random variables, then the sets E_i and F_j in (2.1.1) can be taken as intervals.

In actually obtaining the value of the information, the following result due to I.M.Gelfand, A.M.Yaglom and A.Perez [24, 27] plays an important role.

THEOREM 2.1.2. (1) If the distribution $P_{\xi\eta}$ *is not absolutely continuous with respect to the distribution* $P_{\xi \times \eta}$, *then* $I(\xi, \eta) = \infty$. *(2) If the distribution* $P_{\xi\eta}$ *is absolutely continuous with respect to* $P_{\xi \times \eta}$, *then*

$$I(\xi, \eta) = \int_{X \times Y} \log a_{\xi\eta}(x, y) P_{\xi\eta}(dxdy) = \int_{X \times Y} i_{\xi\eta}(x, y) P_{\xi\eta}(dxdy), \tag{2.1.4}$$

where $a_{\xi\eta}(x, y)$ *is the density of* $P_{\xi\eta}(\cdot)$ *with respect to* $P_{\xi \times \eta}(\cdot)$.

The function $i_{\xi\eta}(x, y) = \log a_{\xi\eta}(x, y)$ is called the **information density** of the random variables ξ and η. Formula (2.1.4) is meaningful, since the integral of the negative part of $i_{\xi\eta}(x, y)$ is not less than $-1/e$.

The expressions $a_{\xi\eta}(\xi, \eta)$ and $i_{\xi\eta}(\xi, \eta) = \log a_{\xi\eta}(\xi, \eta)$ are measurable functions of the random variable (ξ, η) and are therefore themselves random variables, which we will denote by

$$a_{\xi\eta}(\xi, \eta) = a(\xi, \eta), \qquad i_{\xi\eta}(\xi, \eta) = i(\xi, \eta)$$

dropping subscripts. Obviously

$$I(\xi, \eta) = Ei(\xi, \eta). \tag{2.1.5}$$

In many cases it is easy to obtain the form of $i_{\xi\eta}(x, y)$. If the spaces X and Y contain countably many points $x_1, x_2, \ldots$ and

$y_1, y_2, \ldots$, and if S_x and S_y consist of all subsets of X and Y, then

$$i_{\xi\eta}(x_i, y_j) = \log\frac{P_{\xi\eta}(x_i, y_j)}{P_\xi(x_i)P_\eta(y_j)}; \qquad I(\xi, \eta) = \sum_{i,j} P_{\xi\eta}(x_i, y_j)\log\frac{P_{\xi\eta}(x_i, y_j)}{P_\xi(x_i)P_\eta(y_j)}. \tag{2.1.6}$$

However, if the distributions $P_\xi(\cdot)$, $P_\eta(\cdot)$ and $P_{\xi\eta}(\cdot)$ are given in terms of densities $p_\xi(x)$, $p_\eta(y)$ and $p_{\xi\eta}(x, y)$ with respect to some measures $\mu_x(\cdot)$, $\mu_y(\cdot)$ and $\mu_x(\cdot) \times \mu_y(\cdot)$ defined on (X, S_x), (Y, S_y) and $(X \times Y, S_x \times S_y)$ (e.g., if X and Y are finite-dimensional spaces and μ_x, μ_y are Lebesgue measure), then

$$i_{\xi\eta}(x, y) = \log\frac{p_{\xi\eta}(x, y)}{p_\xi(x)p_\eta(y)} \tag{2.1.7}$$

and

$$I(\xi, \eta) = \int_{X\times Y} p_{\xi\eta}(x, y)\log\frac{p_{\xi\eta}(x, y)}{p_\xi(x)p_\eta(y)}\mu_x(dx)\mu_y(dy). \tag{2.1.8}$$

2.2. BASIC PROPERTIES OF INFORMATION

(1) $I(\xi, \eta) \geqslant 0.$ (2.2.1)

$I(\xi, \eta) = 0$ *if and only if* ξ *and* η *are independent.*

(2) $I(\xi, \eta) = I(\eta, \xi).$ (2.2.2)

(3) If the random variables $\xi = (\xi_1, \xi_2)$ *and* $\eta = (\eta_1, \eta_2)$ *are independent, then:*

$$I((\xi_1, \eta_1), (\xi_2, \eta_2)) = I(\xi_1, \xi_2) + I(\eta_1, \eta_2), \tag{2.2.3}$$

and with probability one

$$i((\xi_1, \xi_2), (\eta_1, \eta_2)) = i(\xi_1, \xi_2) + i(\eta_1, \eta_2). \tag{2.2.4}$$

(4) If the random variable $\eta = f(\zeta)$ *is a measurable function of the random variable* ζ, *then*

$$I(\xi, \eta) \leqslant I(\zeta, \eta). \tag{2.2.5}$$

(5) If $\xi = (\xi_1, \xi_2, \ldots)$, *then*

$$I(\xi, \eta) = \lim_{n\to\infty} I((\xi_1, \ldots, \xi_n), \eta). \tag{2.2.6}$$

PROOF. If the random variables $\eta, \xi_1, \xi_2, \ldots$ take values in the measurable spaces (Y, S_y), (X_1, S_{x_1}), $(X_2, S_{x_2}), \ldots,$ then the random variable $\xi = (\xi_1, \xi_2, \ldots)$ takes values in the measurable space $(X_1 \times X_2 \times \ldots, S_{x_1} \times S_{x_2} \times \ldots) = (X, S_x)$. Since $(\xi_1, \xi_2, \ldots, \xi_n)$ is a function both of the random variable $(\xi_1, \ldots, \xi_n, \xi_{n+1})$ and of the random variable ξ, it follows that

$$I(\xi, \eta) \geqslant ((\xi_1, \ldots, \xi_n, \xi_{n+1}), \eta) \geqslant I((\xi_1 \ldots, \xi_n), \eta), \tag{2.2.7}$$

and consequently

$$I(\xi, \eta) \geqslant \lim_{n \to \infty} I((\xi_1, \ldots, \xi_n), \eta). \tag{2.2.8}$$

In order to prove the reverse inequality, we note that on the one hand, the algebra $\mathscr{L}$ consisting of finite sums of sets of the form

$$E_1 \times E_2 \times \ldots \times E_n \times X_{n+1} \times \ldots \times F; \; E_1 \in S_{x_1}, E_2 \in S_{x_2}, \ldots, F \in S_y, \tag{2.2.9}$$

generates the σ-algebra $S_x \times S_y$; and on the other hand, for every partition of $X \times Y$ consisting of elements of $\mathscr{L}$, there is a subpartition consisting of sets of the form (2.2.9).

Therefore, by Dobrushin's theorem we may take the supremum in (2.1.1) only over partitions $\{N_j\}$ consisting of sets of the form (2.2.9), i.e.,

$$I(\xi, \eta) = \sup_{\{N_j\}} \sum_j P_{\xi\eta}(N_j) \log \frac{P_{\xi\eta}(N_j)}{P_{\xi \times \eta}(N_j)}. \tag{2.2.10}$$

Now let the partition $\{N_j\}$ be fixed. Since $\{N_j\}$ consists of a finite number of elements, we may choose n so large that every N_j is of the form (2.2.9) with the same n. If we use the identities

$$P_{\xi_1 \xi_2 \ldots \xi_n}(E_1 \times E_2 \times \ldots \times E_n) = P_\xi(E_1 \times E_2 \times \ldots \times E_n \times X_{n+1} \times \ldots);$$

$$P_{\xi_1 \xi_2 \ldots \xi_n \eta}(E_1 \times E_2 \times \ldots \times E_n \times F) = P_{\xi\eta}(E_1 \times E_2 \times \ldots \times E_n \times X_{n+1} \times \ldots \times F);$$

it follows that for every sum on the right side of (2.2.10) there is an n such that this sum is equal to some sum appearing in (2.1.1) for $I((\xi_1, \ldots, \xi_n), \eta)$.
Thus

$$I(\xi, \eta) \leqslant \overline{\lim_{n \to \infty}} I((\xi_1 \ldots, \xi_n), \eta) \tag{2.2.11}$$

which, combined with (2.2.8), yields (2.2.6).

(6) Let $\xi_1, \xi_2, \ldots, \xi$ *and* η *be random variables taking values in the spaces* (X, S_x) *and* (Y, S_y) *respectively. Then if the distribution* $P_{\xi_i\eta}$ *converges to the distribution* $P_{\xi\eta}$, *we have*

$$I(\xi, \eta) \leqslant \lim_{n\to\infty} I(\xi_n, \eta). \tag{2.2.12}$$

PROOF. By the convergence of distributions is meant that for every $N \epsilon S_x \times S_y$

$$\lim_{n\to\infty} P_{\xi_n\eta}(N) = P_{\xi\eta}(N). \tag{2.2.13}$$

Thus for any fixed partitions $\{E_i\}$ and $\{F_j\}$ of X and Y which satisfy $P_\xi(E_i) \neq 0, P_\eta(F_j) \neq 0$

$$\lim_{n\to\infty} \sum_{i,j} P_{\xi_n\eta}(E_i \times F_j) \log \frac{P_{\xi_n\eta}(E_i \times F_j)}{P_{\xi_n}(E_i)P_\eta(F_j)}$$

$$= \sum_{i,j} P_{\xi\eta}(E_i \times F_j) \log \frac{P_{\xi\eta}(E_i \times F_j)}{P_\xi(E_i)P_\eta(F_j)}. \tag{2.2.14}$$

The desired result now follows by comparing (2.2.14) with (2.1.1), which defines information.

2.3 INFORMATION

For future use in deriving a series of results, it will be important to exhibit various relations between the quantity of information $I(\xi, \eta) = \int_{X\times Y} i_{\xi\eta}(x, y)P_{\xi\eta}(dxdy)$ and $T(\xi, \eta)$, the mathematical expectation of the absolute value of the information density $i(\xi, \eta)$,

$$T(\xi, \eta) = \int_{X\times Y} |i_{\xi\eta}(x, y)|P_{\xi\eta}(dx\,dy) = \mathbf{E}|i(\xi, \eta)|. \tag{2.3.1}$$

We note first of all that since the integral with respect to the measure $P_{\xi\eta}$ of the negative part of the function $i_{\xi\eta}(x, y)$ is not less than $-1/e$, then

$$T(\xi, \eta) \leqslant I(\xi, \eta) + \frac{2}{e}. \tag{2.3.2}$$

For small values of $I(\xi, \eta)$ the following inequality proves to be useful:

$$T(\xi, \eta) \leqslant I(\xi, \eta) + \Gamma\sqrt{I(\xi, \eta)}, \tag{2.3.3}$$

where Γ is a positive constant which does not depend upon (ξ, η).

To verify (2.3.3) it suffices to show that the integral of the negative part of $i_{\xi\eta}(x, y)$ with respect to $P_{\xi\eta}$ is not less than $-\Gamma_1\sqrt{I(\xi, \eta)}$, where $\Gamma_1 > 0$ is a fixed number.

Let Q_ϵ denote the set of points (x, y) for which $i_{\xi\eta}(x, y) < -\epsilon$ and consider the expression

$$P_{\xi\eta}(Q_\epsilon)\log\frac{P_{\xi\eta}(Q_\epsilon)}{P_{\xi\times\eta}(Q_\epsilon)} + (1 - P_{\xi\eta}(Q_\epsilon))\log\frac{1 - P_{\xi\eta}(Q_\epsilon)}{1 - P_{\xi\times\eta}(Q_\epsilon)}. \tag{2.3.4}$$

This sum (corresponding to the partition of $X \times Y$ into Q_ϵ and $X \times Y - Q_\epsilon$) has the same form as the sums appearing in the definition (2.1.1) of the information $I(\xi, \eta)$. Hence (2.3.4) is not greater than $I(\xi, \eta)$. Further, since $i_{\xi\eta}(x, y) = \log a_{\xi\eta}(x, y) < -\epsilon$ for $(x, y)\epsilon Q_\epsilon$,

$$\frac{P_{\xi\eta}(Q_\epsilon)}{P_{\xi\times\eta}(Q_\epsilon)} = \frac{\int_{Q_\epsilon} a_{\xi\eta}(x, y)P_{\xi\times\eta}(dx\, dy)}{P_{\xi\times\eta}(Q_\epsilon)} = \frac{\int_{Q_\epsilon} e^{i_{\xi\eta}(x, y)}P_{\xi\times\eta}(dx\, dy)}{P_{\xi\times\eta}(Q_\epsilon)}$$

$$\leqslant \frac{\int_{Q_\epsilon} e^{-\epsilon}P_{\xi\times\eta}(dx\, dy)}{P_{\xi\times\eta}(Q_\epsilon)} = e^{-\epsilon}. \tag{2.3.5}$$

Combining (2.3.5) with the remark that (2.3.4) does not exceed $I(\xi, \eta)$, we conclude that $P_{\xi\eta}(Q_\epsilon)$ does not exceed the supremum over all values of u which satisfy the system of inequalities

$$\begin{cases} u \log \dfrac{u}{r} + (1 - u) \log\dfrac{1 - u}{1 - r} \leqslant I(\xi, \eta); \\ \dfrac{u}{r} \leqslant e^{-\epsilon}; \qquad 0 \leqslant u \leqslant r \leqslant 1. \end{cases} \tag{2.3.6}$$

Differentiating the left side of the first of the above inequalities with respect to u, we see that it is a decreasing function of u for $u \leqslant r$. Thus, without decreasing the supremum over u, we may replace the inequality $u/r \leqslant e^{-\epsilon}$ by the equality $u = re^{-\epsilon}$. Substituting $r = ue^{\epsilon}$ into the first of the inequalities (2.3.6), we obtain instead of (2.3.6) the inequality

$$-u\epsilon + (1 - u) \log\frac{1 - u}{1 - ue^{\epsilon}} \leqslant I(\xi, \eta); \qquad 0 \leqslant u \leqslant 1 \tag{2.3.7}$$

We estimate the term $\log\dfrac{1 - u}{1 - ue^{\epsilon}}$ by using the inequality $\log u \geqslant 1 - 1/u$. The result is

$$\log\frac{1-u}{1-ue^{\epsilon}} \geqslant 1-\frac{1-ue^{\epsilon}}{1-u} = \frac{u(e^{\epsilon}-1)}{1-u}.$$

Substituting $\frac{u(e^{\epsilon}-1)}{1-u}$ for $\log\frac{1-u}{1-ue^{\epsilon}}$ in (2.3.7), we obtain the inequality

$$u(-\epsilon+e^{\epsilon}-1) \leqslant I(\xi,\eta). \tag{2.3.8}$$

It follows, from what we have done, that every value u which satisfies the system (2.3.6) also satisfies (2.3.8), and therefore $P_{\xi\eta}(Q_\epsilon)$ does not exceed the largest value of u satisfying (2.3.8). Thus:

$$P_{\xi\eta}(Q_\epsilon) \leqslant u_{\max} \leqslant \frac{I(\xi,\eta)}{e^{\epsilon}-1-\epsilon} < \frac{I(\xi,\eta)}{\epsilon^2/2} \tag{2.3.9}$$

We can now estimate the integral with respect to $P_{\xi\eta}$ of the negative part of $i_{\xi\eta}(x,y)$, which may be written in the form

$$\int_{i_{\xi\eta}(x,y)<0} i_{\xi\eta}(x,y)P_{\xi\eta}(dx\,dy) = \int_{-\sqrt{I(\xi,\eta)}\leqslant i_{\xi\eta}(x,y)<0} i_{\xi\eta}(x,y)P_{\xi\eta}(dx\,dy)$$

$$+\int_{i_{\xi\eta}(x,y)<-\sqrt{I(\xi,\eta)}} i_{\xi\eta}(x,y)P_{\xi\eta}(dx\,dy). \tag{2.3.10}$$

Obviously

$$\int_{-\sqrt{I(\xi,\eta)}\leqslant i_{\xi\eta}(x,y)<0} i_{\xi\eta}(x,y)P_{\xi\eta}(dx\,dy) \geqslant \int_{X\times Y} -\sqrt{I(\xi,\eta)}P_{\xi\eta}(dx\,dy)$$

$$= -\sqrt{I(\xi,\eta)} \tag{2.3.11}$$

and

$$\int_{i_{\xi\eta}(x,y)<-\sqrt{I(\xi,\eta)}} i_{\xi\eta}(x,y)P_{\xi\eta}(dx\,dy) = \int_{-\infty}^{-\sqrt{I(\xi,\eta)}} \epsilon\, d_\epsilon P\{i(\xi,\eta)\leqslant\epsilon\}.$$

$$= \int_{-\infty}^{-\sqrt{I(\xi,\eta)}} \epsilon\, d_\epsilon P_{\xi\eta}(Q_{-\epsilon}) \geqslant \int_{-\infty}^{-\sqrt{I(\xi,\eta)}} \epsilon\, d_\epsilon \frac{2I(\xi,\eta)}{\epsilon^2} \tag{2.3.12}$$

$$= -\int_{-\infty}^{-\sqrt{I(\xi,\eta)}} \frac{4I(\xi,\eta)}{\epsilon^2}d\epsilon = -4\sqrt{I(\xi,\eta)}.$$

Comparing (2.3.10) with (2.3.11) and (2.3.12), we obtain

$$\int_{i_{\xi\eta}(x,y)<0} i_{\xi\eta}(x,y)P_{\xi\eta}(dx\,dy) \geqslant -\Gamma_1\sqrt{I(\xi,\eta)}, \tag{2.3.13}$$

where Γ_1 is a fixed number.

As mentioned earlier, (2.3.3) follows from (2.3.13), and (2.3.3) in turn enables us to estimate the variation $V(P_{\xi\eta}, P_{\xi\times\eta})$ of the measures $P_{\xi\eta}$ and $P_{\xi\times\eta}$ in terms of the information $I(\xi,\eta)$. In fact, we will establish the inequality

$$V(P_{\xi\eta}, P_{\xi\times\eta}) \leqslant 2T(\xi,\eta). \tag{2.3.14}$$

It clearly suffices to verify (2.3.14) for the case when $I(\xi,\eta) \leqslant T(\xi,\eta) < \infty$, and hence when $P_{\xi\eta}$ is absolutely continuous with respect to $P_{\xi\times\eta}$.

Let E be the set of (x, y) on which $a_{\xi\eta}(x, y) \geqslant 1$, and let $\overline{E}$ denote the complement of E. Using equation (1.3.5), we write the following chain of equalities:

$$\begin{aligned} V(P_{\xi\eta}, P_{\xi\times\eta}) &= \int_{X\times Y} |a_{\xi\eta}(x, y) - 1| P_{\xi\times\eta}(dx\, dy) \\ &= \int_E (a_{\xi\eta}(x, y) - 1) P_{\xi\times\eta}(dx\, dy) + \int_{\overline{E}} (1 - a_{\xi\eta}(x, y)) P_{\xi\times\eta}(dx\, dy) \\ &= (P_{\xi\eta}(E) - P_{\xi\times\eta}(E)) + (P_{\xi\times\eta}(\overline{E}) - P_{\xi\eta}(\overline{E})) = 2(P_{\xi\eta}(E) - P_{\xi\times\eta}(E)) \\ &= 2\int_E (a_{\xi\eta}(x, y) - 1) P_{\xi\times\eta}(dx\, dy). \end{aligned} \tag{2.3.15}$$

The last step follows from

$$\begin{aligned} &(P_{\xi\eta}(E) - P_{\xi\times\eta}(E)) - (P_{\xi\times\eta}(\overline{E}) - P_{\xi\eta}(\overline{E})) \\ &= (P_{\xi\eta}(E) + P_{\xi\eta}(\overline{E})) - (P_{\xi\times\eta}(E) + P_{\xi\times\eta}(\overline{E})) = 1 - 1 = 0. \end{aligned}$$

Moreover, using standard results of integration theory, we obtain

$$\begin{aligned} &\int_E (a_{\xi\eta}(x, y) - 1) P_{\xi\times\eta}(dx\, dy) \\ &= \int_E \left(1 - \frac{1}{a_{\xi\eta}(x, y)}\right) P_{\xi\eta}(dx\, dy) \leqslant \int_E \log a_{\xi\eta}(x, y) P_{\xi\eta}(dx\, dy) \\ &\leqslant \int_{X\times Y} |i_{\xi\eta}(x, y)| P_{\xi\eta}(dx\, dy) = T(\xi, \eta). \end{aligned} \tag{2.3.16}$$

Comparing (2.3.15) and (2.3.16) proves (2.3.14).

COROLLARY. If $\lim_{n\to\infty} I(\xi_n, \eta_n) = 0$, *then* $\lim_{n\to\infty} V(P_{\xi_n\eta_n}, P_{\xi_n\times\eta_n}) = 0$.

Finally we establish an inequality which is in a certain sense the reverse of (2.3.14), i.e.

$$P_{\xi\eta}\{|i_{\xi\eta}(x, y)| \leqslant \epsilon\} \geqslant 1 - V(P_{\xi\eta}, P_{\xi\times\eta})\frac{1+\epsilon}{\epsilon}; \qquad \epsilon > 0, \tag{2.3.17}$$

or what amounts to the same thing,

$$P_{\xi\eta}\{|i_{\xi\eta}(x, y)| > \epsilon\} \leqslant V(P_{\xi\eta}, P_{\xi\times\eta})\frac{1+\epsilon}{\epsilon}. \tag{2.3.18}$$

PROOF. The inequality

$$|\log a_{\xi\eta}(x, y)| = |i_{\xi\eta}(x, y)| > \epsilon \tag{2.3.19}$$

is equivalent to

$$\log a_{\xi\eta}(x, y) > \epsilon \qquad \text{or} \qquad \log a_{\xi\eta}(x, y) < -\epsilon \tag{2.3.20}$$

Furthermore, since $\epsilon \geqslant \log(1+\epsilon)$ and $\log a_{\xi\eta}(x, y) \geqslant 1 - \frac{1}{a_{\xi\eta}(x, y)}$, at any point (x, y) for which (2.3.20) holds the inequality

$$\log a_{\xi\eta}(x, y) > \log(1+\epsilon) \qquad \text{or} \qquad 1 - \frac{1}{a_{\xi\eta}(x, y)} < -\epsilon \tag{2.3.21}$$

will also hold. Transforming (2.3.21), we obtain the following equivalent inequalities:

$$a_{\xi\eta}(x, y) > 1 + \epsilon \qquad \text{or} \qquad 1 - \frac{1}{a_{\xi\eta}(x, y)} < -\epsilon \tag{2.3.22}$$

$$\frac{1}{a_{\xi\eta}(x, y)} < \frac{1}{1+\epsilon} \qquad \text{or} \qquad 1 - \frac{1}{a_{\xi\eta}(x, y)} < -\epsilon \tag{2.3.23}$$

$$1 - \frac{1}{a_{\xi\eta}(x, y)} > \frac{\epsilon}{1+\epsilon} \qquad \text{or} \qquad 1 - \frac{1}{a_{\xi\eta}(x, y)} < -\epsilon \tag{2.3.24}$$

It follows that the set of points (x, y) which satisfy (2.3.24), and hence (2.3.18), is contained in the set K of points which satisfy

$$1 - \frac{1}{a_{\xi\eta}(x, y)} > \frac{\epsilon}{1+\epsilon} \tag{2.3.25}$$

i.e.,

$$P_{\xi\eta}\{|i_{\xi\eta}(x, y)| > \epsilon\} \leqslant P_{\xi\eta}\{|1 - \frac{1}{a_{\xi\eta}(x, y)}| > \frac{\epsilon}{1+\epsilon}\} = P_{\xi\eta}(K). \tag{2.3.26}$$

It remains to estimate $P_{\xi\eta}(K)$. Letting N denote the set of points where $a_{\xi\eta}(x, y) = 0$, we have

$$P_{\xi\eta}(N) = \int_N a_{\xi\eta}(x, y) P_{\xi\times\eta}(dx\,dy) = \int_N 0 \cdot P_{\xi\times\eta}(dx\,dy) = 0, \tag{2.3.27}$$

and therefore

$$P_{\xi\eta}(\hat{K}) = P_{\xi\eta}(K - KN) = P_{\xi\eta}(K) \tag{2.3.28}$$

where $\hat{K} = K - KN$.

According to (1.3.5), (2.3.26) and (2.3.28),

$$V(P_{\xi\eta}, P_{\xi\times\eta}) = \int_{X\times Y} |a_{\xi\eta}(x, y) - 1| P_{\xi\times\eta}(dx\,dy)$$

$$\geqslant \int_{\hat{K}} |a_{\xi\eta}(x, y) - 1| P_{\xi\times\eta}(dx\,dy)$$

$$= \int_{\hat{K}} |a_{\xi\eta}(x, y) - 1| \frac{P_{\xi\eta}(dx\,dy)}{a_{\xi\eta}(x, y)} = \int_{\hat{K}} \left|1 - \frac{1}{a_{\xi\eta}(x, y)}\right| P_{\xi\eta}(dx\,dy)$$

$$\geqslant \int_{\hat{K}} \frac{\epsilon}{1+\epsilon} P_{\xi\eta}(dx\,dy) = \frac{\epsilon}{1+\epsilon} P_{\xi\eta}(\hat{K}) \geqslant \frac{\epsilon}{1+\epsilon} P_{\xi\eta}\{|i_{\xi\eta}(x, y)| > \epsilon\} \tag{2.3.29}$$

which is precisely (2.3.18).

Remark Inequalities (2.3.17) and (2.3.18) remain valid even if $P_{\xi\eta}$ is not absolutely continuous with respect to $P_{\xi\times\eta}$. All that is required is to replace the whole space $X \times Y$ by the set K of absolute continuity of $P_{\xi\eta}$ with respect to $P_{\xi\times\eta}$.

COROLLARY. *If* $\lim_{n\to\infty} V(P_{\xi_n\eta_n}, P_{\xi_n\times\eta_n}) = 0$, *then* $i(\xi_n, \eta_n)$ *converges in probability to zero.*

2.4 ENTROPY

Let us consider how the information changes if $\xi = \eta$. In this case the information $I(\xi, \eta) = I(\xi, \xi)$, as was stated earlier, is called the **entropy** $H(\xi)$. If the entropy is finite, then $P_{\xi\xi}$ must be absolutely continuous with respect to $P_{\xi\times\xi}$, so that for $E, F \in S_x$ we have

$$P_\xi(EF) = P_{\xi\xi}(E \times F) = \int_{E\times F} a_{\xi\xi}(x, y) P_{\xi\times\xi}(dx\,dy). \tag{2.4.1}$$

Since $EF = 0$ implies $P_{\xi\xi}(E \times F) = P_\xi(EF) = 0$, it follows from (2.4.1) that $a_{\xi\xi}(x, y) = 0$ for $x \neq y$, and consequently

$$P_\xi(E) = P_\xi(EE) = P_{\xi\xi}(E \times E) = \int_{E\times E} a_{\xi\xi}(x, y) P_\xi(dx) P_\xi(dy)$$
$$= \int_E P_\xi(x) a_{\xi\xi}(x, x) P_\xi(dx). \tag{2.4.2}$$

Thus, we see that the measure P_ξ is concentrated on distinct points $x_1, x_2, \ldots$ and that $P_\xi(x) a_{\xi\xi}(x, x) = 1$, i.e., $a_\xi(x) = a_{\xi\xi}(x, x) = 1/P_\xi(x)$ for $x = x_1, x_2, \ldots$, so that

$$H(\xi) = E \log a(\xi, \xi) = E \log a(\xi) = E \log \frac{1}{P_\xi(\xi)}$$

$$= \sum_{n=1}^{\infty} P_\xi(x_n) \log \frac{1}{P_\xi(x_n)} = - \sum_{n=1}^{\infty} P_\xi(x_n) \log P_\xi(x_n).$$

The function $h_\xi(x) = \log a_{\xi\xi}(x, x) = \log 1/P_\xi(x) = -\log P_\xi(x)$ is called the **entropy density** of ξ, and is different from zero only on the countable set of point $x_1, x_2, \ldots$ for which $P_\xi(x_1), P_\xi(x_2), \ldots \neq 0$.

For our purposes, it will be convenient to generalize the concept of entropy (though without a very complete analysis) so that information becomes a special case of entropy. Details concerning this generalization have been considered by S.Kullback [20], A.Perez [24, 27] and M.Rosenblat-Rot [33].

Let P_1 and P_2 be two probability measures defined on the same measurable space (Ω, S_ω) and let $\{E_i\}$ be a partition of Ω. We define the **entropy** $H_{P_2}(P_1)$ of P_1 with respect to P_2 by

$$H_{P_2}(P_1) = \sup \sum_i P_1\{E_i\} \log \frac{P_1\{E_i\}}{P_2\{E_i\}}, \tag{2.4.3}$$

where the supremum is taken over all partitions of Ω. Obviously,

$$I(\xi, \eta) = H_{P_{\xi \times \eta}}(P_{\xi\eta}). \tag{2.4.4}$$

In general the properties of the entropy $H_{P_2}(P_1)$ are simply repetitions of the corresponding properties of information, and the proofs of these properties do not differ in any way from those given in the case of information.

(1) *Always*

$$H_{P_2}(P_1) \geqslant 0, \tag{2.4.5}$$

with equality if and only if P_1 and P_2 coincide.

(2) *THEOREM 2.4.1. (Dobrushin's theorem). Let $\mathscr{L}$ be an algebra of sets belonging to S_ω which generates the σ-algebra S_ω, and let R be a family of partitions of Ω whose elements belong to $\mathscr{L}$. If every partition consisting of sets from $\mathscr{L}$ has a subpartition belonging to R, then*

$$H_{P_2}(P_1) = \sup_{\{E_i\} \in R} \sum_i P_1\{E_i\} \log \frac{P_1\{E_i\}}{P_2\{E_i\}}. \tag{2.4.6}$$

(3) *THEOREM 2.4.2. (Theorem of Gelfand, Yaglom and Perez). If the entropy* $H_{P_2}(P_1)$ *is finite, then* P_1 *is absolutely continuous with respect to* P_2, *and*

$$H_{P_2}(P_1) = \int_\Omega \log a(\omega) P_1\{d\omega\} = \int_\Omega h(\omega) P_1\{d\omega\}, \tag{2.4.7}$$

where $a(\omega)$ *is the density of* P_1 *with respect to* P_2.
The function $h_{P_2}(\omega, P_1) = h(\omega) = \log a(\omega)$ is called the **entropy density.**
(4) *Let* $\tilde{\omega} = f(\omega)$ *be a measurable function defined on* (Ω, S_ω) *with values in the measurable space* $(\tilde{\Omega}, S_{\tilde{\omega}})$. *If* P_1, P_2 *are probability measures on* (Ω, S_ω), *we define* $\tilde{P}_1, \tilde{P}_2$ *on* $(\tilde{\Omega}, S_{\tilde{\omega}})$ *by* $\tilde{P}_{1,2}(\tilde{E}) = P_{1,2}(E^{-1})$, *where* $E^{-1} = f^{-1}(\tilde{E})$ *for* $\tilde{E} \in S_{\tilde{\omega}}$. *Then*

$$H_{P_2}(P_1) \geqslant H_{\tilde{P}_2}(\tilde{P}_1). \tag{2.4.8}$$

(5) *If the probability measures* P_{1n} *and* P_{2n}, *defined on* (Ω, S_ω), *converge as* $n \to \infty$ *to* P_1 *and* P_2 *respectively, then*

$$H_{P_2}(P_1) \leqslant \lim_{n\to\infty} H_{P_{2n}}(P_{1n}). \tag{2.4.9}$$

(6) *The following inequalities, analogous to (2.3.2) and (2.3.3), are valid:*

$$H_{P_2}(P_1) \leqslant \int_\Omega |h(\omega)| P_1\{d\omega\} \leqslant H_{P_2}(P_1) + \frac{2}{e} \tag{2.4.10}$$

$$\int_\Omega |h(\omega)| P_1\{d\omega\} \leqslant H_{P_2}(P_1) + \Gamma \sqrt{H_{P_2}(P_1)}, \tag{2.4.11}$$

where Γ *is a fixed number which is independent of* P_1 *and* P_2.
COROLLARY. If

$$\lim_{n\to\infty} H_{P_{2n}}(P_{1n}) = 0, \text{ then } \lim_{n\to\infty} \int_\Omega |h_n(\omega)| P_{1n}\{d\omega\} = 0, \tag{2.4.12}$$

where $h_n(\omega)$ *is the entropy density of* P_{1n} *with respect to* P_{2n}.
(7) *If* $\lim_{n\to\infty} H_{P_{2n}}(P_{1n}) = 0$, *then* $\lim_{n\to\infty} V(P_{1n}, P_{2n}) = 0$. (2.4.13)

(8) *If* $\lim_{n\to\infty} V(P_{1n}, P_{2n}) = 0$, *then the entropy density* $h_n(\omega)$ *converges to zero in measure* P_{1n}, *i.e., if* $A_\epsilon^n = \{|h_n(\omega)| \geqslant \epsilon\}$, *then* $\lim_{n\to\infty} P_{1n}\{A_\epsilon^n\} = 0$, *for every* $\epsilon > 0$.

Subsequently, P_1 and P_2 will frequently be the distributions of the random variables ξ and η, taking values in the same space

(X, S_x). In this case our notation for the entropy and entropy density will be

$$H_{P_2}(P_1) = H_{P_\eta}(P_\xi) = H_\eta(\xi), \ \log a(x) = h(x) = h_{P_\eta}(x, P_\xi) = h_\eta(x, \xi). \tag{2.4.14}$$

The quantities $\alpha_\eta(\xi, \xi) = a_\eta(\xi)$ and $h_\eta(\xi, \xi) = h_\eta(\xi) = \log \alpha_\eta(\xi)$, being measurable functions of the random variable ξ, are themselves random variables, and

$$H_\eta(\xi) = \mathbf{E} h_\eta(\xi). \tag{2.4.15}$$

TRANSLATOR'S REMARKS TO CHAPTER 2

1. PROOF OF DOBRUSHIN'S THEOREM. Before proving Dobrushin's theorem, a few remarks are in order. First, in defining $I(\xi, \eta)$ it should be added that we take $0 \log 0/a = 0$ for $a \geqslant 0$ and $a \log a/0 = 0$ for $a > 0$. Second, in the statement of the theorem, the condition that the partitions in R have elements in $\mathscr{L}$ is unnecessary, as will be evident from the proof, which follows Dobrushin [3].

We will actually prove Theorem 2.4.1, since Theorem 2.1.1 follows from it by setting $\mathscr{L} = S_x \times S_y$, $P_1 = P_{\xi\eta}$, $P_2 = P_{\xi \times \eta}$ and letting R be the family of all partitions of $X \times Y$ of the form $\{E_i \times F_j\}$, where $\{E_i\}$ and $\{F_j\}$ are partitions of X and Y respectively.

Let us write $H(\mathscr{R})$ for the right side of (2.4.3) when the supremum is taken over all partitions whose elements belong to some algebra $\mathscr{R}$ of measurable sets. Then $H(S_\omega) = H_{P_2}(P_1)$. Similarly, we write $H(R)$ for the right side of (2.4.3) when the supremum is taken over all partitions belonging to the family R. The proof of the theorem is carried out in two steps.

(1) We show that the summation on the right side of (2.4.3) does not decrease when we replace the partition $\{E_i\}$ by an arbitrary subpartition $\{E_i'\}$ of $\{E_i\}$. Since by hypothesis any partition with elements in $\mathscr{L}$ has a subpartition in R, we see at once that $H(R) \geqslant H(\mathscr{L})$.

(2) We show that inasmuch as $\mathscr{L}$ generates S_ω, $H(\mathscr{L}) \geqslant H(S_\omega)$. Since $\mathscr{L} \subseteq S_\omega$, it is obvious that $H(\mathscr{L}) \leqslant H(S_\omega)$. It is equally clear that $H(R) \leqslant H(S_\omega)$, and so we obtain $H(\mathscr{L}) = H(R) = H(S_\omega)$.

PROOF (1) We need the inequality

$$\sum_{i=1}^{m} r_i \log \frac{r_i}{u_i} \geqslant (r_1 + \ldots + r_m) \log \frac{(r_1 + \ldots + r_m)}{(u_1 + \ldots + u_m)},$$

where the r_i and u_i are non-negative. Clearly, we may assume without loss of generality that $r_1 + \ldots + r_m = 1$, as the case $r_1 = \ldots = r_m = 0$ is trivial. Thus we wish to show that

$$\sum_{i=1}^{m} r_i \log \frac{r_i}{u_i} + \log (u_1 + \ldots + u_m) \geqslant 0.$$

Using the inequality $\log x \leqslant x - 1$ which follows from the fact that the derivative of $x - 1 - \log x$ is positive for $x > 1$ and negative for $x < 1$, we have:

$$\sum_{i=1}^{m} r_i \log \frac{r_i}{u_i} + \log (u_1 + \ldots + u_m) = - \sum_{i=1}^{m} r_i \left[\log \frac{u_i}{r_i(u_1 + \ldots + u_m)} \right]$$

$$\geqslant - \sum_{i=1}^{m} r_i \left[\frac{u_i}{r_i(u_1 + \ldots + u_m)} - 1 \right] = 0.$$

Now suppose that $\{F_j\}$ is a subpartition of $\{E_i\}$, where $i = 1, \ldots, n$ and $j = 1, \ldots, m$. Then the set $\{1, \ldots, m\}$ can be broken up into n disjoint sets $N_1, \ldots, N_n$ such that

$$E_i = \bigcup_{j \in N_i} F_j, \; i = 1, \ldots, n. \text{ Thus } P_k(E_i) = \sum_{j \in N_i} P_k(F_j), \; i = 1, \ldots, n,$$

$k = 1, 2$, and using the inequality derived above we obtain

$$\sum_{j \in N_i} P_1(F_j) \log \frac{P_1(F_j)}{P_2(F_j)} \geqslant P_1(E_i) \log \frac{P_1(E_i)}{P_2(E_i)}, \; i = 1, \ldots, n.$$

Summing over i we obtain:

$$\sum_{j=1}^{m} P_1(F_j) \log \frac{P_1(F_j)}{P_2(F_j)} \geqslant \sum_{i=1}^{n} P_1(E_i) \log \frac{P_1(E_i)}{P_2(E_i)},$$

which proves part (1).
(2) Let $\{C_i\}$ be a partition of Ω. Since $\mathscr{L}$ generates S_ω, applying Theorem D of Section 13, Halmos [12], to the measure $\mu = P_1 + P_2$, we can find for any $\delta > 0$ sets $E_i' \in \mathscr{L}$ such that $P_k(C_i \Delta E_i')$ $\leqslant \mu(C_i \Delta E_i') \leqslant \delta, k = 1, 2; i = 1, \ldots, n$. Define $E_1 = E_1'$; $E_2 = E_2' - E_1$; $\ldots$; $E_{n-1} = E_{n-1}' - (E_1 \cup \ldots \cup E_{n-2})$; $E_n = \Omega - (E_1 \cup \ldots \cup E_{n-1})$. Clearly we can take $P_k(C_i \Delta E_i)$ as small as we choose by taking δ sufficiently small, from which it follows that

$$\sum_{i=1}^{n} P_1(E_i) \log \frac{P_1(E_i)}{P_2(E_i)}$$

will approximate

$$\sum_{i=1}^{n} P_1(C_i) \log \frac{P_1(C_i)}{P_2(C_i)}$$

as closely as desired if the latter is finite, while if the latter is infinite the former will be arbitrarily large for δ sufficiently small. Clearly this implies that $H(\mathscr{L}) \geqslant H(S_\omega)$, which completes the proof of Dobrushin's theorem.

2. We prove the theorem of Gelfand, Yaglom and Perez in its most general form, Theorem 2.4.2. The proof follows Dobrushin [3].

If P_1 is not absolutely continuous with respect to P_2, then there exists a set B such that $P_1(B) > 0$ and $P_2(B) = 0$. Taking $E_1 = B$ and $E_2 = \Omega - B$, we see at once that the sum on the right side of (2.4.3) will be infinite. Let us therefore assume that $P_1 \ll P_2$. We will need the inequality

$$\int_0^\infty u \log u \, dF(u) \geqslant \int_0^\infty u \, dF(u) \log \int_0^\infty u \, dF(u)$$

which holds for any probability distribution F which is concentrated on the interval $[0, \infty]$. This is just Jensen's inequality (see Hardy, Littlewood, Polya, "Inequalities") as applied to the convex function $\varphi(u) = -u \log u$, and is the continuous version of the inequality used in proving Dobrushin's theorem. For a given set B such that $P_2(B) > 0$, we define

$$F_B(u) = \frac{P_2(\{a(\omega) < u\} \cap B)}{P_2(B)}.$$

Then

$$\int_0^\infty u \, dF_B(u) = \frac{1}{P_2(B)} \int_B a(\omega) P_2(d\omega) = \frac{P_1(B)}{P_2(B)}$$

and

$$\int_0^\infty u \log u \, dF_B(u) = \frac{1}{P_2(B)} \int_B a(\omega) \log a(\omega) P_2(d\omega)$$

$$= \frac{1}{P_2(B)} \int_B \log a(\omega) P_1(d\omega)$$

where we have used Theorem B of Section 32, Halmos [12]. We note that since $u \log u \geqslant -e^{-1}$ there is no question about the existence of any of the integrals which appear. Substituting into the inequality derived earlier, we obtain

$$\int_B \log a(\omega) P_1(d\omega) \geqslant P_1(B) \log \frac{P_1(B)}{P_2(B)}.$$

Since $P_1 \ll P_2$, it is clear that this inequality reduces to $0 = 0$ if $P_2(B) = 0$. Now let $\{E_i\}$ be a partition of Ω. Applying the foregoing to each set E_i and summing the resulting inequalities with respect to i, we obtain

$$\sum_{i=1}^{n} P_1(E_i) \log \frac{P_1(E_i)}{P_2(E_i)} \leqslant \sum_{i=1}^{n} \int_{E_i} \log a(\omega) P_1(d\omega) = \int_\Omega \log a(\omega) P_1(d\omega).$$

Thus

$$H_{P_2}(P_1) \leqslant \int_\Omega \log a(\omega) P_1(d\omega).$$

To obtain the reverse inequality, we choose an $\epsilon > 0$ and then take $K > 0$ so large that

$$0 \geqslant P_1\{|\log a(\omega)| > K\} \log P_1\{|\log a(\omega)| > K\} \geqslant -\frac{\epsilon}{2}. \qquad (1)$$

This is always possible because $x \log x \to 0$ as $x \to 0$. Since $a(\omega)$ is bounded on the set $\{|\log a(\omega)| \leqslant K\}$, we can find disjoint sets $C_1, \ldots, C_n$ such that

$$\bigcup_{i=1}^{n} C_i = \{|\log a(\omega)| \leqslant K\},$$

and

$$\log \overline{h}_i - \log \underline{h}_i \leqslant \frac{\epsilon}{2}, \qquad (2)$$

where $\overline{h}_i = \sup_{\omega \in C_i} a(\omega)$, $\underline{h}_i = \inf_{\omega \in C_i} a(\omega)$.

We see also that $\underline{h}_i P_2(C_i) \leqslant P_1(C_i) \leqslant \overline{h}_i P_2(C_i)$, and

$$P_1(C_i) \log \overline{h}_i \geqslant \int_{C_i} \log a(\omega) P_1(d\omega) \geqslant P_1(C_i) \log \underline{h}_i.$$

It follows that

$$\left| P_1(C_i) \log \frac{P_1(C_i)}{P_2(C_i)} - \int_{C_i} \log a(\omega) P_1(d\omega) \right| \leqslant (\log \overline{h}_i - \log \underline{h}_i) P_1(C_i).$$

Summing over i and using (2), we find that

$$\left|\sum_{i=1}^{n} P_1(C_i)\log\frac{P_1(C_i)}{P_2(C_i)} - \int_{\Omega - C_{n+1}} \log a(\omega)P_1(d\omega)\right| \leqslant \frac{\epsilon}{2},$$

where $C_{n+1} = \{|\log a(\omega)| > K\}$. Using (1), we obtain

$$\sum_{i=1}^{n+1} P_1(C_i)\log\frac{P_1(C_i)}{P_2(C_i)} \geqslant \int_{\Omega - C_{n+1}} \log a(\omega)P_1(d\omega) - \epsilon.$$

It follows at once that

$$H_{P_2}(P_1) \geqslant \int_{\{|\log a(\omega)| \leqslant K\}} \log a(\omega)P_1(d\omega) - \epsilon.$$

Letting $K \to \infty$ and then $\epsilon \to 0$, we have finally

$$H_{P_2}(P_1) \geqslant \int_{\Omega} \log a(\omega)P_1(d\omega),$$

which completes the proof.

3. The opening remarks in Section 2.4 assume implicitly that the diagonal set $\{(x, x) | x \epsilon X\}$ is measurable. Without this assumption it still follows that the entropy will be finite only if the measure P_ξ is atomic, but one cannot conclude that P_ξ is concentrated on some denumerable set of points.

This result is obtained as follows. As in the text, one finds immediately that $P_{\xi\xi}(E) = P_\xi(\{x | (x, x) \epsilon E\})$ for any set $E \epsilon S_x \times S_x$. Let $A \epsilon S_x$ be any set containing no atoms. Then for any integer $n > 0$ we can find (see, e.g., Halmos [12], Section 41, exercise 2) disjoint sets $B_{1n}, \ldots, B_{nn} \epsilon S_x, \bigcup_{i=1}^{n} B_{in} = A$ such that $P_\xi(B_{1n}) = \ldots = P_\xi(B_{nn}) = 1/n\, P_\xi(A)$. Now clearly

$$\left\{x | (x,x) \epsilon \bigcup_{i=1}^{n} (B_{in} \times B_{in})\right\} = A,$$

and so

$$P_{\xi\xi}(\bigcup_{i=1}^{n} (B_{in} \times B_{in})) = P_\xi(A). \tag{3}$$

Moreover,

$$P_{\xi\times\xi}(\bigcup_{i=1}^{n} (B_{in} \times B_{in})) = \sum_{i=1}^{n} P_{\xi\times\xi}(B_{in} \times B_{in}) = \sum_{i=1}^{n} \frac{1}{n^2} P_\xi^2(A) = \frac{1}{n} P_\xi^2(A).$$

Thus

$$P_{\xi\times\xi}(\bigcap_{n=1}^{\infty} \bigcup_{i=1}^{n} (B_{in} \times B_{in})) = 0.$$ Since by hypothesis $P_{\xi\xi} \ll P_{\xi\times\xi}$,

we have

$$P_{\xi\xi}(\bigcap_{n=1}^{\infty} \bigcup_{i=1}^{n} (B_{in} \times B_{in})) = 0. \tag{4}$$

Now $P_{\xi\xi}(A \times A) = P_{\xi}\{x | (x, x) \in (A \times A)\} = P_{\xi}(A)$.

Since $\bigcup_{i=1}^{n} (B_{in} \times B_{in}) \subset A \times A$ for every $n = 1, 2, \ldots,$ it follows from (3) that

$$P_{\xi\xi}(\bigcap_{n=1}^{\infty} \bigcup_{i=1}^{n} (B_{in} \times B_{in})) = P_{\xi\xi}(A \times A) = P_{\xi}(A),$$

and so (4) shows that $P_{\xi}(A) = 0$.

Thus P_{ξ} is purely atomic. To complete the proof we remark first that a measurable function f is necessarily almost everywhere equal to some constant on every atom. In fact, if A is an atom with respect to some measure μ, then $f(x)$ equals almost everywhere on A (with respect to μ) the smallest value λ for which $\mu(\{f(x) \leq \lambda\}) = \mu(A)$. Using this result, we now show that if A is an atom with respect to P_{ξ}, then $A \times A$ is an atom with respect to $P_{\xi\times\xi}$. Suppose that $B \epsilon S_x \times S_x$ is a subset of $A \times A$. Then the section B_x of B at x (it is immaterial for the argument to specify in which coordinate space x lies) is a measurable set in A, and therefore has P_{ξ} measure either zero or $P_{\xi}(A)$. But $P_{\xi}(B_x)$ is a measurable function of x, and is therefore almost everywhere equal to a constant on A, which constant can only be either zero or $P_{\xi}(A)$. We see, therefore, that $P_{\xi\times\xi}(B)$ is equal either to zero or to $P_{\xi}^2(A) = P_{\xi\times\xi}(A \times A)$, which proves the assertion.

Now let $A_1, A_2, \ldots$ be disjoint atoms (with respect to P_{ξ}) whose union is Ω. Then

$$P_{\xi\xi}(\bigcup_i (A_i \times A_i)) = P_{\xi}(\bigcup_i (A_i)) = 1,$$

and so for convenience we can assume that $a_{\xi\xi}$ vanishes off $\bigcup_i (A_i \times A_i)$. Since each set $A_i \times A_i$ is an atom with respect to $P_{\xi\times\xi}$, we have $a_{\xi\xi} = c_i$ almost everywhere $P_{\xi\times\xi}$ on $A_i \times A_i$. Next,

$$P_{\xi}(A_i) = P_{\xi\xi}(A_i \times A_i) = \int_{A_i \times A_i} a_{\xi\xi} \, dP_{\xi\times\xi} = c_i P_{\xi\times\xi}(A_i \times A_i)$$
$$= c_i P_{\xi}^2(A_i),$$

and so $c_i = P_\xi(A_i)^{-1}$. It follows that

$$H(\xi) = \int_{\Omega\times\Omega} \log a_{\xi\xi} dP_{\xi\xi} = \sum_i \int_{A_i\times A_i} \log \frac{1}{P_\xi(A_i)} dP_{\xi\xi}$$

$$= -\sum_i P_\xi(A_i) \log P_\xi(A_i).$$

Chapter 3 Conditional information

The present chapter is devoted to defining and studying various properties of conditional information, which plays as important a role in the solution of fundamental problems of information theory as the concept of information itself. Certain of the properties which we consider are new and are not encountered in the literature.

The definition of conditional information is based upon the concept of entropy density, in which form it was introduced by R.L.Dobrushin [3]. Naturally, some of the properties of conditional information can be obtained as corollaries of corresponding properties of entropy. Conversely, in this chapter we shall obtain a number of properties of information which have not been considered in the preceding sections. These results will be obtained as a consequence of the fact that the concept of information itself is a special case of the concept of average conditional information.

Finally, we shall introduce the notion of average conditional entropy and indicate certain of its properties.

As everywhere else, we shall omit proofs* of results which can be found in Dobrushin's paper [3].

3.1. AVERAGE CONDITIONAL INFORMATION AND ITS REPRESENTATIONS

Let ξ, η, and ζ be random variables taking values in the measurable spaces (X, S_x), (Y, S_y), and (Z, S_z) respectively.

For any set $F \epsilon S_y$ we can consider the conditional probability $P\{\eta \epsilon F/\xi = x\} = P_{\eta/\xi}(F/x)$. As is well known, the function

---

* For these proofs, see the remarks following this chapter. – Tr.

$P_{\eta/\xi}(F/x)$ is, for fixed F, a measurable function of $x \in X$ which is defined up to an x-set of P_ξ measure zero, and for any sequence of disjoint sets $F_1, F_2, \ldots \in S_y$ we have the identity

$$\sum_{i=1}^{\infty} P_{\eta/\xi}(F_i/x) = P_{\eta/\xi}\left(\bigcup_{i=1}^{\infty} F_i/x\right)$$

almost everywhere with respect to P_ξ.

In his paper [3], R.L.Dobrushin introduced the function

$$\overline{P}_{\eta \times \zeta/\xi}(E \times F \times N) = \int_E P_{\eta/\xi}(F/x) P_{\zeta/\xi}(N/x) P_\xi(dx), \tag{3.1.1}$$

which is completely additive on the family of sets of the form $E \times F \times N$, $E \in S_x$, $F \in S_y$, $N \in S_z$, and can therefore be extended in a unique way to a probability measure defined on the σ-algebra $S_x \times S_y \times S_z$. We will denote this extension by $\overline{P}_{\eta \times \zeta/\xi}$.

The entropy $H_{\overline{P}_{\eta \times \zeta/\xi}}(P_{\xi\eta\zeta})$ of the measure $P_{\xi\eta\zeta}$ with respect to the measure $\overline{P}_{\eta \times \zeta/\xi}$ will be called **the average conditional information of the pair** η and ζ, given ξ, and will be denoted by $\mathbf{E}I(\eta, \zeta/\xi)$.

In the case where $P_{\xi\eta\zeta}$ is absolutely continuous with respect to $\overline{P}_{\eta \times \zeta/\xi}$ (in particular, whenever the average conditional information is finite) then by Section 2.4 we can express $\mathbf{E}I(\eta, \zeta/\xi)$ in terms of the density $\overline{a}_{\eta\zeta/\xi}(\cdot)$ of $P_{\xi\eta\zeta}(\cdot)$ with respect to $\overline{P}_{\eta \times \zeta/\xi}(\cdot)$:

$$\mathbf{E}I(\eta, \zeta/\xi) = H_{\overline{P}_{\eta \times \zeta/\xi}}(P_{\xi\eta\zeta}) = \int_{X \times Y \times Z} \log \overline{a}_{\eta\zeta/\xi}(x, y, z) P_{\xi\eta\zeta}(dx\, dy\, dz) \tag{3.1.2}$$

The function $\overline{i}_{\eta\zeta/\xi}(x, y, z) = \log \overline{a}_{\eta\zeta/\xi}(x, y, z)$, which is defined up to a set of $P_{\eta \times \zeta/\xi}$ measure zero, is called the **conditional information density** of the pair η, ζ given ξ. Clearly, the conditional information density is also the entropy density of $P_{\xi\eta\zeta}$ with respect to $\overline{P}_{\eta \times \zeta/\xi}$.

The expressions $\overline{a}_{\eta\zeta/\xi}(\xi, \eta, \zeta)$ and $\overline{i}_{\eta\zeta/\xi}(\xi, \eta, \zeta)$ are measurable functions of the random variable (ξ, η, ζ) and are therefore also random variables. Omitting subscripts, we will denote them by

$$\overline{a}_{\eta\zeta/\xi}(\xi, \eta, \zeta) = \overline{a}(\eta, \zeta/\xi), \qquad \overline{i}_{\eta\zeta/\xi}(\xi, \eta, \zeta) = \overline{i}(\eta, \zeta/\xi).$$

It is clear that

$$\mathbf{E}I(\eta, \zeta/\xi) = \mathbf{E}\overline{i}(\eta, \zeta/\xi). \tag{3.1.3}$$

If $\eta = \zeta$, then

$$\mathbf{E}I(\eta, \zeta/\xi) = \mathbf{E}I(\eta, \eta/\xi) = \mathbf{E}H(\eta/\xi) \tag{3.1.4}$$

will be called the **average conditional entropy** of the random variable η given ξ.

We now introduce the concept of conditional information in such a way that the symbol **E** may be considered the usual mathematical expectation of a quantity which we call **conditional information.**

According to (1.3.3) we have the representation

$$P_{\xi\eta\zeta}(N) = \int_{N(X\times Y\times Z-C)} \bar{a}_{\eta\zeta/\xi}(x, y, z)\bar{P}_{\eta\times\zeta/\xi}(dx\,dy\,dz) + P_{\xi\eta\zeta}(NC),\ N\epsilon S_x$$

$$\times S_y \times S_z,\ C\epsilon S_x \times S_y \times S_z,\ \bar{P}_{\eta\times\zeta/\xi}(C) = 0.$$

The function $\bar{a}_{\eta\zeta/\xi}(x, y, z)$ is defined on the set $X\times Y\times Z - C$. We extend its domain to all of $X\times Y\times Z$ by setting it equal to $+\infty$ on C. Let $\mathscr{F}$ be the σ-algebra of sets in $X\times Y\times Z$ of the form $E\times Y\times Z$, $E\epsilon S_x$, and let $P(C/\mathscr{F})$ denote the conditional probability of C with respect to $\mathscr{F}$ (cf [4]). Because of the special form of $\mathscr{F}$, $P(C/\mathscr{F})$ can be taken as a function of x only, which is defined up to a set of P_ξ measure zero. We define $I(\eta, \zeta/x) = +\infty$ if $P(C/\mathscr{F})$ is positive at the point x, and $I(\eta, \zeta/x) = \mathbf{E}(\log \bar{a}_{\eta\zeta/\xi}/\mathscr{F})$, the conditional expectation of $\log \bar{a}_{\eta\zeta/\xi}$ with respect to $\mathscr{F}$, if $P(C/\mathscr{F})$ vanishes at x. Then

$$\int_X I(\eta, \zeta/x)P_\xi(dx) = \mathbf{E}I(\eta, \zeta/\xi). \tag{3.1.5}$$

Indeed, if $P_{\xi\eta\zeta}(C) > 0$, then the right side of (3.1.5) is equal to $+\infty$ by Theorem 2.4.2; while, since $P(C/\mathscr{F})$ will be positive on a set of positive P_ξ measure, the left side of (3.1.5) will also equal $+\infty$. Finally, if $P_{\xi\eta\zeta}(C) = 0$, then (3.1.5) is an immediate consequence of the definition of $\mathbf{E}(\log \bar{a}_{\eta\zeta/\xi}/\mathscr{F})$.

We consider now the representation of the conditional information density in certain particular cases.

1. Suppose that the distributions $P_{\xi\eta\zeta}$, $P_{\xi\eta}$, $P_{\xi\zeta}$, and P_ξ relating to the random variables ξ, η, ζ are defined by means of densities $p_{\xi\eta\zeta}(x, y, z)$, $p_{\xi\eta}(x, y)$, $p_{\xi\zeta}(x, z)$, and $p_\xi(x)$ respectively. Then the densities of the conditional distributions $P_{\eta\zeta/\xi}$, $P_{\eta/\xi}$, and $P_{\zeta/\xi}$ are given by

$$p_{\eta\zeta/\xi}(y, z/x) = \frac{p_{\xi\eta\zeta}(x, y, z)}{p_\xi(x)};$$

$$p_{\eta/\xi}(y/x) = \frac{p_{\xi\eta}(x, y)}{p_\xi(x)}; \qquad P_{\eta/\xi}(F/x) = \int_F p_{\eta/\xi}(y/x)dy,\ F\epsilon S_y;$$

$$p_{\zeta/\xi}(z/x) = \frac{p_{\xi\zeta}(x, y)}{p_\xi(x)}; \qquad P_{\zeta/\xi}(N/x) = \int_N p_{\zeta/\xi}(z/x)dz,\ N\epsilon S_z.$$

Hence

$$\overline{P}_{\eta\times\zeta/\xi}(E \times F \times N) = \int_E P_{\eta/\xi}(F/x)P_{\zeta/\xi}(N/x)P_\xi(dx)$$

$$= \int_E\left(\int_F p_{\eta/\xi}(y/x)dy\right)\left(\int_N p_{\zeta/\xi}(z/x)dz\right)P_\xi(dx)$$

$$= \int_{E\times F\times N} p_{\eta/\xi}(y/x)p_{\zeta/\xi}(z/x)p_\xi(x)dx\,dy\,dz;$$

$E \in S_x$, $F \in S_y$, $N \in S_z$.

But this implies that

$$\overline{P}_{\eta\times\zeta/\xi}(K) = \int_K p_{\eta/\xi}(y/x)p_{\zeta/\xi}(z/x)p_\xi(x)dx\,dy\,dz$$

for every $K \in S_x \times S_y \times S_z$. Recalling that $\bar{a}_{\eta\zeta/\xi}(x, y, z)$ is the derivative of the measure $P_{\xi\eta\zeta}$ with respect to the measure $P_{\eta\times\zeta/\xi}$, we obtain, according to the known properties of measures, the following expression for $P_{\xi\eta\zeta}(K)$:

$$P_{\xi\eta\zeta}(K) = \int_K \bar{a}_{\eta\zeta/\xi}(x, y, z)\overline{P}_{\eta\times\zeta/\xi}(dx\,dy\,dz)$$

$$= \int_K \bar{a}_{\eta\zeta/\xi}(x, y, z)p_{\eta/\xi}(y/x)p_{\zeta/\xi}(z/x)p_\xi(x)dx\,dy\,dz.$$

Comparing this expression with

$$P_{\xi\eta\zeta}(K) = \int_K p_{\xi\eta\zeta}(x, y, z)dx\,dy\,dz,$$

we find that

$$p_{\xi\eta\zeta}(x, y, z) = \bar{a}_{\eta\zeta/\xi}(x, y, z)\, p_{\eta/\xi}(y/x)p_{\zeta/\xi}(z/x)p_\xi(x),$$

i.e., $$\bar{a}_{\eta\zeta/\xi}(x, y, z) = \frac{p_{\xi\eta\zeta}(x, y, z)}{p_\xi(x)p_{\eta/\xi}(y/x)p_{\zeta/\xi}(z/x)}.$$

Therefore

$$\bar{i}_{\eta\zeta/\xi}(x, y, z) = \log\frac{p_{\eta\zeta/\xi}(y, z/x)}{p_{\eta/\xi}(y/x)p_{\zeta/\xi}(z/x)}$$

and

$$EI(\eta, \zeta/\xi) \int_X \int_Y \int_Z p_{\xi\eta\zeta}(x, y, z) \log\frac{p_{\eta\zeta/\xi}(y, z/x)}{p_{\eta/\xi}(y/x)p_{\zeta/\xi}(z/x)}\, dx\,dy\,dz$$

$$= \int_X\left\{\int_Y\int_Z p_{\eta\zeta/\xi}(y, z/x)\log\frac{p_{\eta\zeta/\xi}(y, z/x)}{p_{\eta/\xi}(y/x)p_{\zeta/\xi}(z/x)}dy\,dz\right\}p_\xi(x)dx$$

$$= \int_X I(\eta, \zeta/x)p_\xi(x)dx, \qquad (3.1.6)$$

where

$$I(\eta, \zeta/x) = \int_Y \int_Z p_{\eta\zeta/\xi}(y, z/x) \log \frac{p_{\eta\zeta/\xi}(y, z/x)}{p_{\eta/\xi}(y/x) p_{\zeta/\xi}(z/x)} dy\, dz,$$

the conditional information, is just the entropy of the (conditional) distribution

$$P_{\eta\zeta/\xi}(N/x) = \int_N p_{\eta\zeta/\xi}(y, z/x) dy\, dz$$

with respect to the (conditional) distribution

$$P_{\eta\times\zeta/\xi}(N/x) = \int_N p_{\eta/\xi}(y/x) p_{\zeta/\xi}(z/x) dy\, dz, \quad N \in S_y \times S_z.$$

2. Let $\mathscr{F}$ denote the σ-algebra of sets of $X \times Y \times Z$ of the form $E \times Y \times Z$, $E \in S_x$. For every $N \in S_y \times S_z$ the conditional probability $P_{\xi\eta\zeta}(N/\mathscr{F})$ can be taken to be a measurable function of x. Let us assume that for each N it is possible to alter the function $P_{\xi\eta\zeta}(N/\mathscr{F})$ on a set of P_ξ measure zero in such a way that the resulting function, which we will denote by $P_{\eta\zeta/\xi}(N/x)$, is for each x a probability measure of sets N. We are assuming, in essence, the existence of a conditional probability distribution of N sets with respect to the σ-algebra $\mathscr{F}$. Obviously, the expressions $P_{\eta/\xi}(F/x) = P_{\eta\zeta/\xi}(F \times Z/x)$ and $P_{\zeta/\xi}(K/x) = P_{\eta\zeta/\xi}(Y \times K/x)$, $F \in S_y$, $K \in S_z$ are conditional probability distributions of the random variables η and ζ with respect to ξ. It follows that for fixed x, $P_{\eta\times\zeta/\xi}(F \times K/x) = P_{\eta/\xi}(F/x)\, P_{\zeta/\xi}(K/x)$ is completely additive on the family of sets of the form $F \times K$, $F \in S_y$, $K \in S_z$, and may be uniquely extended to a probability measure $P_{\eta\times\zeta/\xi}(N/x)$ defined on the σ-algebra $S_y \times S_z$.

Let us assume, further, that for almost every x (with respect to P_ξ) the conditional distribution $P_{\eta\zeta/\xi}(N/x)$ is absolutely continuous with respect to the conditional distribution $P_{\eta\times\zeta/\xi}(N/x)$, and that the density $a_{\eta\zeta/\xi}(y, z/x)$ of $P_{\eta\zeta/\xi}(N/x)$ with respect to $P_{\eta\times\zeta/\xi}(N/x)$ can be chosen (for each x) in such a way that for almost every x with respect to P_ξ, the function $a_{\eta\zeta/\xi}(y, z/x)$ coincides with some function $\tilde{a}_{\eta\zeta/\xi}(x, y, z)$ which is measurable with respect to the σ-algebra $S_x \times S_y \times S_z$. Then we may put

$$\bar{a}_{\eta\zeta/\xi}(x, y, z) = \tilde{a}_{\eta\zeta/\xi}(x, y, z), \tag{3.1.7}$$

i.e., the right side may be chosen as one version of the left side.

We prove this assertion. By hypothesis

$$P_{\eta\zeta/\xi}(F \times K/x) = \int_{F\times K} \tilde{a}_{\eta\zeta/\xi}(x, y, z)\, P_{\eta\times\zeta/\xi}(dy\, dz/x),$$

$F \in S_y$, $K \in S_z$ for almost every x with respect to P_ξ. Therefore, according to the definition of the conditional distribution $P_{\eta\zeta/\xi}(N/x)$,

$$P_{\xi\eta\zeta}(E \times F \times K) = \int_E P_{\eta\zeta/\xi}(F \times K/x) P_\xi(dx)$$
$$= \int_E \left(\int_{F\times K} \tilde{a}_{\eta\zeta/\xi}(x, y, z) P_{\eta\times\zeta/\xi}(dy\, dz/x) \right) P_\xi(dx). \qquad (3.1.8)$$

We note that for any function $f(x, y, z)$ which is measurable with respect to the σ-algebra $S_x \times S_y \times S_z$,

$$\int_X \left\{ \int_{Y\times Z} f(x, y, z) P_{\eta\times\zeta/\xi}(dy\, dz/x) \right\} P_\xi(dx)$$
$$= \int_{X\times Y\times Z} f(x, y, z) \overline{P}_{\eta\times\zeta/\xi}(dy\, dz\, dx). \qquad (3.1.9)$$

In fact, if

$$f(x, y, z) = \begin{cases} 1 \text{ for } (x, y, z) \in E \times F \times K; \\ 0 \text{ for } (x, y, z) \notin E \times F \times K; \end{cases}$$
$$E \in S_x, \; F \in S_y, \; K \in S_z, \qquad (3.1.10)$$

then the right and left side of (3.1.9) both equal $\overline{P}_{\eta\times\zeta/\xi}(E \times F \times K)$. Since the σ-algebra $S_x \times S_y \times S_z$ is generated by sets of the form $E \times F \times K$, any function measurable with respect to $S_x \times S_y \times S_z$ can be approximated by linear combinations of functions of the form (3.1.10), from which follows the validity of (3.1.9).

Applying (3.1.9) to the function

$$f(x, y, z) = \begin{cases} \tilde{a}_{\eta\zeta/\xi}(x, y, z) \text{ for } (x, y, z) \in E \times F \times K \\ 0 \qquad \text{for} \qquad (x, y, z) \in E \times F \times K \end{cases}$$

we obtain from (3.1.8) that

$$P_{\xi\eta\zeta}(E \times F \times K) = \int_{E\times F\times K} \tilde{a}_{\eta\zeta/\xi}(x, y, z)\, \overline{P}_{\eta\times\zeta/\xi}(dx\, dy\, dz). \qquad (3.1.11)$$

Because the σ-algebra $S_x \times S_y \times S_z$ is generated by sets of the form $E \times F \times K$, it follows from (3.1.11) that

$$P_{\xi\eta\zeta}(N) = \int_N \tilde{a}_{\eta\zeta/\xi}(x, y, z)\, \overline{P}_{\eta\times\zeta/\xi}(dx\, dy\, dz) \qquad (3.1.12)$$

for any set $N \in S_x \times S_y \times S_z$, i.e., $\tilde{a}_{\eta\zeta/\xi}(x, y, z)$ is the density of the measure $P_{\xi\eta\zeta}$ with respect to the measure $\overline{P}_{\eta\times\zeta/\xi}$.

From this it follows that for almost every x with respect to P_ξ

$$\int_{Y \times Z} \log a_{\eta\zeta/\xi}(y, z/x) P_{\eta\zeta/\xi}(dy\, dz/x) = I(\eta, \zeta/x). \tag{3.1.13}$$

In particular, if the conditional distribution $P_{\eta\zeta/\xi}(N/x)$ is defined by means of a density $p_{\eta\zeta/\xi}(y, z/x)$ which is a measurable function with respect to $S_x \times S_y \times S_z$, then

$$I(\eta, \zeta/ x) \int_{X \times Z} \log \frac{p_{\eta\zeta/\xi}(y, z/x)}{p_{\eta/\xi}(y/x)p_{\zeta/\xi}(z/x)} p_{\eta\zeta/\xi}(y, z/x)dy\, dz, \tag{3.1.14}$$

where

$$p_{\eta/\xi}(y/x) = \int_Z p_{\eta\zeta/\xi}(y, z/x)\, dz, \qquad p_{\zeta/\xi}(z/x) = \int_Y p_{\eta\zeta/\xi}(y, z/x)\, dy.$$

It should be noted, in the foregoing, that we have not assumed the existence of densities for the unconditional distributions $P_{\xi\eta\zeta}$, $P_{\xi\eta}$, etc.

3. Suppose that the random variables η and ζ take on only finitely many values $y_1, \ldots, y_n$ and $z_1, \ldots, z_m$. Then there is a version of the conditional distribution $P_{\eta\zeta/\xi}(N/x)$ which is measurable with respect to S_x for fixed $N \epsilon S_y \times S_z$. Therefore

$$a_{\eta\zeta/\xi}(y, z/x) = a_{\eta\zeta/\xi}(y_i, z_j/x) = \frac{P_{\eta\zeta/\xi}(y_i, z_j/x)}{P_{\eta/\xi}(y_i/x)P_{\zeta/\xi}(z_j/x)} \tag{3.1.15}$$

is measurable with respect to $S_x \times S_y \times S_z$, and we can compute the conditional information by means of (3.1.13).

It is easily seen that for almost every x

$$a_{\eta\zeta/\xi}(y, z/x) = \frac{P\{(\eta,\zeta) = (y_i,z_j)/\xi = x\}}{P\{\eta = y_i/\xi = x\}\, P\{\zeta = z_j/\xi = x\}};$$

therefore $$I(\eta,\zeta/x) = \sum_{i=1}^{l} \sum_{j=1}^{m} P\{(\eta,\zeta)$$

$$= (y_i, z_j)/\xi = x\} \log \frac{P\{(\eta, \zeta) = (y_i, z_j)/\xi = x\}}{P\{\eta = y_i/\xi = x\}P\{\zeta = z_j/\xi = x\}}. \tag{3.1.16}$$

3.2. NON-NEGATIVITY AND SYMMETRY OF THE AVERAGE CONDITIONAL INFORMATION

The **non-negativity** of the average conditional information

$$\mathbf{E}I(\eta, \zeta/\xi) \geqslant 0 \tag{3.2.1}$$

follows from the definition of $\mathbf{E}I(\eta, \zeta/\xi)$ as the entropy $H_{\bar{P}_{\eta \times \zeta/\xi}}(P_{\xi\eta\zeta})$, and the non-negativity of entropy. The **symmetry** of the average conditional information

$$\mathbf{E}I(\eta, \zeta/\xi) = \mathbf{E}I(\zeta, \eta/\xi) \tag{3.2.2}$$

is obvious.

3.3. AVERAGE CONDITIONAL INFORMATION AND THE VARIATION OF A DISTRIBUTION

Properties 6, 7, 8 (Section 2.4) of entropy, when applied to the average conditional information, take the form

$$\mathbf{E}I(\eta, \zeta/\xi) \leqslant \int_{X\times Y\times Z} |\bar{i}_{\eta\zeta/\xi}(x, y, z)| P_{\xi\eta\zeta}(dx\,dy\,dz)$$
$$\leqslant \mathbf{E}I(\eta, \zeta/\xi) + \frac{2}{e} \tag{3.3.1}$$

$$\int_{X\times Y\times Z} |\bar{i}_{\eta\zeta/\xi}(x, y, z)| P_{\xi\eta\zeta}(dx\,dy\,dz) \leqslant \mathbf{E}I(\eta, \zeta/\xi) + \Gamma\sqrt{\mathbf{E}I(\eta, \zeta/\xi)}, \tag{3.3.2}$$

where Γ is a fixed constant.

If $\lim_{n\to\infty} \mathbf{E}I(\eta_n, \zeta_n/\xi_n) = 0$, *then* $\lim_{n\to\infty} V(P_{\xi_n\eta_n\zeta_n}, \bar{P}_{\eta_n\times\zeta_n/\xi_n}) = 0.$ (3. 3. 3)

Conversely, if the variation $V(P_{\xi_n\eta_n\zeta_n}, \bar{P}_{\eta_n\times\zeta_n/\xi_n})$ *goes to zero as* $n\to\infty$, *then the conditional information density* $\bar{i}(\eta_n, \zeta_n/\xi_n)$ *converges in probability to zero as* $n\to\infty$.

From (3.3.2) it follows that

if $\lim_{n\to\infty} \mathbf{E}I(\eta_n, \zeta_n/\xi_n) = 0$, *then*

$$\lim_{n\to\infty} \int_{\infty} |\bar{i}_{\eta_n\zeta_n/\xi_n}(x_n, y_n, z_n)| P_{\xi_n\eta_n\zeta_n}(dx_n dy_n dz_n) = 0. \tag{3.3.4}$$

In particular, if $\mathbf{E}I(\eta, \zeta - \xi) = 0$, *then with probability one* $\bar{i}(\eta, \zeta/\xi) = 0$.

3.4. THE AVERAGE CONDITIONAL INFORMATION OF RANDOM VARIABLES WHICH FORM A MARKOV CHAIN

Suppose that the random variables ξ_1, ξ_2, ξ_3, taking values in the measurable spaces (X_1, S_{x_1}), (X_2, S_{x_2}), (X_3, S_{x_3}), form a Markov chain, i.e., for any $E_3 \in S_{x_3}$

$$P\{\xi_3 \in E_3/\xi_2\} = P\{\xi_3 \in E_3/(\xi_1, \xi_2)\} \tag{3.4.1}$$

with probability one. As is known [4], a Markov chain satisfies the following characteristic property with probability one:

$$P\{\xi_1 \epsilon E_1/\xi_2\}P\{\xi_3 \epsilon E_3/\xi_2\} = P\{\xi_1 \epsilon E_1,\ \xi_3 \epsilon E_3/\xi_2\},\ E_1 \epsilon S_{x_1},\ E_2 \epsilon S_{x_2}. \tag{3.4.2}$$

According to the definition of conditional probability, it follows from this that, for any set $E_2 \epsilon S_{x_2}$

$$P_{\xi_1\xi_2\xi_3}(E_1 \times E_2 \times E_3) = P\{\xi_1 \epsilon E_1,\ \xi_2 \epsilon E_2,\ \xi_3 \epsilon E_3\}$$

$$= \int_{E_2} P\{\xi_1 \epsilon E_1,\ \xi_3 \epsilon E_3/x_2\}\, P_{\xi_2}(dx_2)$$

$$= \int_{E_2} P\{\xi_1 \epsilon E_1/x_2\}\, P\{\xi_3 \epsilon E_3/x_2\}\, P_{\xi_2}(dx_2). \tag{3.4.3}$$

Comparing (3.4.3) with equation (3.1.1), which defines $\overline{P}_{\xi_1 \times \xi_3/\xi_2}$, we see that for any $E_1 \epsilon S_{x_1}$, $E_2 \epsilon S_{x_2}$, and $E_3 \epsilon S_{x_3}$

$$P_{\xi_1\xi_2\xi_3}(E_1 \times E_2 \times E_3) = \overline{P}_{\xi_1 \times \xi_3/\xi_2}(E_1 \times E_2 \times E_3). \tag{3.4.4}$$

Since the σ-algebra $S_{x_1} \times S_{x_2} \times S_{x_3}$ is generated by sets of the form $E_1 \times E_2 \times E_3$, it follows that $P_{\xi_1\xi_2\xi_3}$ and $\overline{P}_{\xi_1 \times \xi_3/\xi_2}$ coincide on $S_{x_1} \times S_{x_2} \times S_{x_3}$. Therefore

$$\mathbf{E}I(\xi_1, \xi_3/\xi_2) = H_{\overline{P}_{\xi_1 \times \xi_3/\xi_2}}(P_{\xi_1\xi_2\xi_3}) = 0. \tag{3.4.5}$$

Conversely, if $\mathbf{E}I(\xi_1, \xi_3/\xi_2) = \mathbf{H}_{\overline{P}_{\xi_1 \times \xi_3/\xi_2}}(P_{\xi_1\xi_2\xi_3}) = 0$

then by virtue of (3.3.2), $\bar{i}(\xi_1, \xi_3/\xi_2) = 0$ with probability one, and consequently the measures $\overline{P}_{\xi_1 \xi_3/\xi_2}$ and $P_{\xi_1\xi_2\xi_3}$ coincide. This, however, implies that (3.4.3) is satisfied for any $E_1 \epsilon S_{x_1}$, $E_2 \epsilon S_{x_2}$, $E_3 \epsilon S_{x_3}$, and as a consequence (3.4.2) holds with probability one.

Thus, a necessary and sufficient condition for the vanishing of the average conditional information $\mathbf{E}I(\xi_1, \xi_3/\xi_2)$ *is that the random variables* ξ_1, ξ_2, ξ_3 *form a Markov chain.*

3.5. THE THEOREM OF R. L. DOBRUSHIN

THEOREM 3.5.1. Let $\mathscr{L}$ *be an algebra which generates the* σ*-algebra* $S_x \times S_y \times S_z$*, and let* $\mathbf{R}$ *be some class of partitions of* $X \times Y \times Z$ *whose elements belong to* $\mathscr{L}$. *If every partition with elements in* $\mathscr{L}$ *has a subpartition belong to* $\mathbf{R}$, *then*

$$\mathbf{E}I(\eta, \zeta/\xi) = \sup_{\{E_i\}\epsilon R} \sum_i P_{\xi\eta\zeta}(E_i) \log \frac{P_{\xi\eta\zeta}(E_i)}{\overline{P}_{\eta\times\zeta/\xi}(E_i)},\ E_i \epsilon S_x \times S_y \times S_z. \tag{3.5.1}$$

This theorem is obviously a special case of the corresponding theorem for entropy (see Section 2.4). Since the family of all partitions $\{E_i \times F_j \times N_k\}$, consisting of sets of the form $E_i \times F_j \times N_k$, $E_i \in S_x$, $F_j \in S_y$, $N_k \in S_z$, forms a class R which satisfies the conditions of the theorem, it follows that

$$\mathbf{E}I(\eta, \zeta/\xi)$$

$$= \sup_{\{E_i \times F_j \times N_k\}} \sum_{i,j,k} P_{\xi\eta\zeta}(E_i \times F_j \times N_k) \log \frac{P_{\xi\eta\zeta}(E_i \times F_j \times N_k)}{\overline{P}_{\eta \times \zeta/\xi}(E_i \times F_j \times N_k)}. \tag{3.5.2}$$

3.6. KOLMOGOROV'S FORMULA AND A RESULT OF DOBRUSHIN

R.L.Dobrushin has proved [3] the following assertion.

THEOREM 3.6.1. If $P_{\xi\zeta} \ll P_{\xi \times \zeta}$, *and* $P_{\xi\eta\zeta} \ll \overline{P}_{\eta \times \zeta/\xi}$, *then* $P_{\xi\eta\zeta} \ll P_{(\xi,\eta) \times \zeta}$. *Conversely, the last relation implies the first two. Furthermore, if these relations are all satisfied, then*

$$a(\xi, \eta)\, \overline{a}(\eta, \zeta/\xi) = a((\xi, \eta), \zeta); \tag{3.6.1}$$

$$i(\xi, \eta) + \overline{i}(\eta, \zeta/\xi) = i((\xi, \eta), \zeta) \tag{3.6.2}$$

with probability one. As usual, ξ, η, *and* ζ *are random variables taking values in measurable spaces* (X, S_x), (Y, S_y), *and* (Z, S_z).

Taking the mathematical expectation of both sides of (3.6.2), we obtain **Kolmogorov's formula**

$$I(\xi, \eta) + \mathbf{E}I(\eta, \zeta/\xi) = I((\xi, \eta), \zeta). \tag{3.6.3}$$

For our work we need a certain generalization of Dobrushin's result, namely:

THEOREM 3.6.2. If $P_{\nu\xi\zeta} \ll \overline{P}_{\xi \times \zeta/\nu}$ *and* $P_{\nu\xi\eta\zeta} \ll \overline{P}_{\eta \times \zeta/(\nu,\xi)}$, *then* $P_{\nu\xi\eta\zeta} \ll \overline{P}_{(\xi,\eta) \times \zeta/\nu}$. *Conversely, the last relation implies the first two. Here,* ν *is a random variable taking values in the measurable space* (U, S_u). *Furthermore, if these relations are all satisfied, then*

$$\overline{a}(\xi, \zeta/\nu)\, \overline{a}(\eta, \zeta/(\nu, \xi)) = \overline{a}((\xi, \eta), \zeta/\nu); \tag{3.6.4}$$

$$\overline{i}(\xi, \zeta/\nu) + \overline{i}(\eta, \zeta/(\nu, \xi)) = \overline{i}((\xi, \eta), \zeta/\nu) \tag{3.6.5}$$

with probability one, where $\bar{a}_{\eta\zeta/(\nu,\xi)}(u, x, y, z)$ *and* $\bar{a}_{(\xi,\eta)\zeta/\nu}(u, x, y, z)$ *are the densities of* $P_{\nu\xi\eta\zeta}$ *with respect to* $\bar{P}_{\eta\times\zeta/(\nu,\xi)}$ *and* $\bar{P}_{(\xi,\eta)\times\zeta/\nu}$.

Taking the mathematical expectation of both sides of (3.6.5), we obtain a generalization of Kolmogorov's formula

$$\mathbf{E}I(\xi, \zeta/\nu) + \mathbf{E}I(\eta, \zeta/(\nu, \xi)) = \mathbf{E}I(\xi,\eta), \zeta/\nu). \tag{3.6.6}$$

We observe that formula (3.6.6) remains valid even when one of the densities appearing in (3.6.5) does not exist. In fact, according to Theorems 3.6.2 and 2.1.2, both sides of (3.6.6) will then equal $+\infty$. The proof of Theorem 3.6.2 is similar to that of Theorem 3.6.1 of Dobrushin, and will therefore not be carried out here.

Let us note that formula (3.6.6) cannot be obtained from (3.6.3), for the quantities $I(\xi,\eta)$, $\mathbf{E}I(\nu, \xi/\zeta)$, etc. may turn out to be infinite. However, formula (3.6.3) **is** a special case of formula (3.6.6), and can be obtained simply by taking the random variable ν to be a constant.

Remark. It is possible to go still further in generalizing the result of Dobrushin, and to prove the following assertion, which is very useful in solving problems concerning the information stability of random processes.

Let $E \in S_u \times S_x \times S_z$ be the set of absolute continuity of $P_{\nu\xi\zeta}$ with respect to $\bar{P}_{\xi\times\zeta/\nu}$, and $F \in S_u \times S_x \times S_y \times S_z$ be the set of absolute continuity of $P_{\nu\xi\eta\zeta}$ with respect to $\bar{P}_{\eta\times\zeta/(\nu,\xi)}$. Then $(E \times Y \cap F = N \in S_u \times S_x \times S_y \times S_z$ is the set of absolute continuity of $P_{\nu\xi\eta\zeta}$ with respect to $\bar{P}_{(\xi,\eta)\times\zeta/\nu}$, and relations (3.6.4) and (3.6.5) hold for every point $(u, x, y, z) \in N$.

3.7. AVERAGE CONDITIONAL INFORMATION OF FUNCTIONS OF RANDOM VARIABLES

THEOREM 3.7.1. Let the random variables ξ, η, $\tilde{\eta}$, *and* ζ *take values in the measurable spaces* (X, S_x), (Y, S_y), $(\tilde{Y}, S_{\tilde{y}})$, *and* (Z, S_z) *respectively, and let* $\tilde{\eta}$ *be a measurable function of* η, $\tilde{\eta} = f(\eta)$. *Then*

$$EI(f(\eta), \zeta/\xi) = EI(\tilde{\eta}, \zeta/\xi) \leq EI(\eta, \zeta/\xi). \tag{3.7.1}$$

If $\tilde{\eta}$ *is everywhere dense in* η, *then equality holds in (3.7.1), i.e.,*

$$EI(\tilde{\eta}, \zeta/\xi) = EI(\eta, \zeta/\xi) \tag{3.7.2}$$

and with probability one

$$\bar{i}(\tilde{\eta}, \zeta/\xi) = \bar{i}(\eta, \zeta/\xi). \tag{3.7.3}$$

PROOF. Let us denote by $F = \tilde{F}^{-1} \epsilon S_y$ the inverse image $f^{-1}(\tilde{F})$ of the set $\tilde{F} \epsilon S_{\tilde{y}}$. Clearly,

$$P_{\xi\tilde{\eta}\zeta}(E \times \tilde{F} \times N) = P_{\xi\eta\zeta}(E \times F \times N) \tag{3.7.4}$$

for any $E \epsilon S_x$, $\tilde{F} \epsilon S_{\tilde{y}}$, and $N \epsilon S_z$, and

$$P_{\tilde{\eta}/\xi}(\tilde{F}/\xi) = P_{\eta/\xi}(F/\xi), \tag{3.7.5}$$

with probability one. Therefore

$$\overline{P}_{\tilde{\eta}\times\zeta/\xi}(E \times \tilde{F} \times N) = \int_E P_{\tilde{\eta}/\xi}(\tilde{F}/x) P_{\zeta/\xi}(N/x) P_\xi(dx)$$

$$= \int_E P_{\eta/\xi}(F/x) P_{\zeta/\xi}(N/x) P_\xi(dx) = \overline{P}_{\eta\times\zeta/\xi}(E \times F \times N). \tag{3.7.6}$$

If the system of sets $\{\tilde{F}_j\}$ forms a partition of the space $\tilde{Y}$, then obviously the system $\{F_j\}$ forms a partition of the space Y. Together with (3.7.4) and (3.7.6), this implies that any sum which occurs in the supremum (3.5.2) defining $\mathbf{EI}(\tilde{\eta}, \zeta/\xi)$ also occurs in the supremum which defines $\mathbf{EI}(\eta, \zeta/\xi)$. From this follows (3.7.1).

If $\tilde{\eta}$ is everywhere dense in η, then, as was shown in Section 1.2, Chapter 1, for any partition $\{F_j\}$ of the space Y there is a partition $\{\tilde{F}_j\}$ of $\tilde{Y}$ such that

$$P\{\eta \epsilon F_j, \tilde{\eta} \epsilon \tilde{F}_j\} = P_\eta(F_j) = P_{\tilde{\eta}}(\tilde{F}_j). \tag{3.7.7}$$

From (3.7.7) it follows that for any $E_i \epsilon S_x$, $N_k \epsilon S_z$

$$P_{\xi\eta\zeta}(E_i \times F_j \times N_k) = P_{\xi\tilde{\eta}\zeta}(E_i \times \tilde{F}_j \times N_k) \tag{3.7.8}$$

and, with probability one

$$P_{\eta/\xi}(F_j/\xi) = P_{\tilde{\eta}/\xi}(\tilde{F}_j/\xi) \tag{3.7.9}$$

and thus, from (3.7.6) that

$$\overline{P}_{\eta\times\zeta/\xi}(E_i \times F_j \times N_k) = \overline{P}_{\tilde{\eta}\times\zeta/\xi}(E_i \times \tilde{F}_j \times N_k). \tag{3.7.10}$$

Equations (3.7.8) and (3.7.10) show that any sum which occurs in the supremum (3.5.2) defining $\mathbf{EI}(\eta, \zeta/\xi)$ is equal to some one which occurs in the supremum defining $\mathbf{EI}(\tilde{\eta}, \zeta/\xi)$, i.e.,

$$\mathbf{EI}(\eta, \zeta/\xi) \leqslant \mathbf{EI}(\tilde{\eta}, \zeta/\xi). \tag{3.7.11}$$

In conjunction with inequality (3.7.1), this proves (3.7.2). It remains to prove (3.7.3). Since η is everywhere dense in the random variable $(\eta, \tilde{\eta})$, equation (3.7.2) implies that

$$\mathbf{E}I((\eta, \tilde{\eta}), \zeta/\xi) = \mathbf{E}I(\eta, \zeta/\xi) = \mathbf{E}I(\tilde{\eta}, \zeta/\xi). \qquad (3.7.12)$$

On the other hand, by (3.6.6) and (3.6.5)

$$\mathbf{E}I((\eta, \tilde{\eta}), \zeta/\xi) = \mathbf{E}I(\eta, \zeta/\xi) + \mathbf{E}I(\tilde{\eta}, \zeta/(\xi, \eta)); \qquad (3.7.13)$$

and, with probability one

$$\bar{i}((\eta, \tilde{\eta}), \zeta/\xi) = \bar{i}(\eta, \zeta/\xi) + \bar{i}(\tilde{\eta}, \zeta/(\xi, \eta)). \qquad (3.7.14)$$

Similarly

$$\mathbf{E}I((\eta, \tilde{\eta}), \zeta/\xi) = \mathbf{E}I(\tilde{\eta}, \zeta/\xi) + \mathbf{E}I(\eta, \zeta/(\xi, \tilde{\eta})); \qquad (3.7.15)$$

and, with probability one

$$\bar{i}((\eta, \tilde{\eta}), \zeta/\xi) = \bar{i}(\tilde{\eta}, \zeta/\xi) + \bar{i}(\eta, \zeta/(\xi, \tilde{\eta})). \qquad (3.7.16)$$

Comparing equations (3.7.12), (3.7.13), and (3.7.15) shows that

$$\mathbf{E}I(\tilde{\eta}, \zeta/(\xi, \eta)) = \mathbf{E}I(\eta, \zeta/(\xi, \tilde{\eta})) = 0, \qquad (3.7.17)$$

and consequently

$$\bar{i}(\tilde{\eta}, \zeta/(\xi, \eta)) = \bar{i}(\eta, \zeta/(\xi, \tilde{\eta})) = 0 \qquad (3.7.18)$$

with probability one. Finally, comparing (3.7.14), (3.7.16), and (3.7.18) shows that (3.7.3) holds with probability one.

COROLLARY. If the random variable $\tilde{\eta}$ is subordinate to the random variable η, in particular, if $\tilde{\eta}$ is a measurable function of η, then

$$\mathbf{E}I(\eta, \zeta/\xi) = \mathbf{E}I(\tilde{\eta}, \zeta/\xi) + \mathbf{E}I(\eta, \zeta/(\xi, \tilde{\eta})) \qquad (3.7.19)$$

and with probability one

$$\bar{i}(\eta, \zeta/\xi) = \bar{i}(\tilde{\eta}, \zeta/\xi) + \bar{i}(\eta, \zeta/(\xi, \tilde{\eta})). \qquad (3.7.20)$$

If the random variables η and $\tilde{\eta}$, are mutually subordinate, then

$$\mathbf{E}I(\eta, \zeta/\xi) = \mathbf{E}I(\tilde{\eta}, \zeta/\xi) \qquad (3.7.21)$$

and, with probability one

$$\bar{\imath}(\eta, \zeta/\xi) = \bar{\imath}(\tilde{\eta}, \zeta/\xi). \tag{3.7.22}$$

PROOF. If $\tilde{\eta}$ is subordinate to η, then η is everywhere dense in the random variable $(\eta, \tilde{\eta})$, and so by Theorem 3.7.1

$$\mathbf{E}I(\eta, \zeta/\xi) = \mathbf{E}I((\eta, \tilde{\eta}), \zeta/\xi) \tag{3.7.23}$$

and, with probability one

$$\bar{\imath}(\eta, \zeta/\xi) = \bar{\imath}((\eta, \tilde{\eta}), \zeta/\xi). \tag{3.7.24}$$

On the other hand, according to (3.6.6) and (3.6.5),

$$\mathbf{E}I(\tilde{\eta}, \zeta/\xi) + \mathbf{E}I(\eta, \zeta/(\xi, \tilde{\eta})) = \mathbf{E}I((\eta, \tilde{\eta}), \zeta/\xi) \tag{3.7.25}$$

and, with probability one

$$\bar{\imath}(\tilde{\eta}, \zeta/\xi) + \bar{\imath}(\eta, \zeta/(\xi, \tilde{\eta})) = \bar{\imath}((\eta, \tilde{\eta}), \zeta/\xi). \tag{3.7.26}$$

Comparing (3.7.25) with (3.7.23), and (3.7.26) with (3.7.24) verifies (3.7.19) and (3.7.20).

If also η is subordinate to $\tilde{\eta}$, then along with equations (3.7.23) and (3.7.24) we have

$$\mathbf{E}I(\tilde{\eta}, \zeta/\xi) = \mathbf{E}I((\eta, \tilde{\eta}), \zeta/\xi) \tag{3.7.27}$$

and, with probability one

$$\bar{\imath}(\tilde{\eta}, \zeta/\xi) = \bar{\imath}((\tilde{\eta}, \eta), \zeta/\xi). \tag{3.7.28}$$

To verify (3.7.21) and (3.7.22) it suffices to compare (3.7.23) with (3.7.27) and (3.7.24) with (3.7.28).

THEOREM 3.7.2. If the random variable $\tilde{\xi}$ is everywhere dense in ξ, then

$$\mathbf{E}I(\eta, \zeta/\xi) = \mathbf{E}I(\eta, \zeta/\tilde{\xi}) \tag{3.7.29}$$

and, with probability one

$$\bar{\imath}(\eta, \zeta/\xi) = \bar{\imath}(\eta, \zeta/\tilde{\xi}). \tag{3.7.30}$$

PROOF. According to (3.6.6) and (3.6.5)

$$\mathbf{E}I((\eta, \tilde{\xi}), \zeta/\xi) = \mathbf{E}I(\tilde{\xi}, \zeta/\xi) + \mathbf{E}I(\eta, \zeta/(\tilde{\xi}, \xi)) \tag{3.7.31}$$

and, with probability one

$$\bar{i}((\eta, \tilde{\xi}), \zeta/\xi) = \bar{i}(\xi, \zeta/\xi) + \bar{i}(\eta, \zeta/(\tilde{\xi}, \xi)). \tag{3.7.32}$$

By hypotheses $\tilde{\xi}$ is everywhere dense in ξ. Hence $(\eta, \tilde{\xi})$ is everywhere dense in (η, ξ), and it follows from (3.7.2) and (3.7.3) that

$$\mathbf{E}I((\eta, \tilde{\xi}), \zeta/\xi) = \mathbf{E}I((\eta, \xi), \zeta/\xi); \tag{3.7.33}$$

$$\mathbf{E}I(\tilde{\xi}, \zeta/\xi) = \mathbf{E}I(\xi, \zeta/\xi) \tag{3.7.34}$$

and, with probability one

$$\bar{i}((\eta, \tilde{\xi}), \zeta/\xi) = \bar{i}((\eta, \xi), \zeta/\xi); \tag{3.7.35}$$

$$\bar{i}(\tilde{\xi}, \zeta/\xi) = \bar{i}(\xi, \zeta/\xi). \tag{3.7.36}$$

If we substitute the right sides of equations (3.7.33)–(3.7.36) for those terms in (3.7.31) and (3.7.32) which appear on the left sides of (3.7.33)–(3.7.36), we obtain

$$\mathbf{E}I((\eta, \xi), \zeta/\xi) = \mathbf{E}I(\xi, \zeta/\xi) + \mathbf{E}I(\eta, \zeta/(\tilde{\xi}, \xi)) \tag{3.7.37}$$

and, with probability one

$$\bar{i}(\eta, \xi), \zeta/\xi) = \bar{i}(\xi, \zeta/\xi) + \bar{i}(\eta, \zeta/(\tilde{\xi}, \xi)). \tag{3.7.38}$$

According to (3.6.6) and (3.6.5)

$$\mathbf{E}I((\eta, \xi), \zeta/\xi) = \mathbf{E}I(\xi, \zeta/\xi) + \mathbf{E}I(\eta, \zeta/(\xi, \xi)).$$
$$= \mathbf{E}I(\xi, \zeta/\xi) + \mathbf{E}I(\eta, \zeta/\xi) \tag{3.7.39}$$

and, with probability one

$$\bar{i}((\eta, \xi), \zeta/\xi) = \bar{i}(\xi, \zeta/\xi) + \bar{i}(\eta, \zeta/\xi). \tag{3.7.40}$$

Comparing (3.7.37) with (3.7.39) and (3.7.38) with (3.7.40), we find that

$$\mathbf{E}I(\eta, \zeta/(\tilde{\xi}, \xi)) = \mathbf{E}I(\eta, \zeta/\xi) \tag{3.7.41}$$

and, with probability one

$$\bar{\imath}(\eta, \zeta/(\tilde{\xi}, \xi)) = \bar{\imath}(\eta, \zeta/\xi). \quad (3.7.42)$$

If we replace ξ by $\tilde{\xi}$ in equations (3.7.31) and (3.7.32), we can show similarly that

$$\mathbf{E}I(\eta, \zeta/(\tilde{\xi}, \xi)) = \mathbf{E}I(\eta, \zeta/\tilde{\xi}) \quad (3.7.43)$$

and, with probability one

$$\bar{\imath}(\eta, \zeta/(\tilde{\xi}, \xi)) = \bar{\imath}(\eta, \zeta/\tilde{\xi}). \quad (3.7.44)$$

To obtain (3.7.29) and (3.7.30), it suffices to compare (3.7.41) with (3.7.43) and (3.7.42) with (3.7.44).

COROLLARY 1. If the random variables ξ and $\tilde{\xi}$ are mutually subordinate, then

$$\mathbf{E}I(\eta, \zeta/\xi) = \mathbf{E}I(\eta, \zeta/\tilde{\xi}) \quad (3.7.45)$$

and, with probability one

$$\bar{\imath}(\eta, \zeta/\xi) = \bar{\imath}(\eta, \zeta/\tilde{\xi}). \quad (3.7.46)$$

PROOF. Both ξ and $\tilde{\xi}$ are, by hypothesis, everywhere dense in the random variable $(\xi, \tilde{\xi})$. Applying Theorem 3.7.2, we obtain equations of the form (3.7.41)–(3.7.44), from which (3.7.45) and (3.7.46) (3.7.46) follow.

COROLLARY 2. If $\tilde{\xi}$ is subordinate to ξ, then

$$\mathbf{E}I((\eta, \tilde{\xi}), \zeta/\xi) = \mathbf{E}I(\eta, \zeta/\xi) \quad (3.7.47)$$

and, with probability one

$$\bar{\imath}((\eta, \tilde{\xi}), \zeta/\xi) = \bar{\imath}(\eta, \zeta/\xi). \quad (3.7.48)$$

In particular,

$$\mathbf{E}I(\tilde{\xi}, \zeta/\xi) = 0, \text{ and with probability one } \bar{\imath}(\tilde{\xi}, \zeta/\xi) = 0. \quad (3.7.49)$$

The proof of this corollary is similar to that of Corollary 1.

The corollaries to Theorems 3.7.1 and 3.7.2 show that as far as any information relation is concerned, mutually subordinate random variables may be considered as equivalent, in the sense that replacing one of them by the other effects no change in such a relation.

To conclude this section, we will obtain another expression for the conditional information $\mathbf{E}I(\eta, \zeta/\xi)$.

Let $\{F_j\}$ be a partition of the space Y of values of the random variable η, and let β be a measurable function of η, whose values are the sets F_j, defined so that $\eta \in F_j$ implies $\beta = F_j$. By Dobrushin's theorem

$$\mathbf{E}I(\beta, \zeta/\xi) = \sup \sum_{i,j,k} P_{\xi\beta\zeta}(E_i \times F_j \times N_k) \log \frac{P_{\xi\beta\zeta}(E_i \times F_j \times N_k)}{\overline{P}_{\beta\times\zeta/\xi}(E_i \times F_j \times N_k)}, \tag{3.7.50}$$

where the upper bound is taken over all partitions $\{E_i\}$ and $\{N_k\}$ of the spaces X and Z respectively. From (3.7.4) and (3.7.6)

$$P_{\xi\beta\zeta}(E_i \times F_j \times N_k) = P_{\xi\eta\zeta}(E_i \times F_j \times N_k), \ \overline{P}_{\beta\times\zeta/\xi}(E_i \times F_j \times N_k)$$
$$= \overline{P}_{\eta\times\zeta/\xi}(E_i \times F_j \times N_k),$$

and therefore, comparing (3.7.50) with (3.5.2), we conclude that

$$\mathbf{E}I(\eta, \zeta/\xi) = \sup_{\{F_j\}} \mathbf{E}I(\beta, \zeta/\xi) = \sup_{\beta} \mathbf{E}I(\beta, \zeta/\xi). \tag{3.7.51}$$

It should be noted that according to Dobrushin's theorem, the upper bound in (3.7.51) may be restricted to partitions from a class R such that any partition, consisting of elements of a given algebra $\mathscr{L}$ which generates S_y, has a subpartition which belongs to the class R.

3.8. DOBRUSHIN'S FORMULA

According to relations (3.6.6) and (3.6.5)

$$\mathbf{E}I((\xi, \eta), \zeta/\nu) = \mathbf{E}I(\xi, \zeta/\nu) + \mathbf{E}I(\eta, \zeta/(\xi, \nu)); \tag{3.8.1}$$

$$\mathbf{E}I(\eta, (\zeta, \xi)/\nu) = \mathbf{E}I(\eta, \xi/\nu) + \mathbf{E}I(\eta, \zeta/(\xi, \nu)) \tag{3.8.2}$$

and with probability one

$$\bar{i}((\xi, \eta), \zeta/\nu) = \bar{i}(\xi, \zeta/\nu) + \bar{i}(\eta, \zeta/(\xi, \nu)); \tag{3.8.3}$$

$$\bar{i}(\eta, (\zeta, \xi)/\nu) = \bar{i}(\eta, \xi/\nu) + \bar{i}(\eta, \zeta/(\xi, \nu)). \tag{3.8.4}$$

Comparing (3.8.1) with (3.8.2) and (3.8.3) with (3.8.4), we obtain **Dobrushin's formula**

$$\mathbf{E}I((\xi, \eta), \zeta/\nu) + \mathbf{E}I(\xi, \eta/\nu) = \mathbf{E}I(\eta, (\xi, \zeta)/\nu) + \mathbf{E}I(\xi, \zeta/\nu) \tag{3.8.5}$$

and, with probability one

$$\bar{i}((\xi, \eta), \zeta/\nu) + \bar{i}(\xi, \eta/\nu) = \bar{i}(\eta, (\xi, \zeta)/\nu) + \bar{i}(\xi, \zeta/\nu). \tag{3.8.6}$$

Dobrushin obtained a special case of this formula, namely

$$I((\xi, \eta), \zeta) + I(\xi, \eta) = I(\eta, (\xi, \zeta)) + I(\xi, \zeta). \tag{3.8.7}$$

3.9. PROPERTIES OF THE ENTROPY OF RANDOM VARIABLES

(1) $\mathbf{E}H(\xi/\zeta) \geqslant 0$ (3.9.1)

and

$\mathbf{E}H(\xi/\zeta) = 0,$ (3.9.2)

if and only if ξ *is subordinate to* ζ.

In fact, $\mathbf{E}H(\xi/\zeta) = \mathbf{E}I(\xi, \xi/\zeta)$, and so (3.9.1) follows from the corresponding property of average conditional information. If ξ is subordinate to ζ, then by Corollary 2 of Theorem 3.7.2

$$\mathbf{E}H(\xi/\zeta) = \mathbf{E}I(\xi, \xi/\zeta) = 0.$$

On the other hand, if the preceding equality holds, then by Section 3.4 the sequence ξ, ζ, ξ forms a Markov chain. According to (3.4.2), then,

$$P\{\xi\epsilon E/\zeta\} = P\{\xi\epsilon E, \xi\epsilon E/\zeta\} = P\{\xi\epsilon E/\zeta\}P\{\xi\epsilon E/\zeta\},$$
$$E\epsilon S_x, P_\xi(E) > 0 \tag{3.9.3}$$

with probability one, where $E\epsilon S_x$ and $P_\xi(E) > 0$. But (3.9.3) can hold only if, with probability one, $P\{\xi\epsilon E/\zeta\}$ takes only the values zero and one. Let $F\epsilon Z$, the space of values of ζ, be the set on which $P\{\xi\epsilon E/\zeta\} = 1$; then

$$P\{\xi\epsilon E\} = \int_Z P\{\xi\epsilon E/z\}P_\zeta(dz) = \int_F P_\zeta(dz) = P_\zeta(F)$$

and

$$P\{\xi\epsilon E\} = \int_Z P\{\xi\epsilon E/z\}P_\zeta(dz) = \int_F P\{\xi\epsilon E/z\}P_\zeta(dz) = P_{\xi\zeta}(E \times F),$$

i.e., for any set $E \in S_x$ there is a set $F \in S_z$ such that

$$P_{\xi}(E) = P_{\zeta}(F) = P_{\xi\zeta}(E \times F).$$

But this implies that ζ is everywhere dense in (ξ, ζ), i.e., that ξ is subordinate to ζ.

(2) $$\mathbf{E}H(\xi/\zeta) \geqslant \mathbf{E}I(\eta, \xi/\zeta), \tag{3.9.4}$$

in particular

$$H(\xi) \geqslant I(\eta, \xi). \tag{3.9.5}$$

$$\mathbf{E}H(\xi/\zeta) = \mathbf{E}I(\eta, \xi/\zeta) \tag{3.9.6}$$

if and only if ξ *is subordinate to the random variable* (η, ζ); *in particular*

$$H(\xi) = I(\eta, \xi) \tag{3.9.7}$$

if and only if ξ *is subordinate to* η.

In fact, $\mathbf{E}I(\eta, \xi/\zeta) \leqslant \mathbf{E}I(\eta, \xi), \xi/\zeta) = \mathbf{E}I(\xi, \xi/\zeta) + \mathbf{E}I(\eta, \xi/(\xi, \zeta)) = \mathbf{E}H(\xi/\zeta) + \mathbf{E}I(\eta, \xi/(\xi, \zeta))$, where the inequality follows from (3.7.1) and the equality from (3.6.6). Since ξ is subordinate to (ξ, ζ), the very last term vanishes by virtue of (3.7.49), which yields precisely (3.9.4).

If now ξ is subordinate to (η, ζ), then $\mathbf{E}H(\xi/\zeta)$

$$= \mathbf{E}I(\xi, \xi/\zeta) \leqslant \mathbf{E}I((\eta, \zeta), \xi/\zeta) = \mathbf{E}I(\eta, \xi/\zeta) + \mathbf{E}I(\zeta, \xi/(\eta, \zeta)).$$

Since $\mathbf{E}I(\zeta, \xi/(\eta, \zeta)) = 0$,

$$\mathbf{E}H(\xi/\zeta) \leqslant \mathbf{E}I(\eta, \xi/\zeta), \tag{3.9.8}$$

and together with (3.9.4), this implies (3.9.6). Conversely, suppose that (3.9.6) holds. Since ξ is subordinate to $((\xi, \eta), \zeta)$, (3.9.6) holds with η replaced by (ξ, η), i.e.,

$$\mathbf{E}H(\xi/\zeta) = \mathbf{E}I((\xi, \eta), \xi/\zeta).$$

Using (3.6.6)

$$\mathbf{E}I((\xi, \eta), \xi/\zeta) = \mathbf{E}I(\eta, \xi/\zeta) + \mathbf{E}I(\xi, \xi/(\eta, \zeta)).$$

Comparing this with (3.9.6), which holds by hypothesis, we see that

$$0 = \mathbf{E}I(\xi, \xi/(\eta, \zeta)) = \mathbf{E}H(\xi/(\eta, \zeta))$$

which, according to property 1, implies that ξ is subordinate to (η, ζ).

(3) If the random variable $\tilde{\xi}$ *is subordinate to* ξ, *then*

$$\mathbf{E}H(\xi/\zeta) = \mathbf{E}H(\tilde{\xi}/\zeta) + \mathbf{E}H(\xi/(\zeta, \tilde{\xi})). \tag{3.9.9}$$

In particular

$$H(\xi) = H(\tilde{\xi}) + \mathbf{E}H(\xi/\tilde{\xi}). \tag{3.9.10}$$

PROOF. We have

$$\mathbf{E}H(\xi/\zeta) = \mathbf{E}I(\xi, \xi/\zeta) = \mathbf{E}I((\xi, \tilde{\xi}), \xi/\zeta) = \mathbf{E}I(\tilde{\xi}, \xi/\zeta) + \mathbf{E}I(\xi, \xi/(\tilde{\xi}, \zeta))$$

$$= \mathbf{E}I(\tilde{\xi}, \xi/\zeta) + \mathbf{E}H(\xi/(\tilde{\xi}, \zeta)).$$

Since $\tilde{\xi}$ is certainly subordinate to (ξ, ζ), according to property 2

$$\mathbf{E}I(\tilde{\xi}, \xi/\zeta) = \mathbf{E}H(\tilde{\xi}/\zeta).$$

Comparing the last two equations, we obtain (3.9.9).

COROLLARY (a)

$$\mathbf{E}H((\xi, \eta)/\zeta) = \mathbf{E}H(\xi/\zeta) + \mathbf{E}H(\eta/(\xi, \zeta)), \tag{3.9.11}$$

in particular

$$H((\xi, \eta)) = H(\xi) + \mathbf{E}H(\eta/\xi). \tag{3.9.12}$$

(b) If ξ *and* $\tilde{\xi}$ *are mutually subordinate, then*

$$\mathbf{E}H(\xi/\zeta) = \mathbf{E}H(\tilde{\xi}/\zeta), \tag{3.9.13}$$

in particular

$$H(\xi) = H(\tilde{\xi}). \tag{3.9.14}$$

Equality (3.9.11) follows from (3.6.6) and the use of (3.9.6), and (3.9.13) follows from a double application of (3.7.21). The special cases (3.9.12) and (3.9.14) are obtained by letting ζ be a constant random variable.

(4) If the random variable $\tilde{\zeta}$ *is subordinate to* ζ, *then*

$$\mathbf{E}H(\xi/\tilde{\zeta}) \geqslant \mathbf{E}H(\xi/\zeta), \tag{3.9.15}$$

in particular

$$H(\xi) \geqslant \mathbf{E}H(\xi/\zeta). \tag{3.9.16}$$

In fact, by property 2

$$\mathbf{E}H(\xi/\tilde{\zeta}) = \mathbf{E}I(\xi, \xi/\tilde{\zeta}) = \mathbf{E}I(\xi, (\xi, \zeta)/\tilde{\zeta}).$$

and, according to (3.6.6)

$$\mathbf{E}I(\xi, (\xi, \zeta)/\tilde{\zeta}) = \mathbf{E}I(\xi, \zeta/\tilde{\zeta}) + \mathbf{E}I(\xi, \xi/(\zeta, \tilde{\zeta})).$$

Since ζ and $(\zeta, \tilde{\zeta})$ are mutally subordinate

$$\mathbf{E}I(\xi, \xi/(\zeta, \tilde{\zeta})) = \mathbf{E}I(\xi, \xi/\zeta) = \mathbf{E}H(\xi/\zeta).$$

Comparing the last three equalities yields (3.9.15).

COROLLARY (a) $EH(\xi/\zeta) \geqslant EH(\xi/(\eta, \zeta))$ (3.9.17)

and in particular

$$H(\xi) \geqslant EH(\xi/\eta). \tag{3.9.18}$$

(b) If ζ *and* $\tilde{\zeta}$ *are mutually subordinate, then*

$$EH(\xi/\tilde{\zeta}) = EH(\xi/\zeta). \tag{3.9.19}$$

3.10. LIMIT RELATIONS FOR AVERAGE CONDITIONAL INFORMATION

We formulate the main result of this section as a theorem.

THEOREM 3.10.1.

(1)

$$\lim_{n\to\infty} \mathbf{E}I((\eta_1, \ldots, \eta_n), \zeta/\xi) = \mathbf{E}I((\eta_1\eta_2, \ldots), \zeta/\xi) = \mathbf{E}I(\eta, \zeta/\xi) \tag{3.10.1}$$

and

$$\lim_{n\to\infty} \mathbf{E}|\bar{i}((\eta_1, \ldots, \eta_n), \zeta/\xi) - \bar{i}(\eta, \zeta/\xi)| = 0, \tag{3.10.2}$$

i.e., as $n \to \infty$, *the conditional information density* $\bar{i}((\eta_1, \ldots, \eta_n), \zeta/\xi)$ *converges in the mean to the information density* $\bar{i}(\eta, \zeta/\xi)$.

$$\varliminf_{n\to\infty} \mathbf{E}I(\eta, \zeta/(\xi_1, \ldots, \xi_n)) \geqslant \mathbf{E}I(\eta, \zeta/\xi) \tag{3.10.3}$$

and if

$$\lim_{n\to\infty} \mathbf{E}I(\eta, \zeta/(\xi_1, \ldots, \xi_n)) = \mathbf{E}I(\eta, \zeta/\xi), \tag{3.10.4}$$

then

$$\lim_{n\to\infty} \mathbf{E}\, |\bar{i}(\eta, \zeta/(\xi_1, \ldots, \xi_n)) - \bar{i}(\eta, \zeta/\xi)| = 0. \tag{3.10.5}$$

i.e., as $n \to \infty$, *the information density* $\bar{i}(\eta, \zeta/(\xi_1, \ldots, \xi_n))$ *converges in the mean to the information density* $\bar{i}(\eta, \zeta/\xi)$.
Here, $\xi = (\xi_1, \xi_2, \ldots)$, $\eta = (\eta_1, \eta_2, \ldots)$, $\xi_1, \xi_2, \ldots, \eta_1, \eta_2, \ldots,$ and ζ are random variables taking values in the measurable spaces (X, S_x), (Y, S_y), (X_1, S_{x_1}), $(X_2, S_{x_2}), \ldots,$ (Y_1, S_{y_1}), $(Y_2, S_{y_2}), \ldots,$ and (Z, S_z) respectively.

PROOF. (1) The proof of equality (3.10.1) follows from Dobrushin's theorem in a manner analogous to the proof of (2.2.6), which is the corresponding result for the unconditional information, if we note that

$$P_{\xi(\eta_1\ldots\eta_n)\zeta}(E \times F_1 \times \ldots \times F_n \times N)$$
$$= P_{\xi(\eta_1\ldots\eta_n\eta_{n+1}\ldots)\zeta}(E \times F_1 \times \ldots \times F_n \times Y_{n+1} \times \ldots \times N) \tag{3.10.6}$$

and

$$\overline{P}_{(\eta_1\ldots\eta_n)\times\zeta/\xi}(E \times F_1 \times \ldots \times F_n \times N)$$
$$= \int_E P_{(\eta_1\ldots\eta_n)/\xi}(F_1 \times \ldots \times F_n/x) P_{\zeta/\xi}(N/x) P_\xi(dx)$$
$$= \int_E P_{(\eta_1\ldots\eta_n\eta_{n+1}\ldots)/\xi}(F_1 \times \ldots\ F_n \times Y_{n+1}$$
$$\times \ldots/x) P_{\zeta/\xi}(N/x) P_\xi(dx) = \overline{P}(\eta_1\ldots\eta_n\eta_{n+1}\ldots)\times_{\zeta/\xi}(E \times F_1$$
$$\times \ldots \times F_n \times Y_{n+1} \times \ldots \times N) \tag{3.10.7}$$

To obtain (3.10.2), we use (3.6.6) and (3.6.5):

$$\mathbf{E}I(\eta, \zeta/\xi) = \mathbf{E}I((\eta_1, \ldots, \eta_n, \eta_{n+1}, \ldots), \zeta/\xi) = \mathbf{E}I((\eta_1, \ldots, \eta_n), \zeta/\xi)$$
$$+ \mathbf{E}I((\eta_{n+1}, \ldots), \zeta/(\xi, \eta_1, \ldots, \eta_n)); \tag{3.10.8}$$

$$\bar{i}(\eta, \zeta/\xi) = \bar{i}((\eta_1, \ldots, \eta_n, \eta_{n+1}, \ldots), \zeta/\xi)$$
$$= \bar{i}((\eta_1, \ldots, \eta_n), \zeta/\xi) + \bar{i}((\eta_{n+1}, \ldots), \zeta/(\xi, \eta_1, \ldots, \eta_n)).\text{*} \tag{3.10.9}$$

---

*Henceforth we will frequently omit the phrase "with probability one."

Comparing (3.10.1) with (3.10.8) shows that

$$\lim_{n\to\infty} \mathbf{E}I((\eta_{n+1}, \ldots), \zeta/(\xi, \eta_1, \ldots, \eta_n))$$
$$= \lim_{n\to\infty} \mathbf{E}\bar{i}((\eta_{n+1}, \ldots), \zeta/(\xi, \eta_1, \ldots, \eta_n)) = 0. \qquad (3.10.10)$$

But in view of (3.3.2), this implies that

$$\lim_{n\to\infty} \mathbf{E}|\bar{i}((\eta_{n+1}, \ldots), \zeta/(\xi, \eta_1, \ldots, \eta_n))| = 0. \qquad (3.10.11)$$

Combining (3.10.9 and (3.10.11) proves (3.10.2)

(2) Let us assume first that the random variable η takes on only finitely many values, so that the information $I(\eta, (\xi, \zeta)) \leqslant H(\eta)$ is finite, and by (3.6.3) and (3.6.2)

$$I(\eta, (\xi, \zeta)) = I(\eta, \xi) + \mathbf{E}I(\eta, \zeta/\xi);$$
$$I(\eta, ((\xi_1, \ldots, \xi_n), \zeta)) = I(\eta, (\xi_1, \ldots, \xi_n)) + \mathbf{E}I(\eta, \zeta/(\xi_1, \ldots, \xi_n));$$
$$i(\eta, (\xi, \zeta)) = i(\eta, \xi) + \bar{i}(\eta, \zeta/\xi); \quad i(\eta, (\xi_1, \ldots, \xi_n, \zeta))$$
$$= i(\eta, (\xi_1, \ldots, \xi_n)) + \bar{i}(\eta, \zeta/(\xi_1, \ldots, \xi_n)).$$

Hence

$$\mathbf{E}I(\eta, \zeta/\xi) - \mathbf{E}I(\eta, \zeta/(\xi_1, \ldots, \xi_n))$$
$$= [I(\eta, (\xi, \zeta)) - I(\eta, (\xi_1, \ldots, \xi_n, \zeta))] - [I(\eta, \xi) - I(\eta, (\xi_1, \ldots, \xi_n))]; \qquad (3.10.12)$$

$$\bar{i}(\eta, \zeta/\xi) - \bar{i}(\eta, \zeta/(\xi_1, \ldots, \xi_n))$$
$$= [i(\eta, (\xi, \zeta)) - i(\eta, (\xi_1, \ldots, \xi_n, \zeta)] - [i(\eta, \xi) - i(\eta, (\xi_1, \ldots, \xi_n))]. \qquad (3.10.13)$$

As we have just proved, the right side of (3.10.12) converges to zero as $n \to \infty$, and the right side of (3.10.13) converges in the mean to zero, i.e., in the present case

$$\lim_{n\to\infty} \mathbf{E}I(\eta, \zeta/(\xi_1, \ldots, \xi_n)) = \mathbf{E}I(\eta, \zeta/\xi)$$

and

$$\lim_{n\to\infty} \mathbf{E}|\bar{i}(\eta, \zeta/(\xi_1, \ldots, \xi_n)) - \bar{i}(\eta, \zeta/\xi)| = 0.$$

We consider now the general case. According to (3.7.51)

$$\mathbf{E}I(\eta, \zeta/\xi) = \sup_{\beta} \mathbf{E}I(\beta, \zeta/\xi), \qquad (3.10.14)$$

where β is a random variable which is a measurable function of η and which takes on only finitely many values. But then, as we have just shown,

$$\lim_{n\to\infty} \mathbf{E}\mathrm{I}(\beta, \zeta/(\xi_1, \ldots, \xi_n)) = \mathbf{E}\mathrm{I}(\beta, \zeta/\xi),$$

and

$$\mathbf{E}\mathrm{I}(\eta, \zeta/(\xi_1, \ldots, \xi_n)) \geqslant \mathbf{E}\mathrm{I}(\beta, \zeta/(\xi_1, \ldots, \xi_n))$$

from which it follows that

$$\varliminf_{n\to\infty} \mathbf{E}\mathrm{I}(\eta, \zeta/(\xi_1, \ldots, \xi_n)) \geqslant \mathbf{E}\mathrm{I}(\beta, \zeta/\xi). \tag{3.10.15}$$

Comparing (3.10.14) with (3.10.15) proves (3.10.3).

It remains to consider the case when (3.10.4) holds. According to (3.7.19) and (3.7.20)

$$\mathbf{E}\mathrm{I}(\eta, \zeta/\xi) = \mathbf{E}\mathrm{I}(\beta, \zeta/\xi) + \mathbf{E}\mathrm{I}(\eta, \zeta/(\beta, \xi)); \tag{3.10.16}$$

$$\mathbf{E}\mathrm{I}(\eta, \zeta/(\xi_1, \ldots, \xi_n)) = \mathbf{E}\mathrm{I}(\beta, \zeta/(\xi_1, \ldots, \xi_n)) + \mathbf{E}\mathrm{I}(\eta, \zeta/(\beta, \xi_1, \ldots, \xi_n)) \tag{3.10.17}$$

and

$$\bar{\mathrm{i}}(\eta, \zeta/\xi) = \bar{\mathrm{i}}(\beta, \zeta/\xi) + \bar{\mathrm{i}}(\eta, \zeta/(\beta, \xi));$$
$$\bar{\mathrm{i}}(\eta, \zeta/(\xi_1, \ldots, \xi_n)) = \bar{\mathrm{i}}(\beta, \zeta/(\xi_1, \ldots, \xi_n)) + \bar{\mathrm{i}}(\eta, \zeta/(\beta, \xi_1, \ldots, \xi_n))$$

from which

$$|\bar{\mathrm{i}}(\eta, \zeta/\xi) - \bar{\mathrm{i}}(\eta, \zeta/(\xi_1, \ldots, \xi_n))| \leqslant |\bar{\mathrm{i}}(\beta, \zeta/\xi) - \bar{\mathrm{i}}(\beta, \zeta/(\xi_1, \ldots, \xi_n))| + |\bar{\mathrm{i}}(\eta, \zeta/(\beta, \xi))| + |\bar{\mathrm{i}}(\eta, \zeta/(\beta, \xi_1, \ldots, \xi_n))|. \tag{3.10.18}$$

Let us estimate the expectations of the terms on the right side of (3.10.18). We have proved that

$$\lim_{n\to\infty} \mathbf{E}|\bar{\mathrm{i}}(\beta, \zeta/\xi) - \bar{\mathrm{i}}(\beta, \zeta/(\xi_1, \ldots, \xi_n)| = 0,$$

and therefore for any $\epsilon > 0$ we have

$$\mathbf{E}|\bar{\mathrm{i}}(\beta, \zeta/\xi) - \bar{\mathrm{i}}(\beta, \zeta/(\xi_1, \ldots, \xi_n))| < \epsilon \tag{3.10.19}$$

for all n sufficiently large. In view of (3.10.14) we can choose β so that

$$\mathbf{E}\bar{i}(\eta, \zeta/(\beta, \xi)) = \mathbf{E}I(\eta, \zeta/(\beta, \xi)) = \mathbf{E}I(\eta, \zeta/\xi) - \mathbf{E}I(\beta, \zeta/\xi) < \epsilon \tag{3.10.20}$$

Now $\mathbf{E}I(\eta, \zeta/(\xi_1, \ldots, \xi_n))$ converges to $\mathbf{E}I(\eta, \zeta/\xi)$ by assumption, and we have proved that $\mathbf{E}I(\beta, \zeta/(\xi_1, \ldots, \xi_n))$ converges to $\mathbf{E}I(\beta, \zeta/\xi)$. In conjunction with (3.10.16) and (3.10.17) this shows that $\mathbf{E}I(\eta, \zeta/(\beta, \xi_1, \ldots, \xi_n))$ converges to $\mathbf{E}I(\eta, \zeta/(\beta, \xi))$, and consequently

$$\mathbf{E}\bar{i}(\eta, \zeta/(\beta, \xi_1, \ldots, \xi_n)) = \mathbf{E}I(\eta, \zeta/(\beta, \xi_1, \ldots, \xi_n)) \leqslant \mathbf{E}I(\eta, \zeta/(\beta, \xi)) + \epsilon \leqslant 2\epsilon \tag{3.10.21}$$

for all n sufficiently large.
Now (3.10.20) and (3.10.21) imply, according to (3.3.2), that

$$\mathbf{E}|\bar{i}(\eta, \zeta/(\beta, \xi))| \leqslant \epsilon + \Gamma\sqrt{\epsilon},$$
$$\mathbf{E}|\bar{i}(\eta, \zeta/(\beta, \xi_1, \ldots, \xi_n)| \leqslant 2\epsilon + \Gamma\sqrt{2\epsilon} \tag{3.10.22}$$

Comparing (3.10.18), (3.10.19) and (3.10.22) leads to (3.10.5).

COROLLARY 1. The information density $i((\xi_1, \ldots, \xi_n), \eta)$ *of the random variables* $(\xi_1, \ldots, \xi_n)$ *and* η *converges in the mean to the information density* $i(\xi, \eta)$ *of the random variables* $\xi = (\xi_1, \xi_2, \ldots)$ *and* η, *i.e.*,

$$\lim_{n\to\infty} \mathbf{E}|i((\xi_1, \ldots, \xi_n), \eta) - i(\xi, \eta)| = 0. \tag{3.10.23}$$

COROLLARY 2. Let $\eta = (\eta_1, \eta_2, \ldots)$, $\zeta = (\zeta_1, \zeta_2, \ldots)$, *and* $\xi = (\xi_1, \xi_2, \ldots)$. *Then*

$$\underline{\lim}_{n,k,l\to\infty} \mathbf{E}I((\eta_1, \ldots, \eta_k), (\zeta_1, \ldots, \zeta_l)/(\xi_1, \ldots, \xi_n)) \geqslant \mathbf{E}I(\eta, \zeta/\xi). \tag{3.10.24}$$

If, however,

$$\lim_{n,k,l\to\infty} \mathbf{E}I((\eta_1, \ldots, \eta_k), (\zeta_1, \ldots, \zeta_l)/(\xi_1, \ldots, \xi_n)) = \mathbf{E}I(\eta, \zeta/\xi), \tag{3.10.25}$$

then

$$\lim_{n,k,l\to\infty} \mathbf{E}|\bar{i}((\eta_1, \ldots, \eta_k), (\zeta_1, \ldots, \zeta_l)/(\xi_1, \ldots, \xi_n)) - \bar{i}(\eta, \zeta/\xi)| = 0. \tag{3.10.26}$$

In particular, the equality holds when $\eta_1 = \eta_2 = \ldots$ *and* $\eta_1, \eta_2, \ldots$ *take on only finitely many values.*

THEOREM 3.10.2. Let $\xi, \xi_1, \zeta_2, \ldots, \eta, \zeta$ *be random variables taking values respectively in the measurable spaces* $(\tilde{X}, S_{\tilde{x}})$, (X_1, S_{x_1}), $(X_2, S_{x_2}), \ldots, (Y, S_y)$, (Z, S_z), *and let* S_x', $S_x'^{(n)}$ *and* $S_x''^{(n)}$ *be* σ*-sub-*

algebras of the σ*-algebra* $S_x = S_{\tilde{x}} \times \overset{\infty}{\underset{i=1}{\times}} S_{x_i}$, *generated respectively by sets of the form* $\tilde{E} \times X_1 \times X_2 \times \ldots ; \tilde{E} \times X_1 \times \ldots \times X_{n-1} \times E_n \times E_{n+1} \times \ldots ; \tilde{X} \times X_1 \times X \ldots \times X_{n-1} \times E_n \times E_{n+1} \times \ldots ; \tilde{E} \in S_{\tilde{x}}, E_j \in S_{x_j}$, $j = 1, 2, \ldots$.

Then: (1) If the σ*-algebra* S'_x *is everywhere dense in the* σ*-algebra* $\bar{S}'_x = \bigcap_{n=1}^{\infty} S'^{(n)}_x$ *with respect to the measure* $P_\xi = P_{\tilde{\xi}\xi_1\xi_2\ldots}$, *then*

$$\varliminf_{n\to\infty} \mathbf{E}I(\eta, \zeta/(\tilde{\xi}, \xi_n, \xi_{n+1}, \ldots)) \geqslant \mathbf{E}I(\eta, \zeta/\tilde{\xi}). \tag{3.10.27}$$

If, however,

$$\lim_{n\to\infty} \mathbf{E}I(\eta, \zeta/(\tilde{\xi}, \xi_n, \xi_{n+1}, \ldots)) = \mathbf{E}I(\eta, \zeta/\tilde{\xi}), \tag{3.10.28}$$

then

$$\lim_{n\to\infty} \mathbf{E}|\bar{i}(\eta, \zeta/(\tilde{\xi}, \xi_n, \xi_{n+1}, \ldots)) - \bar{i}(\eta, \zeta/\tilde{\xi})| = 0, \tag{3.10.29}$$

i.e., as $n \to \infty$, *the information density* $\bar{i}(\eta, \zeta/(\tilde{\xi}, \xi_n, \xi_{n+1} \ldots))$ *converges in the mean to the information density* $\bar{i}(\eta, \zeta/\tilde{\xi})$.

(2) If the σ*-algebras* $\bar{S}''_x = \bigcap_{n=1}^{\infty} S''^{(n)}_x$ *and* S'_x *are everywhere dense in the* σ*-algebra* $\bar{S}'_x$ *with respect to the measure* P_ξ, *then*

$$\varliminf_{n\to\infty} \mathbf{E}I(\eta, \zeta/(\xi_n, \xi_{n+1}, \ldots)) \geqslant \mathbf{E}I(\eta, \zeta/\tilde{\xi}). \tag{3.10.30}$$

If, however,

$$\lim_{n\to\infty} \mathbf{E}I(\eta, \zeta/(\xi_n, \xi_{n+1}, \ldots)) = \mathbf{E}I(\eta, \zeta/\tilde{\xi}), \tag{3.10.31}$$

then

$$\lim_{n\to\infty} \mathbf{E}|\bar{i}(\eta, \zeta/(\xi_n, \xi_{n+1}, \ldots)) - \bar{i}(\eta, \zeta/\tilde{\xi})| = 0, \tag{3.10.32}$$

i.e., the information density $\bar{i}(\eta, \zeta/(\xi_n, \xi_{n+1}, \ldots))$ *converges in the mean to the information density* $\bar{i}(\eta, \zeta/\tilde{\xi})$.

COROLLARY. *Let* S^n_x *be the* σ*-subalgebra of the* σ*-algebra* $S_x = S_{x_1} \times S_{x_2} \times \ldots$, *generated by sets of the form* $X_1 \times \ldots \times X_{n-1} \times E_n \times E_{n+1} \times \ldots$, $E_j \in S_{x_j}$, $j = 1, 2, \ldots$. *If the* σ*-algebra* $\bar{S}_x = \bigcap_{n=1}^{\infty} S^n_x$ *contains only sets of measure zero or one with respect to the measure* $P_\xi = P_{\xi_1\xi_2\ldots}$, *then*

$$\varliminf_{n\to\infty} \mathbf{E}I(\eta, \zeta/(\xi_n, \xi_{n+1}, \ldots)) \geqslant I(\eta, \zeta); \tag{3.10.33}$$

and if

$$\lim_{n\to\infty} \mathbf{E} I(\eta, \zeta/(\xi_n, \xi_{n+1}, \ldots)) = I(\eta, \zeta), \tag{3.10.34}$$

then

$$\lim_{n\to\infty} \mathbf{E} |\bar{i}(\eta, \zeta/(\xi_n, \xi_{n+1}, \ldots)) - i(\eta, \zeta)| = 0. \tag{3.10.35}$$

3.11. CONDITIONAL ENTROPY

The concept of conditional information is contained, in a natural way, in the concept of conditional entropy.

Let P_1 and P_2 be two probability measures defined on the measurable space $(\Omega, S_\omega) = (\Omega' \times \Omega'', S_{\omega'} \times S_{\omega''})$, and suppose that the measure $P_1'\{E\} = P_1\{E \times \Omega''\}$, $E \in S_{\omega'}$, defined on the measurable space Ω', is absolutely continuous with respect to the measure $P_2'\{E\} = P_2\{E \times \Omega''\}$, and that $a(\omega') = a\, P_2'(\omega', P_1')$ is the density of $P_1'\{\cdot\}$ with respect to $P_2'\{\cdot\}$.

For fixed $F \in S_{\omega''}$ the conditional probability $P_2\{F/\omega'\} = P_2\{\omega'' \in F/\omega'\}$ is a measurable function of $\omega' \in \Omega'$, defined up to an ω'-set of P_2' measure zero, and for any disjoint sequence of sets $F_1, F_2, \ldots \in S_{\omega''}$ we have

$$\sum_{i=1}^{\infty} P_2\{F_i/\omega'\} = P_2\left\{\bigcup_{i=1}^{\infty} F_i/\omega'\right\}$$

almost everywhere with respect to P_2'. The function

$$\begin{aligned}\bar{P}_2\{E \times F/S_{\omega'}\} &= \int_E P_2\{F/\omega'\} a(\omega') P_2'\{d\omega'\} \\ &= \int_E P_2\{F/\omega'\} P_1'\{d\omega'\}\end{aligned} \tag{3.11.1}$$

is completely additive on the family of sets of the form $E \times F$, $E \in S_{\omega'}$, $F \in S_{\omega''}$ and may therefore be extended to a **probability measure** $\bar{P}_2\{\cdot/S_{\omega'}\}$ defined on the σ-algebra $S_\omega = S_{\omega'} \times S_{\omega''}$.*

---

*In fact, it is easy to show that $\bar{P}_2\{N/S_{\omega'}\} = \int_N a(\omega') dP_2$ for any $N \in S_\omega$. Tr.

The entropy of the measure $P_1\{\cdot\}$ with respect to the measure $\bar{P}_2\{\cdot/S_{\omega}'\}$, denoted by

$$\mathbf{E}H_{P_2}(P_1/S_{\omega}') = H_{\bar{P}_2\{\cdot/S_{\omega}'\}}(P_1), \tag{3.11.2}$$

is called the **average conditional entropy** of P_1 with respect to P_2 and the σ-algebra S_{ω}'. The function

$$\bar{h}_{P_2}(\omega, P_1/S_{\omega}') = h_{\bar{P}_2}\{\cdot/S_{\omega}'\}(\omega, P_1), \ \omega\in\Omega = \Omega' \times \Omega'' \tag{3.11.3}$$

is called the **conditional entropy density**. In general, those facts which we have established for the average conditional information continue to hold for the average conditional entropy. We will only repeat here the formulation of Dobrushin's result and write down Kolmogorov's formula.

THEOREM 3.11.1. If $P_1' \ll P_2'$ and $P_1 \ll \bar{P}_2'[\{\cdot/S_{\omega}'\}$, then $P_1 \ll P_2$. Conversely, the validity of the last relation implies that of the first two.

If all the above relations hold, then

$$h_{P_2}(\cdot, P_1) = h_{P_2'}(\cdot, P_1') + \bar{h}_{P_2}(\cdot, P_1/S_{\omega'}) \tag{3.11.4}$$

almost everywhere with respect to P_1. Taking the mathematical expectation of both sides of (3.11.4) with respect to P_1, we obtain Kolmogorov's formula

$$H_{P_2}(P_1) = H_{P_2'}(P_1') + \mathbf{E}H_{P_2}(P_1/S_{\omega}'). \tag{3.11.5}$$

TRANSLATOR'S REMARKS TO CHAPTER 3

1. The assertion that the set function defined by (3.1.1) is obviously completely additive is taken directly from Dobrushin* [3], where no supporting evidence is given. The translator has not been able to supply a proof, and is inclined to doubt its general validity. If, however, $P_{\eta/\xi}(\cdot/x)$ and $P_{\zeta/\xi}(\cdot/x)$ can be chosen to be measures for almost every x with respect to P_ξ, then the assertion is certainly true, and the proof is practically identical with the proof of the complete additivity of an ordinary product measure (see Halmos [12]). Actually, it is sufficient that one of the conditional probabilities, say $P_{\eta/\xi}(\cdot/x)$, be a measure for almost every x. In fact, repeating the steps following (6) below, one finds that $\bar{P}_{\eta\times\zeta/\xi}(E \times F \times N) = \int_{E\times N} P_{\eta/\xi}(F/x)P_{\xi\zeta}(dx, dz)$,

*Note added in proof: Dobrushin has informed the translator that this assertion is incorrect.

and the remarks two sentences back apply here as well.

Another condition under which $\overline{P}_{\eta \times \zeta/\xi}$ is a measure is given by part 2 below, namely, that $P_{\xi\zeta}$ be absolutely continuous with respect to $P_{\xi \times \zeta}$ (or, interchanging η and ζ, that $P_{\xi\eta} \ll P_{\xi \times \eta}$).

This gap does not really cause much inconvenience here, as the author is mainly interested in real or complex valued random variables. In this case conditional probabilities (in the wide sense, which is really what the author is considering) can always be taken to be measures (see Doob [4], Chap. 1). In fact, Doob's proof, with the aid of the Kolmogorov extension theorem, is easily seen to be valid for a random variable whose values lie in a denumerably infinite dimensional Euclidean space. Since all random processes are here assumed to be continuous (see Chapter 5 below), it is not difficult to see that this last result is adequate in considering real or complex valued n-dimensional random processes.

2. We prove Theorem 3.6.1, following Dobrushin [3].

It clearly suffices to show the following:

(a) $P_{\xi\zeta} \ll P_{\xi \times \zeta}$ implies $\overline{P}_{\eta \times \zeta/\xi} \ll P_{(\xi\eta) \times \zeta}$;

(b) $P_{\xi\eta\zeta} \ll P_{(\xi\eta) \times \zeta}$ implies $P_{\xi\zeta} \ll P_{\xi \times \zeta}$ and $P_{\xi\eta\zeta} \ll \overline{P}_{\eta \times \zeta/\xi}$;
formula (3.6.1) will be an easy consequence of a result which will appear in the course of the proof. It is interesting to note that the assumption that $\overline{P}_{\eta \times \zeta/\xi}$ is indeed a measure is not required; as will be seen, it is a direct consequence of $P_{\xi\zeta} \ll P_{\xi \times \zeta}$. Let us now proceed to the proof.

PROOF. (a) First of all we show that for function $f(x, z)$ which is measurable with respect to $S_x \times S_z$ and for any set $A \in S_y$ we have

$$\int_{X \times A \times Z} f(x, z) P_{\xi\eta} \times P_\zeta(dx, dy, dz) = \int_{X \times Z} f(x, z) P_{\eta/\xi}(A/x) P_\xi \times P_\zeta(dx, dz) \qquad (1)$$

in the sense that if either integral exists, then the other one does also, and (1) holds. In fact, if

$$f(x, z) = \begin{cases} 1, & (x, z) \in C \times B, \\ 0, & (x, z) \notin C \times B, \end{cases} \qquad (2)$$

where $C \in S_x$, $B \in S_z$, then (1) is equivalent to

$$\int_{C \times A \times B} P_{\xi\eta} \times P_\zeta(dx, dy, dz) = \int_{C \times A} P_{\xi\eta}(dx, dy) \int_B P_\zeta(dz),$$
$$= \int_C P_{\eta/\xi}(A/x) P_\xi(dx) \int_B P_\zeta(dz) = \int_{C \times B} P_{\eta/\xi}(A/x) P_\xi \times P_\zeta(dx, dz), \qquad (3)$$

which follows at once from the definition of a product measure and conditional probability. Since the σ-algebra $S_x \times S_z$ is generated by all sets of the form $C \times B$, by taking linear combinations of functions of the form (2) and then monotone limits of such we obtain (1) for all $f \geqslant 0$ or $\leqslant 0$, from which our assertion follows at once.

Now we apply (1) to the function

$$f(x, z) = \begin{cases} a_{\xi\zeta}(x, z), & (x, z) \in C \times B, \\ 0, & (x, z) \notin C \times B, \end{cases}$$

where $C \in S_x, B \in S_z$. Then

$$\int_{C \times A \times B} a_{\xi\zeta}(x, z) P_{\xi\eta} \times P_\zeta(dx, dy, dz)$$
$$= \int_{C \times B} a_{\xi\zeta}(x, z) P_{\eta/\xi}(A/x) P_\xi \times P_\zeta(dx, dz). \qquad (4)$$

Using a well-known theorem on "change of variable" ([12]), § 32, Theorem B), we can write (4) in the form

$$\int_{C \times A \times B} a_{\xi\zeta}(x, z) P_{\xi\eta} \times P_\zeta(dx, dy, dz) = \int_{C \times B} P_{\eta/\xi}(A/x) P_{\xi\zeta}(dx, dz). \qquad (5)$$

Now we observe that for any function $f(x)$ which is measurable with respect to S_x, and any set $B \in S_z$ we have

$$\int_{X \times B} f(x) P_{\xi\zeta}(dx, dz) = \int_X f(x) P_{\zeta/\xi}(B/x) P_\xi(dx). \qquad (6)$$

This can be proved in the same manner as was (1), or we may note that it is just a special case obtainable from (1) by letting f in (1) depend only upon x, and interchanging η, ζ and y, z. Setting

$$f(x) = \begin{cases} P_{\eta/\xi}(A/x), & x \in C, \\ 0, & x \notin C \end{cases}$$

applying (6) and then comparing the result with (5), we obtain

$$\int_{C \times A \times B} a_{\xi\zeta}(x, z) P_{\xi\eta} \times P_\zeta(dx, dy, dz)$$
$$= \int_C P_{\eta/\xi}(A/x) P_{\zeta/\xi}(B/x) P_\xi(dx) = P_{\eta \times \zeta/\xi}(C \times A \times B), \qquad (7)$$

which shows that $\overline{P}_{\eta \times \zeta/\xi}$ can be extended to a probability measure on $S_x \times S_y \times S_z$, that it is absolutely continuous with respect to $P_{(\xi\eta) \times \zeta}$, and that

$$\frac{d\overline{P}_{\eta \times \zeta/\xi}}{dP_{(\xi\eta) \times \zeta}} = \frac{dP_{\xi\zeta}}{dP_{\xi \times \zeta}}. \qquad (8)$$

(b) The first assertion is almost trivial. Suppose the assertion $P_{\xi\zeta} \ll P_{\xi \times \zeta}$ is false; then there exists $C \epsilon S_x \times S_z$ such that $P_{\xi\zeta}(C) > 0$ while $P_{\xi \times \zeta}(C) = 0$. Letting $C' = C \times Y \epsilon S_x \times S_y \times S_z$, clearly

$$P_{\xi\eta\zeta}(C') = P_{\xi\zeta}(C) > 0 \qquad \text{and} \qquad P_{(\xi\eta) \times \zeta}(C') = P_{\xi \times \zeta}(C) = 0,$$

which contradicts $P_{\xi\eta\zeta} \ll P_{(\xi\eta) \times \zeta}$.

To show, finally, that $P_{\xi\eta\zeta} \ll P_{\eta \times \zeta/\xi}$, let $E \epsilon S_x \times S_y \times S_z$ be some fixed set for which $\overline{P}_{\eta \times \zeta/\xi}(E) = 0$. By (8) we have

$$P_{\eta \times \zeta/\xi}(E) = \int\int_E\int a_{\xi\zeta}(x, z) P_{\xi\eta} \times P_\zeta(dx, dy, dz). \tag{9}$$

Now let $D = \{(x, z)/a_{\xi\zeta}(x, z) = 0\}$. It follows from (9) that $P_{(\xi\eta) \times \zeta}(E - D \times Y) = 0$, which by hypothesis implies

$$P_{\xi\eta\zeta}(E - D \times Y) = 0. \tag{10}$$

Now by the definition of D and $a_{\xi\zeta}$ we have $P_{\xi\zeta}(D) = 0$, or

$$P_{\xi\eta\zeta}(D \times Y) = 0. \tag{11}$$

Since $E \subset (E - D \times Y) \cup (D \times Y)$, (10) and (11) imply $P_{\xi\eta\zeta}(E) = 0$. As for formula (3.6.1), it is now a direct consequence of (8) and the "chain rule" for differentiating measures (see [12], §32, Theorem A).

3. A few words concerning terminology are in order. These are intended mainly for the reader who has had no previous contact with information theory, and may be wondering why the terminology employed here is actually used.

The quantity $I(\xi, \eta)$ is usually thought of as the average amount of "information" obtained about ξ by being given the value of η (or vice versa), because the mathematical equivalents of many intuitively valid statements concerning information in the colloquial sense are in fact true. One such is (2.2.5), and another is (3.9.5), to mention only two. The quantity $\mathbf{E}I(\xi, \eta/\zeta)$ may similarly be considered as the average amount of information furnished about ξ by a knowledge of η when one already knows the value of ζ. The result of Section 3.4 appears completely obvious in the light of this description of $\mathbf{E}I(\xi, \eta/\zeta)$; as a further example, the reader should have no difficulty in rendering (3.6.6) into simple intuitive language.

Simple remarks apply a fortiori to the information rates of stochastic processes in Chapter 5.

The use of the word "entropy" stems from a similarity of the quantity $H(\xi)$ to the quantity "entropy" as it occurs in statistical mechanics, further consideration of which is impossible here.

Chapter 4 Information stability

The basic theorems of information theory essentially represent asymptotic properties of the distribution of random variables which depend upon a parameter. As in the solution of a series of problems of probability theory, here also a central role is played by the concept of stability, which is encountered under various names in almost every work of a fundamental nature, in particular, those of B.McMillan [21] and A.Y.Khinchin [16], where it is formulated as an ϵ-property. With further details and generalization, the concept of information stability was introduced in the literature by R.L. Dobrushin [3]. Together with information stability, we will define also the concept of quasi-stability. These concepts are sufficient for the purpose of generalizing, in a suitable formulation, the basic theorems of information theory.

If, as in fact the case will be, we prove every assertion which will be made concerning information stability, in the case of quasi-stability we will restrict ourselves to formulating results and remarks. Our reason, first of all, is that in the majority of cases the methods of proof are analogous, and second, that in those cases which one meets in practice, information stability obtains.

At the end of this chapter, a few remarks will be made concerning the concept of entropy stability of a pair of distributions, which is a generalization of the concept of information stability.

4.1 DEFINITION OF INFORMATION STABILITY

Let ξ^t, η^t, ζ^t be random variables, depending upon a parameter t which takes on positive integer or real values. A family of pairs (η^t, ζ^t) which possess an information density $i(\eta^t, \zeta^t)$ for all sufficiently large t will be called **information stable** if $0 < I(\eta^t, \zeta^t)$

$< \infty$ for all t sufficiently large, and if the ratio $i(\eta^t, \zeta^t)/I(\eta^t, \zeta^t)$ converges in probability to one as $t \to \infty$, i.e., if

$$\lim_{t\to\infty} P\left\{\left|\frac{i(\eta^t, \zeta^t)}{I(\eta^t, \zeta^t)} - 1\right| > \epsilon\right\} = 0, \tag{4.1.1}$$

for every $\epsilon > 0$.

A family of pairs (η^t, ζ^t) which, for all t sufficiently large, do not possess an information density, is called **information stable** if, for all sufficiently large t, the distribution $P_{\eta^t \times \zeta^t}$ is singular with respect to the distribution $P_{\eta^t} \times \zeta^t$. In the **general case,** a family of pairs (η^t, ζ^t) is called **information stable** if it can be divided into two disjoint parts which are information stable in each of the preceding senses, respectively.

A family of pairs (η^t, ζ^t) which possess an information density $i(\eta^t, \zeta^t)$ for all t sufficiently large will be called **information quasi-stable** if there exists a function $\varphi(t) \neq 0$ such that as $t \to \infty$, the ratio $i(\eta^t, \zeta^t)/\varphi(t)$ converges to one in probability. The function $\varphi(t)$ is called the function of information stability. Always

$$\overline{\lim_{t\to\infty}} \frac{\varphi(t)}{I(\eta^t, \zeta^t)} \leqslant 1. \tag{4.1.2}$$

A family of pairs (η^t, ζ^t) which, for all t sufficiently large, do not possess an information density, will be called **information quasi-stable** if the $P_{\eta^t \zeta^t}$ measure of the set of absolute continuity of $P_{\eta^t \zeta^t}$ with respect to $P_{\eta^t \times \zeta^t}$ goes to zero as $t \to \infty$.

Just as does the concept of information stability, so does the concept of relative information stability prove to be extremely useful.

A family of pairs (η^t, ζ^t) which possess, for all t sufficiently large, a conditional information density $\overline{i}(\eta^t, \zeta^t/\xi^t)$, is called **information stable relative to the family of random variables** ξ^t, if for sufficiently large t $0 < \mathbf{E}I(\eta^t, \zeta^t/\xi^t) < \infty$, and if for $t \to \infty$ the ratio $\overline{i}(\eta^t, \zeta^t/\xi^t)/\mathbf{E}I(\eta^t, \zeta^t/\xi^t)$ converges in probability to one, i.e., for any $\epsilon > 0$

$$\lim_{t\to\infty} P\left\{\left|\frac{\overline{i}(\eta^t, \zeta^t/\xi^t)}{\mathbf{E}I(\eta^t, \zeta^t/\xi^t)} - 1\right| > \epsilon\right\} 0. \tag{4.1.3}$$

A family of pairs (η^t, ζ^t) which, for all t sufficiently large, do not possess a conditional information density $\overline{i}(\eta^t, \zeta^t/\xi^t)$ is called **information stable with respect to the family** $\{\xi^t\}$ if, for all t sufficiently large, the distributions $P_{\xi^t \eta^t \zeta^t}$ and $\overline{P}_{\eta^t \times \zeta^t/\xi^t}$ are mutually singular. In the **general case,** a family of pairs (η^t, ζ^t) is called **information stable relative to the family of random variables** ξ^t if the family of triples (η^t, ζ^t, ξ^t) can be divided into two disjoint parts such that the pairs (η^t, ζ^t) belonging to each part are information stable relative to the corresponding ξ^t in each of the above senses respectively.

4.2. PROPERTIES OF INFORMATION STABLE FAMILIES OF RANDOM VARIABLES

THEOREM 4.2.1. Let $\xi^t, \eta^t, \tilde{\eta}^t, \zeta^t$ *be random variables depending upon a positive integer or real valued parameter* t, *and suppose that* $\tilde{\eta}^t$ *is subordinate to* η^t. *Then:*
(1) If

$$0 < d \leqslant I(\eta^t, \zeta^t) < \infty \text{ and } \lim_{t\to\infty} \frac{I(\tilde{\eta}^t, \zeta^t)}{I(\eta^t, \zeta^t)} = 1, \tag{4.2.1}$$

then the information stability of either of the families $\{(\eta^t, \zeta^t)\}$ *and* $\{(\tilde{\eta}^t, \zeta^t)\}$ *implies that of the other.*
(2) If

$$0 < d \leqslant \mathbf{E}I(\eta^t, \zeta^t,/\xi^t) < \infty \text{ and } \lim_{t\to\infty} \frac{\mathbf{E}I(\tilde{\eta}^t, \zeta^t/\xi)}{\mathbf{E}I(\eta^t, \zeta^t/\xi^t)} = 1, \tag{4.2.2}$$

then from the information stability relative to $\{\xi^t\}$ *of one of the families* $\{(\eta^t, \zeta^t)\}$ *and* $\{(\tilde{\eta}^t, \zeta^t)\}$ *follows that of the other.*
(3) If, for t *sufficiently large,* $EI(\tilde{\eta}^t, \zeta^t) \neq \infty$, *then the information stability of the family* $\{(\tilde{\eta}^t, \zeta^t)\}$ *implies that of the family* $\{(\eta^t, \zeta^t)\}$.
(4) If $EI(\tilde{\eta}^t, \zeta^t | \xi^t) = \infty$ *for all* t *sufficiently large, then the information stability relative to* $\{\xi^t\}$ *of the family* $\{(\tilde{\eta}^t, \zeta^t)\}$ *implies that of the family* $\{(\tilde{\eta}^t, \zeta^t)\}$ *relative to* $\{\xi^t\}$.

PROOF. According to formulas (3.7.19) and (3.7.20)

$$I(\eta^t, \zeta^t) = I(\tilde{\eta}^t, \zeta^t) + \mathbf{E}I(\eta^t, \zeta^t/\tilde{\eta}^t)$$

and

$$i(\eta^t, \zeta^t) = i(\tilde{\eta}^t, \zeta^t) + \bar{i}(\eta^t, \zeta^t/\tilde{\eta}^t),$$

from which

$$i(\eta^t, \zeta^t) - I(\eta^t, \zeta^t) = i(\tilde{\eta}^t, \zeta^t) - I(\tilde{\eta}^t, \zeta^t) + \bar{i}(\eta^t, \zeta^t/\tilde{\eta}^t)$$
$$- \mathbf{E}I(\eta^t, \zeta^t/\tilde{\eta}^t);$$

$$i(\tilde{\eta}^t, \zeta^t) - I(\tilde{\eta}^t, \zeta^t) = i(\eta^t, \zeta^t) - I(\eta^t, \zeta^t) - \bar{i}(\eta^t, \zeta^t/\tilde{\eta}^t)$$
$$+ \mathbf{E}I(\eta^t, \zeta^t/\tilde{\eta}^t).$$

Dividing these equalities termwise by $I(\eta^t, \zeta^t)$ and $I(\tilde{\eta}^t, \zeta^t)$ respectively, and using the usual inequality for the absolute value of a sum of terms, we obtain

$$\left|\frac{i(\eta^t, \zeta^t)}{I(\eta^t, \zeta^t)} - 1\right| \leqslant \left|\frac{i(\tilde{\eta}^t, \zeta^t)}{I(\tilde{\eta}^t, \zeta^t)} - 1\right| \frac{I(\tilde{\eta}^t, \zeta^t)}{I(\eta^t, \zeta^t)} + \left|\frac{\bar{i}(\eta^t, \zeta^t/\tilde{\eta}^t)}{I(\eta^t, \zeta^t)}\right| + \frac{EI(\eta^t, \zeta^t/\tilde{\eta}^t)}{I(\eta^t, \zeta^t)}; \tag{4.2.3}$$

$$\left|\frac{i(\tilde{\eta}^t, \zeta^t)}{I(\tilde{\eta}^t, \zeta^t)} - 1\right| \leqslant \left|\frac{i(\eta^t, \zeta^t)}{I(\eta^t, \zeta^t)} - 1\right| \frac{I(\eta^t, \zeta^t)}{I(\tilde{\eta}^t, \zeta^t)} + \left|\frac{\bar{i}(\eta^t, \zeta^t/\tilde{\eta}^t)}{I(\tilde{\eta}^t, \zeta^t)}\right| + \frac{EI(\eta^t, \zeta^t/\tilde{\eta}^t)}{I(\tilde{\eta}^t, \zeta^t)}. \tag{4.2.4}$$

Since

$$EI(\eta^t, \zeta^t/\tilde{\eta}^t) = I(\eta^t, \zeta^t) - I(\tilde{\eta}^t, \zeta^t), \tag{4.2.5}$$

then in view of (4.2.1), the last term on the right side of (4.2.3) and of (4.2.4) converges to zero as $t \to \infty$. According to (3.3.2),

$$E|i(\eta^t, \zeta^t/\tilde{\eta}^t| \leqslant EI(\eta^t, \zeta^t/\tilde{\eta}^t) + \Gamma\sqrt{EI(\eta^t, \zeta^t/\tilde{\eta})}, \tag{4.2.6}$$

and it follows from (4.2.5) and (4.2.1) that the second term on the right side of (4.2.3) and (4.2.4) converges to zero in mean, and therefore in probability. But then (4.2.3) and (4.2.4) show that the convergence to one in probability of either $i(\eta^t, \zeta^t)/I(\eta^t, \zeta^t)$ or $i(\tilde{\eta}^t, \zeta^t)/I(\tilde{\eta}^t, \zeta^t)$ implies the convergence to one in probability of the other.

(2) The proof of this part of the theorem is entirely analogous to, and repeats almost word for word, the proof of the first part.

(3) In this case information stability implies that for all t sufficiently large, the distribution $P_{\tilde{\eta}^t\zeta^t}$ is singular with respect to the distribution $P_{\tilde{\eta}^t \times \zeta^t}$, i.e., there exists a set $E^t \in S_{\tilde{y}^t} \times S_{z^t}$ such that

$$P_{\tilde{\eta}^t\zeta^t}(\tilde{E}^t) = 1 \qquad \text{and} \qquad P_{\tilde{\eta}^t \times \zeta^t}(\tilde{E}^t) = 0,$$

where $(\tilde{Y}^t, S_{\tilde{y}^t})$ and (Z^t, S_{z^t}) are the measurable spaces of values of the random variables $\tilde{\eta}^t$ and ζ^t. Since $\tilde{\eta}^t$ is subordinate to η^t, there exists a set $E^t \in S_{y^t} \times S_{z^t}$ such that $P_{\eta^t\zeta^t}(E^t) = P_{\tilde{\eta}^t\zeta^t}(\tilde{E}^t) = 1$ and

$$P_{\eta^t \times \zeta^t}(E^t) = P_{\tilde{\eta}^t \times \zeta^t}(\tilde{E}^t) = 0,$$

where (Y^t, S_{y^t}) is the space of values of η^t.

This implies that the distributions $P_{\eta^t\zeta^t}$ and $P_{\eta^t \times \zeta^t}$ are mutually singular, and hence that the family of pairs (η^t, ζ^t) is information stable.

(4) The proof of this part is analogous to that of part 3.

Remark 1. If $I(\eta^t, \zeta^t) = \infty$ and $\mathbf{E}I(\eta^t, \zeta^t/\tilde{\eta}^t) < \infty$ for all t sufficiently large, then the information stability of one of the families $\{(\eta^t, \zeta^t)\}$, $\{(\tilde{\eta}^t, \zeta^t)\}$ follows from that of the other. If $\mathbf{E}I(\eta^t, \zeta^t/\xi^t) = \infty$ and $\mathbf{E}I(\eta^t, \zeta^t/\xi^t, \tilde{\eta}^t)) < \infty$, then we can similarly strengthen the assertion of part 4 of the theorem. Thus combining these assertions with the preceding theorem, we can state the following:

(1) If $\mathbf{E}I(\eta^t, \zeta^t | \tilde{\eta}^t) < \infty$, $0 < d \leqslant I(\eta^t, \zeta^t)$ and

$$\lim_{t \to \infty} \frac{\mathbf{E}I(\eta^t, \zeta^t/\tilde{\eta}^t)}{I(\eta^t, \zeta^t)} = 0, \tag{4.2.7}$$

then the information stability of one of the families $\{(\eta^t, \zeta^t)\}$, $\{(\tilde{\eta}^t, \zeta^t)\}$ implies that of the other.

(2) If $\mathbf{E}I(\eta^t, \zeta^t | (\xi^t, \tilde{\eta}^t)) < \infty$, $0 < d \leqslant \mathbf{E}I(\eta^t, \zeta^t/\xi^t)$, and

$$\lim_{t \to \infty} \frac{\mathbf{E}I(\eta^t, \zeta^t/(\tilde{\eta}^t, \xi^t))}{\mathbf{E}I(\eta^t, \zeta^t/\xi^t)} = 0, \tag{4.2.8}$$

then the information stability with respect to $\{\xi^t\}$ of one of the families $\{(\eta^t, \zeta^t)\}$, $\{(\tilde{\eta}^t, \zeta^t)\}$ implies that of the other.

Remark 2. In a completely analogous way one can formulate a theorem establishing the connection between the quasi-stability of the families $\{(\eta^t, \zeta^t)\}$ and $\{(\tilde{\eta}^t, \zeta^t)\}$.

We now prove an important assertion, which may be considered a criterion for information stability.

THEOREM 4.2.2. (1) Let $0 < I(\eta^t, \zeta^t) < \infty$ for $0 < t < \infty$. If for every $\delta > 0$ there exist random variables $\tilde{\eta}^t$ which are subordinate to η^t, such that the family $\{(\tilde{\eta}^t, \zeta^t)\}$ is information stable and

$$\varliminf_{t \to \infty} \frac{(\eta^t, \zeta^t)}{(\eta , \zeta^t)} > 1 - \delta; \ \varliminf_{t \to \infty} I(\eta^t, \zeta^t) > d > 0, \tag{4.2.9}$$

then the family $\{(\eta^t, \zeta^t)\}$ is also information stable.

(2) Let $0 < \mathbf{E}I(\eta^t, \zeta^t | \xi^t) < \infty$ for $0 < t < \infty$. If for every $\delta > 0$ there exist random variables $\tilde{\eta}^t$ which are subordinate to η^t, such that the family $\{(\tilde{\eta}^t, \zeta^t)\}$ is information stable relative to $\{\xi^t\}$ and

$$\varliminf_{t \to \infty} \frac{\mathbf{E}I(\tilde{\eta}^t, \zeta^t/\xi^t)}{\mathbf{E}I(\eta^t, \zeta^t/\xi^t)} > 1 - \delta; \ \varliminf_{t \to \infty} \mathbf{E}I(\eta^t, \zeta^t/\xi^t) > d > 0, \tag{4.2.10}$$

then the family $\{(\eta^t, \zeta^t)\}$ *is also information stable relative to* $\{\xi^t\}$.

PROOF. (1) If we consider the inequality (4.2.3), which is valid whenever $\tilde{\eta}^t$ is subordinate to η^t, it is clear that in order that the inequality

$$\left|\frac{i(\eta^t, \zeta^t)}{I(\eta^t, \zeta^t)} - 1\right| > 3\epsilon, \ \epsilon > 0$$

hold, one of the terms on the right side of (4.2.3) must exceed ϵ. Thus, for sufficiently large t

$$P\left\{\left|\frac{i(\eta^t, \zeta^t)}{I(\eta^t, \zeta^t)} - 1\right| > 3\epsilon\right\} \leqslant P\left\{\left|\frac{i(\tilde{\eta}^t, \zeta^t)}{I(\tilde{\eta}^t, \zeta^t)} - 1\right| > \epsilon\right\}$$
$$+ P\left\{\left|\frac{\bar{i}(\eta^t, \zeta^t/\tilde{\eta}^t)}{I(\eta^t, \zeta^t)}\right| > \epsilon\right\} + P\left\{\frac{\mathbf{E}I(\eta^t, \zeta^t/\tilde{\eta}^t)}{I(\eta^t, \zeta^t)} > \epsilon\right\} \tag{4.2.11}$$

where we have used the inequality

$$P\left\{\left|\frac{i(\tilde{\eta}^t, \zeta^t)}{I(\eta^t, \zeta^t)} - 1\right|\frac{I(\tilde{\eta}^t, \zeta^t)}{I(\eta^t, \zeta^t)} > \epsilon\right\} \leqslant P\left\{\left|\frac{i(\tilde{\eta}^t, \zeta^t)}{I(\tilde{\eta}^t, \zeta^t)} - 1\right| > \epsilon\right\},$$

which holds since $I(\tilde{\eta}^t, \zeta^t) \leqslant I(\eta^t, \zeta^t$. Let us estimate the second and third terms on the right side of (4.2.11). Of course the third term is either zero or one, since the "random variable" involved is just a constant. From (4.2.9) and the first equation in the proof of Theorem 4.2.1 it follows at once that

$$\frac{\mathbf{E}I(\eta^t, \zeta^t/\tilde{\eta}^t)}{I(\eta^t, \zeta^t)} = \frac{I(\eta^t, \zeta^t) - I(\tilde{\eta}^t, \zeta^t)}{I(\eta^t, \zeta^t)}$$
$$= 1 - \frac{I(\tilde{\eta}^t, \zeta^t)}{I(\eta^t, \zeta^t)} < 1 - (1 - \delta) = \delta \tag{4.2.12}$$

for all t sufficiently large, and therefore in conjunction with (4.2.6) we obtain, for t sufficiently large

$$\mathbf{E}\left|\frac{i(\eta^t, \zeta^t/\tilde{\eta}^t)}{I(\eta^t, \zeta^t)}\right| \leqslant \frac{\mathbf{E}I(\eta^t, \zeta^t/\tilde{\eta}^t) + \Gamma\sqrt{\mathbf{E}I(\eta^t, \zeta^t/\tilde{\eta}^t)}}{I(\eta^t, \zeta^t)} \leqslant \delta + \frac{\Gamma\sqrt{\delta}}{\sqrt{I(\eta^t, \zeta^t)}}$$
$$\leqslant \delta + \Gamma\sqrt{\frac{\delta}{d}}.$$

Applying Tchebycheff's inequality, we obtain

$$P\left\{\left|\frac{i(\eta^t, \zeta^t/\tilde{\eta}^t)}{I(\eta^t, \zeta^t)}\right| > \epsilon\right\} < \frac{\delta + \Gamma\sqrt{\frac{\delta}{d}}}{\epsilon} \tag{4.2.13}$$

Choosing $\delta < \epsilon$, it follows from (4.2.12) that the third term on the right side of (4.2.11) vanishes for t sufficiently large. Taking into account the information stability of the family $\{(\tilde{\eta}^t, \zeta^t)\}$, and comparing (4.2.11), (4.2.13), and (4.2.12), we find that

$$\overline{\lim_{t\to\infty}} P\left\{\left|\frac{i(\eta^t, \zeta^t)}{I(\eta^t, \zeta^t)} - 1\right| > 3\epsilon\right\} \leqslant 0 + \frac{\delta + \Gamma\sqrt{\frac{\delta}{d}}}{\epsilon} + \delta. \tag{4.2.14}$$

Since ϵ is arbitrary, this implies (4.1.1), which establishes the information stability of the family $\{(\eta^t, \zeta^t)\}$.

(2) The proof of this part of the theorem is completely analogous to that of the first part.

Remark. With appropriate changes in its statement, the preceding theorem can be modified to give a criterion for the quasi-stability of the family $\{(\eta^t, \zeta^t)\}$. In this case the condition (4.2.9) should be replaced by

$$\overline{\lim_{t\to\infty}} \frac{EI(\eta^t, \zeta^t/\tilde{\eta}^t)}{\tilde{\varphi}(t)} < \delta, \ \underline{\lim_{t\to\infty}} \tilde{\varphi}(t) > d > 0, \tag{4.2.15}$$

where $\tilde{\varphi}(t)$ is the function of information stability of the family $\{(\tilde{\eta}^t, \zeta^t)\}$.

4.3. ENTROPY STABILITY

The concept of information stability is generalized in a natural way by the concept of entropy stability.

The family of pairs of distributions (P_1^t, P_2^t), defined on the measurable spaces (Ω^t, S_{ω^t}) and possessing an entropy density $h(\omega^t) = h_{P_2^t}(\omega^t, P_1^t)$ for all t sufficiently large, is called **entropy stable** if $0 < H_{P_2^t}(P_1^t) < \infty$ for all t sufficiently large, and if for every $\epsilon > 0$

$$\lim_{t\to\infty} (P_1^t\left\{\left|\frac{h(\omega^t)}{H_{P_2^t}(P_1^t)} - 1\right| > \epsilon\right\} = 0 \tag{4.3.1}$$

A family of pairs (P_1^t, P_2^t) which, for all t sufficiently large, do not possess an entropy density is called **entropy stable** if, for all t sufficiently large, the measure P_1^t is singular with respect to P_2^t. In the **general case**, the family $\{(P_1^t, P_2^t)\}$ is called **entropy stable** if it can be divided into two disjoint parts which are entropy stable in each of the preceding senses respectively.

PART II

Information rate and information stability of random processes

The first chapter of this part, which is introductory, contains an exposition of known facts of the theory of random processes, principally stationary processes. We introduce several definitions of information rate and information stability for both ordinary and generalized random processes. The central purpose of this part will be to attempt to determine the interrelationships among the various definitions of information rate, and to establish criteria for the information stability of a stationary random process.

At the end of this chapter we will indicate the possibility of generalizing the definition of information rate by defining the entropy rate of one random process with respect to another.

The main results of this part, relating to stationary random processes taking values in an arbitrary abstract space, are apparently new.

Chapter 5 Random processes. Definition of the information rate and information stability of random processes

In order to clarify fully our terminology, and also for completeness of exposition, we will give in this chapter the definitions of a number of concepts in the theory of random processes, and also indicate the properties of various classes of random processes which we will use further on. Various definitions of information rate will be given, including those considered by Shannon [36] and Kolmogorov [18], and we will indicate how to generalize the definition of this concept by defining the entropy rate. In the last paragraphs we will formulate the definition of information stability, relative information stability, and entropy stability of random processes.

5.1. DEFINITION OF RANDOM PROCESS AND STATIONARITY

A family of random variables $\xi(t)$, $-\infty < t < \infty$, which depend upon a variable t which takes on all integer values or all real values, is called a **random process** $\xi = \{\xi(t)\}$. If t takes on all integer values, then $\xi = \{\xi(t)\}$ is called a **discrete parameter random process,** while if t takes on all real values, $\xi = \{\xi(t)\}$ is called a **continuous parameter random process.** We introduce the following notation: ξ_S^T is the random variable consisting of the family of random variables $\xi(t)$, $S < t \leqslant T$, and $\xi = \xi_{-\infty}^{\infty}$. If $S = -\infty$, we will omit the lower index, i.e., $\xi_{-\infty}^T = \xi^T$, while if $T = +\infty$, we will omit the upper index, i.e., $\xi_S^{\infty} = \xi_S$. We say that the random process $\eta = \{\eta(t)\}$ is **subordinate** to the random process $\xi = \{\xi(t)\}$ if the random variable η is subordinate to the random variable ξ. In particular, this will be the case when η is a measurable function of ξ. We will say that the random process $\eta = \{\eta(t)\}$ is **regularly subordinate** to the random process $\xi = \{\xi(t)\}$ if there is a $T > 0$ such that for every t, $\eta(t)$ is subordinate to ξ^{t+T}. Finally, we will say that the random process η is finitely subordinate to the random process ξ if there is $T > 0$ such that $\eta(t)$ is subordinate to ξ_{t-T}^{t+T} for every t. This will be the case, for example, when for every t, $\eta(t)$ is a measurable function of $\xi(t)$, or when $\eta(t)$ is the derivative (i.e., the limit of $\xi(t + \Delta t) - \xi(t)/\Delta t$) of the random process $\xi = \{\xi(t)\}$, where the limit is taken in the sense of convergence with probability one, or in the mean, or in probability, and so on.

Let $\xi_1, \ldots, \xi_n$, $\tilde{\xi}_1, \ldots, \tilde{\xi}_n$ be random variables with values in the measurable spaces

$$(X_1, S_{x_1}), \ldots, (X_n, S_{x_n}), \; (\tilde{X}_1, S_{\tilde{x}_1}), \ldots, (\tilde{X}_n, S_{\tilde{x}_n}),$$

respectively. We say that the systems $\xi_1, \ldots, \xi_n$ and $\tilde{\xi}_1, \ldots, \xi_n$ **have the same joint distribution** if $X_i = \tilde{X}_i$, $S_{x_i} = S_{\tilde{x}_i}$, $i = 1, \ldots, n$, and for $A_i \in S_{x_i}$, $\tilde{A}_i \in S_{\tilde{x}_i}$ and $A_i = \tilde{A}_i$ the equality

$$\begin{aligned} P_{\xi_1 \ldots \xi_n}(A_1 \times \ldots \times A_n) &= P\{\xi_1 \in A_1, \ldots, \xi_n \in A_n\} = P\{\tilde{\xi}_1 \in \tilde{A}_1, \ldots \tilde{\xi}_n \in \tilde{A}_n\} \\ &= P_{\tilde{\xi}_1 \ldots \tilde{\xi}_n}(\tilde{A}_1 \times \ldots \times \tilde{A}_n) \end{aligned} \tag{5.1.1}$$

holds. The equality of two sets is to be understood in the sense of equivalence, not coincidence of the two sets. In what follows, the sense of the equal sign will be clear from the text.

The random process $\xi = \{\xi(t)\}$ is called **stationary**, if the joint distribution of the random variables $\xi = \{\xi(t)\}$ will be called a does not depend upon h, where $t_1, \ldots, t_n$ are possible values of t, and h is an integer in the discrete-parameter case and an arbitrary real number in the continuous-parameter case.*

If the space $X(t)$ of values of the random variable $\xi(t)$ consists of finitely many points, and the σ-algebra $S_{x(t)}$ consists of all subsets of $X(t)$, the process $\xi = \{\xi(t)\}$ will be called a **process with a finite number of states.** The stationary processes $\xi = \{\xi(t)\}$ and $\eta = \{\eta(t)\}$ will be called **stationarily correlated** if the pair $(\xi, \eta) = \{(\xi(t), \eta(t))\}$ forms a stationary process.

---

*In Doob [27] a definition of stationary process is given which is in some sense more general, but with any process which is stationary in Doob's sense there is associated a process which is stationary in our sense, and the two processes, as concerns those properties which we need, will be identical.

Let $\xi = \{\xi(t)\}$ be a stationary random process, and let the random variables $\xi, \xi(t), -\infty < t < \infty$ take values in the measurable spaces $(X, S_x), (X(t), S_x(t))$. Let us consider the one-to-one mapping U_τ of X on itself, which takes the point $x = \{x(t)\} \epsilon X$ into the point $y = \{y(t)\} \epsilon X$; $y(t) = x(t + \tau)$. Then the family of mappings U_τ, $-\infty < \tau < \infty$ is a **group of measure-preserving transformations,** i.e., if $E \epsilon S_x$, then $E_\tau = U_\tau E \epsilon S_x$ and $P_\xi(E) = P\{\xi \epsilon E\} = P\{\xi \epsilon E_\tau\} = P_\xi(E_\tau)$, and if $y = U_\tau x, z = U_t y$, then $z = U_{\tau + t} x$. If t runs over the real line, U_t is called a one-parameter group. If for every $E \epsilon S_x$

$$\lim_{\tau \to 0} P_\xi(E \Delta E_\tau) = 0, \tag{5.1.2}$$

where $E_\tau = U_\tau E$, then the one-parameter group U_t is called **continuous,** and the process $\xi = \{\xi(t)\}$ is called a **continuous random process.** Since we will only consider such processes from now on, the word "continuous" will frequently be omitted.

5.2. ERGODICITY, MIXING, REGULARITY

(1) Ergodicity. A set E will be called **invariant** with respect to the stationary random process $\xi = \{\xi(t)\}$ if $U_t E = E, -\infty < t < \infty$. The process $\xi = \{\xi(t)\}$ will be called **ergodic** if every invariant set E has P_ξ-measure either zero or one, i.e., $U_t E = E$ for all t implies that either $P_\xi(E) = 1$ or $P_\xi(E) = 0$. As is known, if ξ is an ergodic process, then

$$\lim_{n \to \infty} \frac{1}{n} \sum_{k=0}^{n-1} P_\xi(U_k E \cdot F) = P_\xi(E) P_\xi(F) \tag{5.2.1}$$

in the discrete-parameter case, and

$$\lim_{t \to \infty} \frac{1}{t} \int_0^t P_\xi(U_t E \cdot F) dt = P_\xi(E) P_\xi(F) \tag{5.2.2}$$

in the continuous-parameter case, for any two measurable sets $E, F \epsilon S_x$. Correspondingly, for any integrable complex-valued function $f(x)$

$$\lim_{n \to \infty} \frac{1}{n} \sum_{k=0}^{n-1} f(U_k x) = \int_X f(x) P_\xi(dx); \tag{5.2.3}$$

$$\lim_{t \to \infty} \frac{1}{t} \int_0^t f(U_t x) dt = \int_X f(x) P_\xi(dx) \tag{5.2.4}$$

in the discrete and continuous-parameter cases respectively. Conversely, if (5.2.1) or (5.2.2) hold for every $E, F \in S_x$, or if (5.2.3) or (5.2.4) hold for every integrable function $f(x)$, the random process ξ is ergodic. We mention that in order to show the ergodicity of ξ it is sufficient to verify (5.2.1) or (5.2.2) for sets E and F which belong to a family $\mathscr{L}_x$ which generates the σ-algebra S_x, and which is closed under intersections, i.e., which contains, along with any two sets, their intersection also. Similarly, (5.2.3) or (5.2.4) need be verified only for characteristic functions of sets in $\mathscr{L}_x$.

(2) Mixing. The process $\xi = \{\xi(t)\}$ is called **mixing** if for every $E, F \in S_x$

$$\lim_{t\to\infty} (P_\xi(E\cdot U_t F) = P_\xi(E)P_\xi(F) \tag{5.2.5}$$

and **weakly mixing** if

$$\lim_{n\to\infty} \frac{1}{n}\sum_{k=0}^{n-1} (P_\xi(E\cdot U_k F) - P_\xi(E)P_\xi(F))^2 = 0 \tag{5.2.6}$$

in the discrete-parameter case, and

$$\lim_{t\leftarrow\infty} \frac{1}{t}\int_0^t (P_\xi(E\cdot U_\tau F) - P_\xi(E)P_\xi(F))^2 d\tau = 0 \tag{5.2.7}$$

in the continuous-parameter case.

Comparing (5.2.5), (5.2.6) and (5.2.7) with (5.2.1) and (5.2.5) shows that a process which is mixing in either sense is ergodic. We remark that in order to prove that a process is mixing, it is sufficient to verify (5.2.5)(or (5.2.6) and (5.2.7) respectively) for sets E, F belonging to a family $\mathscr{L}_x$ which generates the σ-algebra S_x and which is closed under intersections.

(3) Regularity. Let (X, S_x) and $(X(t), S_{x(t)})$ be the space of values of $\xi = \{\xi(t)\}$ and $\xi(t)$, $-\infty < t < \infty$ respectively. We denote by $S_x^T = S_{x_{\xi T}}^{-1}$ the σ-subalgebra of the σ-algebra S_x which is generated by sets of the form $E_t^{-1} = E(t) \times \underset{\tau\neq t}{\times} X(\tau)$ $t \leqslant T$, $E(t) \in S_{x(t)}$. Let

$$\overline{S}_x = \bigcap_{-\infty<t<\infty} S_x^t. \tag{5.2.8}$$

The stationary random process $\xi = \{\xi(t)\}$ is called **regular** if the σ-algebra $\overline{S}_x$ contains only sets of P_ξ-measure one or zero, and **singular** if $\overline{S}_x$ is everywhere dense in S_x, in other words, if for every t the random variable ξ^t is everywhere dense in ξ. As

Vinokurov [31] has shown*, the following property is equivalent to regularity: for any random variable β which takes on only finitely many values

$$\lim_{\tau \to -\infty} V(P_{\xi^\tau \beta}, P_{\xi^\tau \times \beta}) = 0. \tag{5.2.9}$$

We remark that in order to prove the regularity of a process, it is sufficient to verify (5.2.9) for random variables β which take on only two values, namely the value one on a set $E \epsilon S_x$ and zero on the complement of E, and for a family $\mathscr{L}_x$ of sets E which generates the σ-algebra S_x and which is closed under intersections.

Further on we will use notions of regularity which are stronger and weaker than that just given. A stationary process $\xi = \{\xi(t)\}$ will be called **completely regular** if

$$\lim_{t-\tau \to \infty} V(P_{\xi^\tau \xi_t}, P_{\xi^\tau \times \xi_t}) = 0. \tag{5.2.10}$$

Evidently a completely regular process is regular.

Let $\{E_i(t)\}$ be a finite decomposition of the space $X(t)$ such that $E_i(t) = E_i(0)$ (in the sense of equivalence, as mentioned earlier) for $-\infty < t < \infty$, and let $\beta(t)$ be a random variable taking values in the space $(E(t), S_{e(t)})$ whose points are the sets $E_i(t)$, and the σ-algebra $S_{e(t)}$ consists of all subsets of $E(t)$, with $\beta(t)$ so defined that if $\xi(t) \epsilon E_i(t)$, then $\beta(t) = E_i(t)$. Obviously the random variables $\beta(t)$ form a stationary random process $\beta = \{\beta(t)\}$ with finite state space, and the random variables $\beta^{(h)}(n) = \beta(nh)$, for any fixed $h > 0$ for which nh is a parameter value for all integer n, constitute a discrete-parameter stationary process with finite state space. If for every finite partition $\{E_i(t)\}$ of the space $X(t)$, satisfying the conditions just mentioned, and every admissible $h > 0$, the process $\beta^{(h)} = \{\beta^{(h)}(n)\}$ is regular, then ξ will be called a **weakly regular** random process, while if $\beta^{(h)}$ is always singular, ξ will be called **completely singular.** It is easy to see that a regular process is also weakly regular, and that a completely singular process is singular.

To conclude this section, we pause to consider some particular cases, in which one can establish the ergodicity, mixing, or regularity of a process.

(a) Let the processes $\xi_1 = \{\xi_1(t)\}$ and $\xi = \{\xi(t)\}$ be stationarily correlated, and suppose that ξ_1 is a measurable function of ξ. Then it is obvious that the ergodicity or weak mixing of ξ implies that of ξ_1.

---

*See also J.R.Blum and D.L.Hanson, J. Math. Mech. 11, No. 3, 497-502 (1962).Tr.

(b) Let $\xi = \{\xi(t)\}$ and $\eta = \{\eta(t)\}$ be stationary and stationarily correlated processes with values in (X, S_x) and (Y, S_y) respectively. If ξ and η are independent, then for the ergodicity of the process $\zeta = (\xi, \eta)$ it is sufficient that ξ and η be ergodic, and one of them be weakly mixing. In fact, to prove ergodicity it is sufficient to verify that (5.2.1) or (5.2.2) holds for all sets of the form $E \times F \in S_x \times S_y, E \in S_x, F \in S_y$, since the family of all sets of this form generates the σ-algebra $S_x \times S_y$ and is clearly closed under intersections, as $(E_1 \times F_1) \cdot (E_2 \times F_2) = (E_1 \cdot E_2) \times (F_1 \cdot F_2)$. For two sets $N_1 = E_1 \times F_1$ and $N_2 = E_2 \times F_2, E_1, E_2 \in S_x$ and $F_1, F_2 \in S_y$

$$P_{\xi\eta}(U_t N_1 \cdot N_2) = P_{\xi\eta}(U_t(E_1 \times F_1) \cdot (E_2 \times F_2))$$

$$= P_{\xi\eta}((U_t E_1 \times U_t F_1) \cdot (E_2 \times F_2))$$

$$= P_{\xi\eta}((U_t E_1 \cdot E_2) \times (U_t F_1 \cdot F_2)) = P_\xi(U_t E_1 \cdot E_2) P_\eta(U_t F_1 \cdot F_2)$$

since ξ and η are independent and stationarily correlated, and consequently

$$\frac{1}{t}\int_0^t P_{\xi\eta}(U_\tau N_1 \cdot N_2)d\tau = \frac{1}{t}\int_0^t P_\xi(U_\tau E_1 \cdot E_2)\, P_\eta(U_\tau F_1 \cdot F_2)d\tau$$

$$= \frac{1}{t}\int_0^t [P_\xi(U_\tau E_1 \cdot E_2) - P_\xi(E_1)P_\xi(E_2)]P_\eta(U_\tau F_1 \cdot F_2))d\tau$$

$$+ \frac{1}{t}\int_0^t P_\xi(E_1)P_\xi(E_2)P_\eta(U_\tau F_1 \cdot F_2)d\tau. \tag{5.2.11}$$

Since $P_\xi(U_\tau F_1 \cdot F_2) \leqslant 1$, then from the weak mixing of ξ it follows that the first term on the extreme right of (5.2.11) goes to zero as $t \to \infty$, while, by virtue of the ergodicity of η, the second term converges to $P_\xi(E_1)P_\xi(E_2)P_\eta(F_1)P_\eta(F_2)$. But since ξ and η are independent,

$$P_{\xi\eta}(E_1 \times F_1)P_{\xi\eta}(E_2 \times F_2) = P_\xi(E_1)P_\eta(F_1)P_\xi(E_2)P_\eta(F_2).$$

Thus, for sets of the form $N_1 = E_1 \times F_1$ and $N_2 = E_2 \times F_2$

$$\lim_{t\to\infty} \frac{1}{t}\int_0^t P_{\xi\eta}(U_\tau N_1 \cdot N_2)d\tau = P_{\xi\eta}(N_1)P_{\xi\eta}(N_2),$$

which proves the ergodicity of the process (ξ, η).

Similarly, it can be shown that from the mixing, weak mixing, regularity, complete regularity or weak regularity of both of the processes ξ and η follows the corresponding property for the process (ξ, η).

This situation may be illustrated by the following example, which is encountered in practical applications. Let $\eta(t) = \xi(t)\gamma(t) + \zeta(t)$, where $\xi = \{\xi(t)\}, \gamma = \{\gamma(t)\}$ and $\zeta = \{\zeta(t)\}$ are stationary and mutually independent. Then, for example, it is sufficient, for the ergodicity of the pair (ξ, η), that ξ be ergodic and that both γ and ζ be weakly mixing; for, (ξ, η) is a measurable function of the process (ξ, γ, ζ), which, consisting of the ergodic process ξ and the weakly mixing process (γ, ζ), is itself ergodic.

In exactly the same manner, from the mixing, regularity, complete regularity or weak regularity of ξ, ζ and γ follows the corresponding property for the pair (ξ, η).

5.3. COMPLEX AND REAL-VALUED RANDOM PROCESSES. GENERALIZED RANDOM PROCESSES

In this section we introduce the notion of an n-dimensional complex or real-valued process, which is frequently encountered in applications, and also the related concept of a generalized random process.

The definition of such processes is based upon the concept of n-dimensional complex or real-valued random variables. A random variable γ which takes complex values in which the σ-algebra consists of the Borel sets, is called a **one-dimensional complex-valued** random variable. If γ takes only real values, then it is called a **one-dimensional real-valued** random variable. The random variable $\gamma = (\gamma_1, \ldots, \gamma_n)$, consisting of n complex, or n real-valued one-dimensional random variables $\gamma_j, j = 1, \ldots,$ n is called an **n-dimensional complex or real-valued** random variable, respectively.

A random process $\xi = (\xi_1, \ldots, \xi_n) = \{\xi(t)\} = \{(\xi_1(t), \ldots, \xi_n(t))\}$ consisting of n-dimensional complex or real-valued random variables $\xi(t) = (\xi_1(t), \ldots, \xi_n(t))$ is called an **n-dimensional complex or real-valued random process.**

We consider now the concept of a generalized n-dimensional complex or real-valued random process. The basic facts of the theory of generalized processes were first set forth in the papers [7], [14]. For such processes, among which, for example, so-called "white noise" is included, the notion of the random variable $\xi(t)$ loses meaning, and one can only speak of random variables $\xi_1(\varphi_j)$, $j = 1, \ldots,$ n which are linear functionals on spaces Φ_j of functions $\varphi_j(t)$ of a real variable t. Following [7], we take for $\Phi_j, j = 1, \ldots$ n the space of all infinitely differentiable functions of a real variable t, each of which vanishes outside of some closed finite interval. A **generalized n-dimensional complex or real-valued random process** is a collection of n-dimensional complex or real-valued random variables $\xi(\varphi) = (\xi_1(\varphi_1), \ldots, \xi_n(\varphi_n))$. Here $\xi_j(\varphi_j), j = 1, \ldots, n$ are random variables defined on the spaces Φ_j, linear with respect to $\varphi_j \epsilon \Phi_j$, and satisfying the condition

$$\lim_{m \to \infty} P\{|\xi_j(\varphi_j) - \xi(\varphi_{jm})| > \epsilon\} = 0; \quad \varphi_{jm} \epsilon \Phi_j, \tag{5.3.1}$$

if all of the φ_{jm} vanish outside of one fixed finite interval I and

$$\lim_{m \to \infty} \varphi_{jm} = \varphi_j, \lim_{m \to \infty} \varphi_{jm}^{[k]} = \varphi_j^{[k]}, k = 1, 2, \ldots, j = 1, \ldots, n \tag{5.3.2}$$

uniformly on I, where the superscript [k] denotes k-th derivative (see [7a]).

The concept of a generalized random process includes that of an ordinary complex or real-valued continuous random process which is integrable over any finite interval in the sense of convergence in probability; then we may take

$$\xi_j(\varphi_j) = \int_{-\infty}^{\infty} \xi_j(t) \varphi_j(t) dt.$$

If we denote by ξ_S^T the random variable consisting of the random variables $\xi_j(\varphi_j), j = 1, \ldots, n$, where the functions $\varphi_j \epsilon \Phi_j$ vanish outside the interval (S, T), then we arrive in a natural way at the concept of **subordination** for generalized random processes.

A generalized random process $\xi = \xi(\varphi) = (\xi_1(\varphi_1), \ldots, \xi_n(\varphi_n))$ is called **stationary** if, for any choice of functions $\varphi_{ji}, j = 1, \ldots, n$, $i = 1, \ldots, m, \varphi_{ji} \epsilon \Phi_j$, the joint distribution of the random variables $\xi_j(\varphi_{ji}), j = 1, \ldots, n, i = 1, \ldots, m$ is not altered upon replacing the $\varphi_{ji}(t)$ by $\varphi_{ji}(t + h)$ (translation by h). The generalized random processes ξ and η are **stationarily correlated** if the generalized process (ξ, η) is stationary. Now, just as in the case of non-generalized stationary random processes, a generalized stationary random process generates a one-parameter group of measure preserving transformations. Hence the notions of ergodicity, mixing, mixing in the weak sense, regularity, complete regularity and singularity completely carry over to generalized random processes. A generalized random process is called **weakly regular** or **completely singular** if the random process consisting of the random variables $\xi^t, -\infty < t < \infty$ is, respectively, weakly regular or completely singular.

5.4. DEFINITION OF THE INFORMATION RATE AND ENTROPY RATE

In the present work we will introduce several definitions for the **rate of generation of information about a process** η **by a process** ξ, namely:

$$\bar{I}(\xi, \eta) = \lim_{T\to\infty} \frac{1}{T} I(\xi_0^T, \eta_0^T); \tag{5.4.1}$$

$$\vec{I}(\xi, \eta) = \lim_{T\to\infty} \frac{1}{T} EI(\xi^T, \eta/\xi^0); \tag{5.4.2}$$

$$\tilde{I}(\xi, \eta) = \lim_{T\to\infty} \frac{1}{T} I(\xi_0^T, \eta). \tag{5.4.3}$$

These quantities are defined only when the right sides of the corresponding formulas exist.

Let now $\xi = \{\xi(t)\}$ and $\eta = \{\eta(t)\}$ be non-generalized stationary and stationarily correlated processes, and let (X, S_x), (Y, S_y), $(X(t), S_{x(t)})$, $(Y(t), S_{y(t)})$ be respectively the spaces of values of the random variables $\xi, \eta, \xi(t), \eta(t)$, and let $\{E_i(t)\}, \{F_j(t)\}$ be finite partitions of the spaces $X(t), Y(t)$ respectively, such that $E_i(t) = E_i(0), F_j(t) = F_j(0)$. Thus, as in Section 5.2, we can associate with these partitions stationary random processes $\beta = \{\beta(t)\}, \gamma = \{\gamma(t)\}$ having finite state spaces. Obviously β and γ are stationarily correlated.

When the processes ξ and η are stationary and stationarily correlated, it will be important for our work to introduce still other definitions of information rate:

$$\bar{I}^{(g)}(\xi, \eta) = \sup \frac{1}{h} \bar{I}(\beta^{(h)}, \gamma^{(h)}); \tag{5.4.4}$$

$$\vec{I}^{(g)}(\xi, \eta) = \sup \frac{1}{h} \vec{I}(\beta^{(h)}, \gamma^{(h)}); \tag{5.4.5}$$

$$\tilde{I}^{(g)}(\xi, \eta) = \sup \frac{1}{h} \tilde{I}(\beta^{(h)}, \gamma^{(h)}), \tag{5.4.6}$$

where $\beta^{(h)} = \{\beta^{(h)}(n)\} = \{\beta(nh)\}$ and $\gamma^{(h)} = \{\gamma^{(h)}(n)\} = \{\gamma(nh)\}$ are stationary and stationarily correlated discrete-parameter processes with finite state spaces, and the upper bound is taken over all the random processes β and γ corresponding to all possible partitions $\{E_i(t)\}$ and $\{F_j(t)\}$ and all admissible values of h, as in Section 5.2. For example, if t is discrete, then h must be an integer. In the next chapter it will be shown that the right sides of these formulas always exist and are equal. We remark that if ξ and η are thenselves discrete-parameter processes with finite state spaces, then the last three versions of the information rate coincide respectively with the first three defined in this section. If $\xi = \eta$, then the information rate is called the **entropy rate** of the process ξ. In this case, as usual, we replace the symbol I by H.

To carry over formulas (5.4.4), (5.4.5) and (5.4.6) to the case when ξ and η are generalized stationary random processes, we consider the non-generalized stationary processes $\xi_\varphi = \{\xi_\varphi(\tau)\}$ and $\eta_{\varphi'} = \{\eta_{\varphi'}(\tau)\}$, where

$$\xi_\varphi(\tau) = (\xi_1(\varphi_1(t+\tau)), \ldots, \xi_n(\varphi_n(t+\tau)));$$
$$\eta_{\varphi'}(\tau) = (\eta_1(\varphi'_1(t+\tau)), \ldots, \eta_m(\varphi'_m(t+\tau))).$$

Then the various information rates of ξ, η are defined by taking the supremum, over all families $\varphi = (\varphi_1, \ldots, \varphi_n)$ and $\varphi' = (\varphi'_1, \ldots, \varphi'_n)$, of the corresponding rates for the ordinary processes $\xi_\varphi, \eta_{\varphi'}$, where $\varphi_j \in \Phi_j$ and $\varphi'_j \in \Phi'_j$.

Remark. Occasionally a process ξ may be considered simultaneously generalized and non-generalized, so that ξ_S^T may be taken in two different senses. Nevertheless, the information rates defined by (5.4.1), (5.4.2) and (5.4.3) will be the same in both cases, for it is obvious that the two versions of ξ_S^T will be mutually subordinate.

To conclude this section we shall introduce the definition of the **entropy rate** of one process with respect to another. Let $\xi = \{\xi(\cdot)\}$, $\eta = \{\eta(\cdot)\}$ be random processes, generalized or non-generalized, with the random variables ξ_0^T, η_0^T taking values in the same space $(X_{\xi_0^T}, S_{X_{\xi_0^T}})$, and let P_{ξ^T}, P_{η^T} be the corresponding distributions of ξ_0^T and η_0^T. Then for the **entropy rate** $\overline{H}_{P_\eta}(P_\xi) = \overline{H}_\eta(\xi)$ of the process ξ with respect to the process η we take the quantity

$$\overline{H}_\eta(\xi) = \lim_{T\to\infty} \frac{1}{T} H_{\eta_0^T}(\xi_0^T) = \lim_{T\to\infty} \frac{1}{T} H_{P_{\eta_0^T}}(P_{\xi_0^T}), \qquad (5.4.7)$$

defined only when the right side exists. This formula is a generalization of (5.4.1), for

$$\overline{I}(\xi, \eta) = \lim_{T\to\infty} \frac{1}{T} I(\xi_0^T, \eta_0^T) = \lim_{T\to\infty} \frac{1}{T} H_{P_{\xi_0^T} \times \eta_0^T}(P_{\xi_0^T \eta_0^T})$$

is the entropy rate of the process $\gamma = (\xi, \eta)$ with respect to the process $\theta = (\xi \times \eta)$, defined in the space $X \times Y$ with measure $P_\theta = P_{\xi \times \eta}$, where X and Y are the spaces of values of ξ and η. Similarly, one can define various other entropy rates; it is true that here certain subtleties arise.

5.5. DEFINITION OF INFORMATION AND ENTROPY STABILITY OF RANDOM PROCESSES

A pair (ξ, η) of random processes ξ and η is called

information stable if $\overline{I}(\xi, \eta) = 0$ or if the family of pairs (ξ_0^t, η_0^t), $t > 0$ is information stable in the sense of Chapter 4. The pair (ξ, η) is called **relatively information stable** if $\vec{I}(\xi, \eta) = 0$ or if the family of pairs (ξ^t, η^t) is information stable with respect to the family $\gamma^t = \xi^0$ in the sense of Chapter 4. Finally, the pair (ξ, η) is called **entropy stable** if the random variables ξ_0^t and η_0^t, $0 < t < \infty$ take values in the same space and either $\overline{H}_{P_\eta}(P_\xi) = \overline{H}_\eta(\xi) = 0$ or the family of pairs of distributions $(P_{\xi_0^t}, P_{\eta_0^t})$ is entropy stable in the sense of Chapter 4.

TRANSLATOR'S REMARKS TO CHAPTER 5

It seems inexcusable not to point out that the concept of the so-called entropy invariant of a measure preserving transformation on a probability space is contained in the definitions of Section 5.4. Let T be a one-to-one transformation of a probability space (Ω, P) onto itself such that T and T^{-1} are both measurable and measure preserving. For each integer n let X_n be a replica of Ω; we define $\xi_n(\omega) = T^n\omega \in X_n$. Thus $\{\xi_n\}$ is a stationary discrete-parameter random process. The entropy of the system (Ω, P, T) is defined as $\overline{I}^{(g)}(\xi, \xi) = E(T)$. For those who are familiar with the more usual definition of the entropy invariant, we mention that the complete equivalence of these two definitions follows from the observation that when ξ and η are discrete-parameter processes, the supremum in (5.4.4) is easily seen to be achieved for $h = 1$.

Many of the known properties of the entropy invariant may be found among the results of Chapters 6 and 7. For example, part 7 of Theorem 7.2.1 essentially contains a basic result of Sinai (Dokl. Akad. Nauk. SSSR, vol. 124, no. 4, 768-771, 1959) concerning the actual evaluation of $E(T)$.

If $\{T_t\}$, $-\infty < t < \infty$ is a one-parameter family of one-to-one measure-preserving transformations of (Ω, P) onto itself, then one can define (as above) $E(T_t)$ for every value of t. If t_1/t_2 is rational, it is not difficult to show that $t_1 E(T_{t_1}) = t_2 E(T_{t_2})$. It has been shown by Abramov (Dokl. Akad. Nauk SSSR, vol. 128, no. 5, 1959) that if $\{T_t\}$ is a measurable flow and (Ω, P) is a Lebesgue space (for the definition see e.g. V.A.Rohlin, "Fundamental Ideas of Measure Theory," Amer. Math. Soc. Translations, Series I, no. 71), then $E(T_t) = tE(T_1)$ for all t. If one defines the continuous-parameter process $\{\xi_t\}$ in the same way as $\{\xi_n\}$ was defined earlier, Abramov's result would imply that if we set $\eta = \xi$ in (7.2.5), then the quantity $\frac{1}{h}\overline{I}^{(g)}(\xi^{(h)}, \xi^{(n)})$ is independent of h, so that $\overline{I}^{(g)}(\xi, \xi) = E(T_1)$. Possibly this result can be obtained, at least for the case of a continuous one-parameter flow, by the methods of this book. For a self-contained introduction to this subject see P.R.Halmos, "Entropy and Ergodic Theory," Univ. of Chicago lecture notes, 1959, and for further references see the address of the same author, Bull. Amer. Math. Society, vol. 67, no. 1, 70-80, 1961.

Chapter 6 Information rate and information stability of finite-state discrete-parameter stationary processes

In this chapter it will be shown that for stationary discrete parameter finite-state processes, all versions of the information rate coincide. A number of interesting properties of the information rate and entropy rate are established. It is proved that a sufficient condition for the information stability of such processes is their ergodicity. The possibility of generalizing these results to non-stationary processes is indicated. In the course of establishing these results, a number of lemmas, useful in themselves, will be proved.

The main results of this chapter have already appeared in the literature, for example, in the papers of McMillan [21] and Khinchin [16].

6.1. RELATIONS AMONG THE VARIOUS DEFINITIONS OF INFORMATION RATE.

THEOREM 6.1.1. Let $\xi = \{\xi(t)\}$ *and* $\eta = \{\eta(t)\}$, $t = \ldots, -1, 0, 1, \ldots$ *be stationary and stationarily correlated discrete-parameter finite-state processes. Then*

$$\tilde{I}(\xi, \eta) = \overline{I}(\xi, \eta) = \vec{I}(\xi, \eta) = \mathbf{E}\,\mathrm{I}(\xi, \eta/\xi^0), \tag{6.1.1}$$

$$\lim_{n\to\infty} \frac{1}{n} \mathbf{E}|i(\xi_0^n, \eta_0^n) - \bar{i}(\xi_0^n, \eta/\xi^0)|$$

$$= \lim_{n\to\infty} \frac{1}{n} \mathbf{E}|i(\xi_0^n, \eta) - \bar{i}(\xi_0^n, \eta/\xi^0)| = 0. \tag{6.1.2}$$

The proof of this theorem uses the following lemma.

LEMMA 6.1.1. Let $a_1, a_2, \ldots$ be a sequence of non-negative numbers of the form

$$a_n = \sum_{j=1}^{n} a_{nj},$$

where the a_{nj}, $j = 1, \ldots, n$; $n = 1, 2, \ldots$ are non-negative and bounded, such that

$$\lim_{j,n,n-j\to\infty} a_{nj} = a. \tag{6.1.3}$$

Then

$$\lim_{n\to\infty} \frac{a_n}{n} = \lim_{n\to\infty} \sum_{j=1}^{n} \frac{a_{nj}}{n} = a.$$

The proof is obvious.

We come now to the proof of the theorem. In the case under consideration, the parameter T which occurs in the definitions of the information rates is integer valued, i.e., T = n. Taking into account that $(\xi_Q^T, \xi_T^R) = \xi_Q^R$ for $Q < T \leqslant R$, and applying (3.6.6) n times to the expressions $\mathbf{E}I(\xi^n, \eta/\xi^0)$, $I(\xi_0^n, \eta_0^n)$, $I(\xi_0^n, \eta)$, we obtain

$$\mathbf{E}I(\xi^n, \eta/\xi^0) = \mathbf{E}I(\xi_0^n, \eta/\xi^0) = \mathbf{E}I(\xi_0^1, \eta/\xi^0) + \mathbf{E}I(\xi_1^2, \eta/\xi^1) + \ldots$$

$$+ \mathbf{E}I(\xi_{n-1}^n, \eta/\xi^{n-1}); \tag{6.1.4}$$

$$I(\xi_0^n, \eta_0^n) = I(\xi_0^1, \eta_0^n) + \mathbf{E}I(\xi_1^2, \eta_0^n/\xi_0^1) + \ldots + \mathbf{E}I(\xi_{n-1}^n, \eta_0^n/\xi_0^{n-1}); \tag{6.1.5}$$

$$I(\xi_0^n, \eta) = I(\xi_0^1, \eta) + \mathbf{E}I(\xi_1^2, \eta/\xi_0^1) + \ldots + \mathbf{E}I(\xi_{n-1}^n, \eta/\xi_0^{n-1}). \tag{6.1.6}$$

Let us consider the k-th term on the right side of (6.1.4)–(6.1.6). Since the processes ξ and η are stationarily correlated,

$$\mathbf{E}I(\xi_{k-1}^k, \eta/\xi^{k-1}) = \mathbf{E}I(\xi_0^1, \eta/\xi^0) \leqslant H(\xi_0^1); \tag{6.1.7}$$

$$\mathbf{E}I(\xi_{k-1}^k, \eta_0^n/\xi_0^{k-1}) = \mathbf{E}I(\xi_0^1, \eta_{-k+1}^{n-k+1}/\xi_{-k+1}^0) \leqslant H(\xi_0^1); \tag{6.1.8}$$

$$\mathbf{E}I(\xi_{k-1}^k, \eta/\xi_0^{k-1}) = \mathbf{E}I(\xi_0^1, \eta/\xi_{-k+1}^0) \leqslant H(\xi_0^1). \tag{6.1.9}$$

Since by hypothesis the random variable $\xi_0^1 = \xi(1)$ takes on only finitely many values,

$$\lim_{n, k, n-k\to\infty} \mathbf{E}I(\xi_0^1, \eta_{-k+1}^{n-k+1}/\xi_{-k+1}^0) = \mathbf{E}I(\xi_0^1, \eta/\xi^0); \tag{6.1.10}$$

$$\lim_{k\to\infty} \mathbf{E}I(\xi_0^1, \eta/\xi_{-k+1}^0) = \mathbf{E}I(\xi_0^1, \eta/\xi^0) \tag{6.1.11}$$

by Corollary 2 of Theorem 3.10.1. From (6.1.7)–(6.1.11) it is evident that every term appearing on the right side of (6.1.4)–(6.1.6) is bounded by $H(\xi_0^1)$, and that for $n, k, n-k\to\infty$ each of these terms converges to the same value $\mathbf{E}I(\xi_0^1, \eta/\xi^0)$. Thus, each sequence $\{\mathbf{E}I(\xi_0^n, \eta/\xi^0)\}$, $\{I(\xi_0^n, \eta_0^n)\}$, $\{I(\xi_0^n, \eta)\}$, $n = 1, 2, \ldots$ satisfies the conditions of Lemma 6.1.1 with $a = \mathbf{E}I(\xi_0^1, \eta/\xi^0)$. Therefore, according to the lemma

$$\mathbf{E}I(\xi_0^1, \eta/\xi^0) = \lim_{n\to\infty} \frac{1}{n} \mathbf{E}I(\xi_0^n, \eta/\xi^0) = \lim_{n\to\infty} \frac{1}{n} I(\xi_0^n, \eta_0^n) = \lim_{n\to\infty} \frac{1}{n} I(\xi_0^n, \eta),$$

i.e., formula (6.1.1) is valid.

We note, moreover, that comparing (6.1.4) and (6.1.7) shows that

$$\mathbf{E}I(\xi_0^n, \eta/\xi^0) = n\mathbf{E}I(\xi_0^1, \eta/\xi^0) \tag{6.1.12}$$

and that the ratio $\mathbf{E}I(\xi_0^n, \eta/\xi^0)/n$ does not depend upon n. It remains to prove (6.1.2). Applying (3.6.5) n times to $\bar{i}(\xi_0^n, \eta/\xi^0)$, $i(\xi_0^n, \eta_0^n)$, and $i(\xi_0^n, \eta)$, we obtain

$$\bar{i}(\xi_0^n, \eta/\xi^0) = \bar{i}(\xi_0^1, \eta/\xi^0) + \bar{i}(\xi_1^2, \eta/\xi^1) + \ldots + \bar{i}(\xi_{n-1}^n, \eta/\xi^{n-1}); \tag{6.1.13}$$

$$i(\xi_0^n, \eta_0^n) = i(\xi_0^1, \eta_0^n) + \bar{i}(\xi_1^2, \eta_0^n/\xi_0^1) + \ldots + \bar{i}(\xi_{n-1}^n, \eta_0^n/\xi_0^{n-1}); \tag{6.1.14}$$

$$i(\xi_0^n, \eta) = i(\xi_0^1, \eta) + \bar{i}(\xi_1^2, \eta/\xi_0^1) + \ldots + \bar{i}(\xi_{n-1}^n, \eta/\xi_0^{n-1}). \tag{6.1.15}$$

Subtracting equation (6.1.13) termwise from (6.1.14) and (6.1.15), and using the ordinary inequality for the absolute value of a sum, we find that

$$\mathbf{E}|i(\xi_0^n, \eta_0^n) - \bar{i}(\xi_0^n, \eta/\xi^0)| \leqslant \mathbf{E}|i(\xi_0^1, \eta_0^n) - \bar{i}(\xi_0^1, \eta/\xi^0)| + \mathbf{E}|\bar{i}(\xi_1^2, \eta_0^n/\xi_0^1) - \bar{i}(\xi_1^2, \eta/\xi^1)| + \ldots + \mathbf{E}|\bar{i}(\xi_{n-1}^n, \eta_0^n/\xi_0^{n-1}) - \bar{i}(\xi_{n-1}^n, \eta/\xi^{n-1})|; \tag{6.1.16}$$

$$\mathbf{E}|i(\xi_0^n, \eta) - \bar{i}(\xi_0^n, \eta/\xi^0)| \leqslant \mathbf{E}|i(\xi_0^1, \eta) - \bar{i}(\xi_0^1, \eta/\xi^0)| + \mathbf{E}|\bar{i}(\xi_1^2, \eta/\xi_0^1) - \bar{i}(\xi_1^2, \eta/\xi^1)| + \ldots + \mathbf{E}|\bar{i}(\xi_{n-1}^n, \eta/\xi_0^{n-1}) - \bar{i}(\xi_{n-1}^n, \eta/\xi^{n-1})|. \quad (6.1.17)$$

Since the processes ξ and η are stationarily correlated, the k-th terms on the right side of (6.1.16) and (6.1.17) satisfy

$$\mathbf{E}|\bar{i}(\xi_{k-1}^k, \eta_0^n/\xi_0^{k-1}) - \bar{i}(\xi_{k-1}^k, \eta/\xi^{k-1})|$$
$$= \mathbf{E}|\bar{i}(\xi_0^1, \eta_{-k+1}^{n-k+1}/\xi_{-k+1}^0) - \bar{i}(\xi_0^1, \eta/\xi^0)|; \quad (6.1.18)$$

$$\mathbf{E}|\bar{i}(\xi_{k-1}^k, \eta/\xi_0^{k-1}) - \bar{i}(\xi_{k-1}^k, \eta/\xi^{k-1})|$$
$$= \mathbf{E}|\bar{i}(\xi_{0-1}^1, \eta/\xi_{-k+1}^0) - \bar{i}(\xi_0^1, \eta/\xi^0)|. \quad (6.1.19)$$

Since for any p, s, l, r $\mathbf{E}|\bar{i}(\xi_0^1, \eta_p^r/\xi_s^l)| \leqslant \mathbf{E}I(\xi_0^1, \eta_p^r/\xi_s^l) + 2/e \leqslant H(\xi_0^1) + 2/e$, the right sides of (6.1.18) and (6.1.19) have a common bound. In view of (6.1.10) and (6.1.11) it follows from Corollary 2 of Theorem 3.10.1 that for $n, k, n-k \to \infty$ the right side of (6.1.18) and (6.1.19) converges to zero. Let a_n, b_n denote respectively the terms on the right side of (6.1.16) and (6.1.17). From what has just been shown, it follows that $\{a_n\}$ and $\{b_n\}$ satisfy the conditions of Lemma 6.1.1 with $a = 0$. By the lemma

$$\lim_{n\to\infty} \frac{1}{n} \mathbf{E}|i(\xi_0^n, \eta_0^n) - \bar{i}(\xi_0^n, \eta/\xi^0)|$$
$$\leqslant \lim_{n\to\infty} \frac{\mathbf{E}|i(\xi_0^1, \eta_0^n) - \bar{i}(\xi_0^1, \eta/\xi^0)| + \sum_{k=2}^{n} \mathbf{E}|\bar{i}(\xi_{k-1}^k, \eta_0^n/\xi_0^{k-1}) - \bar{i}(\xi_{k-1}^k, \eta/\xi^{k-1})|}{n} = 0; \quad (6.1.20)$$

$$\lim_{n\to\infty} \frac{1}{n} \mathbf{E}|i(\xi_0^n, \eta) - \bar{i}(\xi_0^n, \eta/\xi^0)|$$
$$\leqslant \lim_{n\to\infty} \frac{\mathbf{E}|i(\xi_0^1, \eta) - \bar{i}(\xi_0^1, \eta/\xi^0)| + \sum_{k=2}^{n} \mathbf{E}|\bar{i}(\xi_{k-1}^k, \eta/\xi_0^{k-1}) - \bar{i}(\xi_{k-1}^k, \eta/\xi^{k-1})|}{n} = 0, \quad (6.1.21)$$

which proves (6.1.2).

COROLLARY. For any pair of stationary and stationarily correlated processes

$$\tilde{I}^{(g)}(\xi, \eta) = \bar{I}^{(g)}(\xi, \eta) = \vec{I}^{(g)}(\xi, \eta). \quad (6.1.22)$$

We remark that (6.1.1) and (6.1.2), which were proved for stationarily correlated processes, remain valid in certain cases, frequently encountered in practice, which involve non-stationary processes. Let us clarify this remark.

(a) If the pair of random variables $(\xi(t), \eta(t))$ and $(\xi(t'), \eta(t'))$, $t \neq t'$ are independent, then (6.1.1) and (6.1.2) are obvious.

(b) Let $\xi = \{\xi(t)\}$, $\eta = \{\eta(t)\}$, $\zeta = \{\zeta(t)\}$ be random processes. We consider the average conditional information rates defined by

$$\mathbf{E}\tilde{\mathrm{I}}(\xi, \eta/\zeta) = \lim_{T\to\infty} \frac{1}{T}\mathbf{E}\mathrm{I}(\xi_0^T, \eta/\zeta); \qquad (6.1.23)$$

$$\mathbf{E}\bar{\mathrm{I}}(\xi, \eta/\zeta) = \lim_{T\to\infty} \frac{1}{T}\mathbf{E}\mathrm{I}(\xi_0^T, \eta_0^T/\zeta); \qquad (6.1.24)$$

$$\mathbf{E}\vec{\mathrm{I}}(\xi, \eta/\zeta) = \lim_{T\to\infty} \frac{1}{T}\mathbf{E}\mathrm{I}(\xi_0^T, \eta/(\zeta, \xi^0)). \qquad (6.1.25)$$

If ξ, η and ζ are stationary and stationarily correlated discrete-parameter processes with finite state spaces, then, just as previously, it can be proved that

$$\mathbf{E}\tilde{\mathrm{I}}(\xi, \eta/\zeta) = \mathbf{E}\bar{\mathrm{I}}(\xi, \eta/\zeta) = \mathbf{E}\vec{\mathrm{I}}(\xi, \eta/\zeta) = \mathbf{E}\mathrm{I}(\xi_0^1, \eta/(\zeta, \xi^0)).$$

Further, it can be shown that the conditional informations $\mathrm{I}(\xi_0^T, \eta/z)$, $\mathrm{I}(\xi_0^T, \eta_0^T/z)$ and $\mathbf{E}\mathrm{I}(\xi_0^T, \eta/(\xi^0, z)$ are defined almost everywhere with respect to P_ζ, that the limits

$$\tilde{\mathrm{I}}(\xi, \eta/z) = \lim_{T\to\infty} \frac{1}{T}\mathrm{I}(\xi_0^T, \eta/z); \qquad (6.1.26)$$

$$\bar{\mathrm{I}}(\xi, \eta/z) = \lim_{T\to\infty} \frac{1}{T}\mathrm{I}(\xi_0^T, \eta_0^T/z); \qquad (6.1.27)$$

$$\vec{\mathrm{I}}(\xi, \eta/z) = \lim_{T\to\infty} \frac{1}{T}\mathbf{E}\mathrm{I}(\xi_0^T, \eta/(\xi^0, z)), \qquad (6.1.28)$$

exist, where z is in the space (Z, S_z) of values of ζ, and that

$$\tilde{\mathrm{I}}(\xi, \eta/z) = \bar{\mathrm{I}}(\xi, \eta/z) = \vec{\mathrm{I}}(\xi, \eta/z) = \mathbf{E}\mathrm{I}(\xi_0^1, \eta/(\xi^0, z)). \qquad (6.1.29)$$

Equation (6.1.29) may be considered as a generalization of (6.1.1) to the case of non-stationary processes which depend upon a parameter z. Equation (6.1.2) can also be generalized in exactly the same way.

6.2. PROPERTIES OF THE INFORMATION RATE.

THEOREM 6.2.1. *Throughout this section, let* $\xi = \{\xi(t)\}$, $\eta = \{\eta(t)\}$, $\zeta = \{\zeta(t)\}$, $\gamma = \{\gamma(t)\}$ *and* $\theta = \{\theta(t)\} = \{(\xi(t), \eta(t), \zeta(t), \gamma(t))\}$ *be stationary discrete-parameter finite-state processes with values in the measurable spaces* (X, S_x), (Y, S_y), (Z, S_z), (U, S_u) *and* $(X \times Y \times Z \times U, S_x \times S_y \times S_z \times S_u)$ *respectively. Then the information rates of these processes have the following properties:*

$$(1)\ 0 \leqslant \bar{I}(\xi, \eta) < \infty . \tag{6.2.1}$$

If one of the processes, say ξ, *is singular, then*

$$\bar{I}(\xi, \eta) = 0. \tag{6.2.2}$$

If, however, ξ *is regular, then* $\bar{I}(\xi, \eta) = 0$ *if and only if the processes* ξ *and* η *are independent.*

$$(2)\ \bar{I}(\xi, \eta) = \bar{I}(\eta, \xi). \tag{6.2.3}$$

(3) If the pair (ξ, η) *is independent of the pair* (ζ, γ), *then*

$$\bar{I}((\xi, \zeta), (\eta, \gamma)) = \bar{I}(\xi, \eta) + \bar{I}(\zeta, \gamma). \tag{6.2.4}$$

(4) Dobrushin's formula

$$\bar{I}((\xi, \eta), \zeta) + \bar{I}(\xi, \eta) = \bar{I}(\xi, (\eta, \zeta)) + \bar{I}(\eta, \zeta). \tag{6.2.5}$$

(5) If the sequence ξ, η, ζ *forms a Markov chain, then*

$$\bar{I}(\xi, (\eta, \zeta)) = \bar{I}(\xi, \eta). \tag{6.2.6}$$

(6) If the random process ζ *is subordinate to the random process* ξ *(in particular, if* ζ *is a measurable function of* ξ*), then*

$$\bar{I}(\zeta, \eta) \leqslant \bar{I}(\xi, \eta). \tag{6.2.7}$$

(7) If

$$H(\zeta(t)) - I(\xi(t), \zeta(t)) < \epsilon, \text{ then } \bar{I}(\zeta, \eta) - \bar{I}(\xi, \eta) < \epsilon. \tag{6.2.8}$$

Moreover, if

$$H(\zeta(t)) - I(\xi, \zeta(t)) < \epsilon, \text{ then } \bar{I}(\zeta, \eta) - \bar{I}(\xi, \eta) < \epsilon. \tag{6.2.9}$$

PROOF. (1) Inequality (6.2.1) follows from the corresponding property of information. If the process ξ is singular, then ξ^0 is everywhere dense in ξ^1. Therefore $\overline{I}(\xi,\eta) = \overline{I}(\xi,\eta) = \mathbf{E}I(\xi_0^1, \eta/\xi^0)$ $= \mathbf{E}I(\xi_0^1, \eta/\xi^1)$. But since the sequence of random variables ξ_0^1, ξ^1, η forms a Markov chain, $\mathbf{E}I(\xi_0^1, \eta/\xi^1) = 0$, i.e., $\overline{I}(\xi,\eta) = 0$. If now ξ and η are independent, then $I(\xi,\eta) = 0$, which *a fortiori* implies $\overline{I}(\xi,\eta) = 0$.

It remains to show only that if the process ξ is regular, then $\overline{I}(\xi,\eta) = 0$ implies the independence of ξ and η. Now by the definition of regularity, the σ-algebra $\overline{S}_x = \cap_n S_x^n$ consists of sets of probability measure one or zero. Therefore by Theorem 4.3, Chapter 7 of Doob [4] it follows that for every $E \epsilon S_x$

$$\lim_{n \to -\infty} P\{\xi \epsilon E/x^n\} = P\{\xi \epsilon E\};$$

$$x = (\ldots, x(-1), x(0), x(1), x(2), \ldots), x^n = (\ldots, x(n-2), x(n-1), x(n)), x \epsilon X \quad x(j) \epsilon X(j) \qquad (6.2.10)$$

almost everywhere with respect to P_ξ. Consider the random variable α which is a measurable function of ξ, whose values are the sets $E_1 = E$ and $E_2 = X - E$, defined so that $\xi \epsilon E$ implies $\alpha = E$. According to (3.1.16)

$$\mathbf{E}H(\alpha/\xi^n) = \mathbf{E}I(\alpha, \alpha/\xi^n) = \mathbf{E} \sum_{i,j=1}^{2} P\{\alpha = E_i, \alpha = E_j/\xi^n\}$$

$$\times \log \frac{P\{\alpha = E_i, \alpha = E_j/\xi^n\}}{P\{\alpha = E_i/\xi^n\} P\{\alpha = E_j/\xi^n\}} = \mathbf{E} \sum_{i=1}^{2} P\{\xi \epsilon E_i/\xi^n\} \log \frac{1}{P\{\xi \epsilon E_i/\xi^n\}}. \qquad (6.2.11)$$

It follows by virtue of (6.2.10) that

$$\lim_{n \to -\infty} \mathbf{E}H(\alpha/\xi^n) = \lim_{n \to -\infty} \mathbf{E} \sum_{i=1}^{2} P\{\xi \epsilon E_i/\xi^n\} \log \frac{1}{P\{\xi \epsilon E_i/\xi^n\}}$$

$$\geqslant \mathbf{E} \sum_{i=1}^{2} P\{\xi \epsilon E_i\} \log \frac{1}{P\{\xi \epsilon E_i\}} = H(\alpha). \qquad (6.2.12)$$

Comparing (6.2.12) with the inequality $H(\alpha) \leq \mathbf{E}H(\alpha)/\xi^n)$ shows that

$$\lim_{n \to -\infty} \mathbf{E}H(\alpha/\xi^n) = H(\alpha). \qquad (6.2.13)$$

Therefore as $n \to -\infty$ the relation $H(\alpha) = I(\alpha, (\alpha, \xi^n)) = I(\alpha, \xi^n) + \mathbf{E}I(\alpha, \alpha/\xi^n) = I(\alpha, \xi^n) + \mathbf{E}H(\alpha/\xi^n)$ goes over into

$$H(\alpha) = \lim_{n \to -\infty} I(\alpha, \xi^n) + H(\alpha), \text{ i.e.,}$$

$$\lim_{n \to -\infty} I(\alpha, \xi^n) = 0. \qquad (6.2.14)$$

Moreover, since ξ and η are stationarily correlated, it follows from $\bar{I}(\xi,\eta) = \vec{I}(\xi,\eta) = 0$ that

$$\mathbf{E}I(\xi, \eta/\xi^n) = \mathbf{E}I(\xi, \eta/\xi^0) = \lim_{n\to\infty} \mathbf{E}I(\xi^n, \eta/\xi^0) = \lim_{n\to\infty} \mathbf{E}I(\xi_0^n, \eta/\xi^0)$$

$$= \lim_{n\to\infty} n\,\vec{I}(\xi, \eta) = 0. \tag{6.2.15}$$

But (6.2.15) and (6.2.14) imply that as $n \to -\infty$ the relation $I(\alpha,\eta) \leqslant I(\alpha,(\eta,\xi^n)) = I(\alpha,\xi^n) + \mathbf{E}I(\alpha,\eta/\xi^n) \leqslant I(\alpha,\xi^n) + \mathbf{E}I(\xi,\eta/\xi^n)$ goes over into the relation $I(\alpha,\eta) = 0$. Thus $I(\alpha,\eta) = 0$ for any set $E \in S_x$, which implies the independence of ξ and η.

(2), (3), (4). The proof of these properties follows from the corresponding properties of information.

(5) Since ξ, η, ζ form a Markov chain, the random variables ξ_0^n, η, ζ likewise form a Markov chain, and therefore

$$\bar{I}(\xi,(\eta,\zeta)) = \tilde{I}(\xi,(\eta,\zeta))$$

$$= \lim_{n\to\infty} \frac{1}{n} I(\xi_0^n, (\eta, \zeta)) = \lim_{n\to\infty} \frac{1}{n} I(\xi_0^n, \eta) = \tilde{I}(\xi, \eta) = \bar{I}(\xi, \eta).$$

(6) The inequality (6.2.7) is implied by the following sequence of relations:

$$\bar{I}(\zeta, \eta) = \bar{I}(\eta, \zeta) = \vec{I}(\eta, \zeta) = \mathbf{E}I(\eta_0^1, \zeta/\eta^0) \leqslant \mathbf{E}I(\eta_0^1, \xi/\eta^0)$$

$$= \vec{I}(\eta, \xi) = \bar{I}(\eta, \xi) = \bar{I}(\xi, \eta). \tag{6.2.15.1}$$

(7) In order to prove (6.2.9) we first write down the following lemma.

LEMMA 6.2.1. If

$$H(\zeta_i) - I(\xi, \zeta_i) < \epsilon_i, \; i = 1, \ldots, n,$$

then $$I((\zeta_1, \ldots, \zeta_n), \nu) - I(\xi, \nu) < \sum_{i=1}^n \epsilon_i, \tag{6.2.16}$$

where ν, ζ_i are random variables and the ϵ_i are arbitrary positive numbers.

For the proof, it suffices to establish the following two inequalities:

$$I(\zeta', \nu) - I(\xi, \nu) \leqslant H(\zeta') - I(\xi, \zeta') \tag{6.2.17}$$

and $H((\zeta_1', \zeta_2')) - I(\xi, (\zeta_1', \zeta_2')) \leqslant [H(\zeta_1')$

$$- I(\xi, \zeta_1')] + [H(\zeta_2') - I(\xi, \zeta_2')] \qquad (6.2.18)$$

where $\zeta', \zeta_1', \zeta_2'$ are any random variables. We have

$$H(\zeta') - I(\xi, \zeta') = I(\zeta', \zeta') - I(\xi, \zeta') = I(\zeta', (\zeta', \nu)) - I(\xi, \zeta')$$

$$\geqslant I(\zeta', (\zeta', \nu)) - I(\xi, (\zeta', \nu)) = I(\zeta', \nu)$$

$$+ \mathbf{E}I(\zeta', \zeta'/\nu) - I(\xi, \nu) - \mathbf{E}I(\xi, \zeta'/\nu) \qquad (6.2.18.1)$$

which implies (6.2.17) since $\mathbf{E}I(\zeta', \zeta'/\nu) - \mathbf{E}I\xi, \zeta'/\nu) = \mathbf{E}H(\zeta'/\nu) - \mathbf{E}I(\xi, \zeta'/\nu) \geqslant 0$. Furthermore, by Dobrushin's formula (3.8.7)

$$I((\zeta_1', \zeta_2'), (\zeta_1', \zeta_2')) + I(\zeta_1', \zeta_2') = I((\zeta_2', \zeta_1', \zeta_2'), \zeta_1') + I(\zeta_2', (\zeta_1', \zeta_2'));$$

$$(6.2.19)$$

$$I(\xi, (\zeta_1', \zeta_2')) + I(\zeta_1', \zeta_2') = I((\xi, \zeta_2'), \zeta_1') + I(\xi, \zeta_2'). \qquad (6.2.20)$$

Taking into account that $I((\zeta_1', \zeta_2'), (\zeta_1', \zeta_2')) = H((\zeta_1', \zeta_2'))$; $I(\zeta_1', (\zeta_2', \zeta_1', \zeta_2')) = H(\zeta_1')$; $I(\zeta_2', (\zeta_1', \zeta_2')) = H(\zeta_2')$, formula (6.2.19) may be written in the form

$$H((\zeta_1', \zeta_2')) + I(\zeta_1', \zeta_2') = H(\zeta_1') + H(\zeta_2'). \qquad (6.2.21)$$

Comparing (6.2.21) and (6.2.20), we obtain (6.2.18), which proves the lemma.

In view of the lemma, from the first inequality of (6.2.9) follows

$$\bar{I}(\zeta, \eta) - \bar{I}(\xi, \eta) = \bar{I}(\eta, \zeta) - \bar{I}(\eta, \xi)$$

$$= \lim_{n \to \infty} \frac{1}{n} [I(\eta_0^n, \zeta_0^n) - I(\eta_0^n, \xi)] \leqslant \lim_{n = \infty} \frac{1}{n} \sum_{k=1}^{n} [I(\zeta(k), \eta_0^n) - I(\xi, \eta_0^n)]$$

$$\leqslant \lim_{n \to \infty} \frac{1}{n}(n\epsilon) = \epsilon \qquad (6.2.22)$$

i.e., we obtain the second inequality in (6.2.9).

6.3. ENTROPY RATE.

Let $\xi = \{\xi(t)\}$ and $\eta = \{\eta(t)\}$ be stationary and stationarily correlated discrete-parameter finite-state processes. The entropy rate has the following properties:

(1) $0 \leqslant \overline{H}(\xi) < \infty$ (6.3.1)

and $\overline{H}(\xi) = 0$ *if and only if the process* $\xi = \{\xi(t)\}$ *is singular.*

(2) $\overline{H}(\xi) \geqslant \overline{I}(\xi, \eta)$. (6.3.2)

(3) If the random variables ξ *and* η *are independent, then*

$$\overline{H}((\xi, \eta)) = \overline{H}(\xi) + \overline{H}(\eta). \tag{6.3.3}$$

(4) If the random process η *is subordinate to the random process* ξ, *then*

$$\overline{H}(\eta) \leqslant \overline{H}(\xi). \tag{6.3.4}$$

(5) If

$$H(\eta(t)) - I(\xi, \eta(t)) < \epsilon, \tag{6.3.5}$$

then

$$\overline{H}(\eta) - \overline{H}(\xi) < \epsilon. \tag{6.3.6}$$

Relations (6.3.1)–(6.3.4) and (6.3.6) follow from the corresponding relations for the information rate. Only the assertion that $\overline{H}(\xi) = 0$ implies that ξ is singular is non-trivial. Let us prove this fact. If $\overline{H}(\xi) = 0$,

$$\mathbf{E}H(\xi/\xi^0) = \mathbf{E}I(\xi, \xi/\xi^0) = \lim_{n\to\infty} \mathbf{E}I(\xi^n, \xi/\xi^0) = \lim_{n\to\infty} \mathbf{E}I(\xi_0^n, \xi/\xi^0)$$

$$= \lim_{n\to\infty} (n\mathbf{E}I(\xi_0^1, \xi/\xi^0)) = \lim_{n\to\infty} (n\vec{I}(\xi, \xi)) = \lim_{n\to\infty} (n\overline{I}(\xi, \xi))$$

$$= \lim_{n\to\infty} (n\overline{H}(\xi)) = 0.$$

By the properties of entropy (see Section 3.9), it follows from the equation $\mathbf{E}H(\xi/\xi^0) = 0$ that ξ is subordinate to ξ^0, i.e., that ξ^0 is everywhere dense in ξ. In view of the stationarity of ξ it follows that for every n, ξ^n is everywhere dense in ξ. But this is just the statement that the process ξ is singular.

6.4. INFORMATION STABILITY.

We prove McMillan's Theorem [21].

THEOREM 6.4.1. Every pair of stationary and stationarily correlated discrete-parameter finite-state processes $\xi = \{\xi(t)\}$

and $\eta = \{\eta(t)\}$, *such that the process* (ξ, η) *is ergodic, is information and relatively information stable.*

PROOF. Applying formula (3.6.5) n times to $\bar{i}(\xi_0^n, \eta/\xi^0)$, we obtain

$$\bar{i}(\xi^n, \eta/\xi^0) = \sum_{k=0}^{n-1} \bar{i}(\xi_k^{k+1}, \eta/\xi^k).$$

Since ξ and η are stationarily correlated, the random variables $\bar{i}(\xi_k^{k+1}, \eta/\xi^k)$, $k = \ldots, -1, 0, 1, 2, \ldots$, with average value

$$\mathbf{E}\bar{i}(\xi_k^{k+1}, \eta/\xi^k) = \mathbf{E}I(\xi_k^{k+1}, \eta/\xi^k) = \mathbf{E}I(\xi^1, \eta/\xi^0) = \bar{I}(\xi, \eta) = \bar{I}(\xi, \eta)$$

also form a stationary ergodic random process. By a well-known ergodic theorem, the ratio

$$\frac{\bar{i}(\xi_0^n, \eta/\xi^0)}{n} = \sum_{k=0}^{n-1} \frac{\bar{i}(\xi_k^{k+1}, \eta/\xi^k)}{n}$$

converges in the mean to $\mathbf{E}I(\xi_0^1, \eta/\xi^0) = \bar{I}(\xi, \eta)$, i.e.,

$$\frac{\bar{i}(\xi_0^n, \eta/\xi^0)}{n\bar{I}(\xi, \eta)} = \frac{\bar{i}(\xi_0^n, \eta/\xi^0)}{\mathbf{E}I(\xi_0^n, \eta/\xi^0)}$$

converges in the mean, and therefore in probability, to one, which is precisely the relative information stability of the pair (ξ, η). The information stability of the pair (ξ, η) follows by virtue of the relative information stability, the inequality

$$\left|\frac{i(\xi_0^n, \eta_0^n)}{I(\xi_0^n, \eta_0^n)} - 1\right| \leqslant \left|\frac{i(\xi_0^n, \eta_0^n) - \bar{i}(\xi_0^n, \eta/\xi^0)}{n}\right| \frac{n}{I(\xi_0^n, \eta_0^n)}$$

$$+ \left|\frac{\bar{i}(\xi_0^n, \eta/\xi^0)}{\mathbf{E}I(\xi_0^n, \eta/\xi^0)} - 1\right| \frac{\mathbf{E}I(\xi_0^n, \eta/\xi^0)}{I(\xi_0^n, \eta_0^n)} + o(1)$$

and relation (6.1.2).

Remark 1. If $\eta = \xi$, then

$$i_{\xi_0^n \xi_0^n}(x_0^n, x_0^n) = -\log P_{\xi_0^n}(x_0^n),$$

where x_0^n is a value of the random variable ξ_0^n. In this case, the information stability assumes the form of convergence to one in probability of the ratio

$$\frac{-\log P_{\xi_0^n}(\xi_0^n)}{H(\xi_0^n)}.$$

Remark 2. The ergodicity of the pair (ξ, η) is not a necessary condition for information stability. We can exhibit a case in which the information stability of the pair (ξ, η) can be established without knowledge as to the ergodicity of the process ξ. For example, let $\xi = (\xi', \xi'')$, ξ', ξ'', η be stationary and pairwise stationarily correlated discrete-parameter finite-state processes such that (ξ', η) is ergodic and ξ'' is singular. Then the pair (ξ, η) is information stable. To prove this fact it suffices, according to Theorem 4.2.1, to verify that

$$\lim_{n\to\infty} \frac{I((\xi')_0^n, \eta_0^n)}{I(\xi_0^n, \eta_0^n)} = 1. \tag{6.4.1}$$

Moreover, we have

$$I(\xi_0^n, \eta_0^n) = I(((\xi')_0^n, (\xi'')_0^n), \eta_0^n) = I((\xi')_0^n, \eta_0^n) + \mathbf{E}I((\xi'')_0^n, \eta_0^n/(\xi')_0^n)$$
$$\leqslant I((\xi')_0^n, \eta_0^n) + H((\xi'')_0^n). \tag{6.4.2}$$

But since ξ'' is a singular process,

$$\lim_{n\to\infty} \frac{1}{n} H((\xi'')_0^n) = \overline{H}(\xi'') = 0. \tag{6.4.3}$$

Comparing (6.4.2) and (6.4.3) proves (6.4.1) and hence the information stability of the pair (ξ, η).

Chapter 7 Information rate of stationary random processes: general case

In this chapter we will study the properties of the information rate of stationary random processes and establish the interrelationships among the various definitions of this quantity. We give a sufficiently general condition under which the variously defined information rates coincide. At the conclusion of the chapter, various remarks are made concerning the existence and determination of the entropy rate of one stationary process with respect to another.

7.1. PROPERTIES OF $\vec{I}(\xi,\eta)$

THEOREM 7.1.1. Let $\xi = \{\xi(t)\}$, $\eta = \{\eta(t)\}$, $\zeta = \{\zeta(t)\}$, $\nu = \{\nu(t)\}$ *and* $\theta = \{\theta(t)\} = \{(\xi(t), \eta(t), \zeta(t), \nu(t))\}$ *be stationary processes. Then the information rate* $\vec{I}(\xi,\eta)$ *is always defined, and has the following properties:*

(1) $T\vec{I}(\xi,\eta) = EI(\xi_0^T, \eta/\xi^0)$. (7.1.1)

(2) $\vec{I}(\xi,\eta) \geq 0$. (7.1.2)

(3) If the pair (ξ,η) *is independent of the pair* (ζ,ν), *Then*

$\vec{I}((\xi,\zeta),(\eta,\nu)) = \vec{I}(\xi,\eta) + \vec{I}(\zeta,\nu)$. (7.1.3)

(4) If the random variables ξ, η, ζ *form a Markov chain, then*

$\vec{I}(\xi,(\eta,\zeta)) = \vec{I}(\xi,\eta)$. (7.1.4)

(5) If the processes $\xi = \{\xi(t)\}$ *and* $\zeta = \{\zeta(t)\}$ *are each regularly*

subordinate to the other, then

$$\vec{I}(\xi, \eta) = \vec{I}(\zeta, \eta). \tag{7.1.5}$$

(6) If $\xi = \{\xi(t)\}$ *is a singular process, then* $\vec{I}(\xi, \eta) = 0$. *If, however,* $\xi = \{\xi(t)\}$ *is a regular process, then* $\vec{I}(\xi, \eta) = 0$ *if and only if* ξ *and* η *are independent.*

PROOF. (1) According to formula (3.6.6), we have for $T_1, T_2 > 0$

$$\mathbf{E}I(\xi_0^{T_1+T_2}, \eta/\xi^0) = \mathbf{E}I(\xi_0^{T_1}, \eta/\xi^0) + \mathbf{E}I(\xi_{T_1}^{T_1+T_2}, \eta/(\xi^0, \xi_0^{T_1}))$$

$$= \mathbf{E}I(\xi_0^{T_1}, \eta/\xi^0) + \mathbf{E}I(\xi_{T_1}^{T_1+T_2}, \eta/\xi^{T_1}). \tag{7.1.6}$$

Since ξ and η are stationarily correlated (θ is stationary),

$$\mathbf{E}I(\xi_{T_1}^{T_1+T_2}, \eta/\xi^{T_1}) = \mathbf{E}I(\xi_0^{T_2}, \eta/\xi^0),$$

and therefore from (7.1.6) we obtain

$$\mathbf{E}I(\xi_0^{T_1+T_2}, \eta/\xi^0) = \mathbf{E}I(\xi_0^{T_1}, \eta/\xi^0) + \mathbf{E}I(\xi_0^{T_2}, \eta/\xi^0). \tag{7.1.7}$$

Since the properties of the average conditional information imply that $\mathbf{E}I(\xi_0^{T_2}, \eta/\xi^0) \geqslant \mathbf{E}I(\xi_0^{T_1}, \eta/\xi^0) \geqslant 0$ for $T_2 \geqslant T_1$, it is seen from (7.1.7) that $\mathbf{E}I(\xi_0^{T}, \eta/\xi^0)$ is a linear function cT of T, and consequently

$$\mathbf{E}I(\xi_0^{T}, \eta/\xi^0) = T\mathbf{E}I(\xi_0^{1}, \eta/\xi^0) \tag{7.1.8}$$

and

$$\vec{I}(\xi, \eta) = \lim_{T\to\infty} \frac{1}{T}\mathbf{E}I(\xi_0^{T}, \eta/\xi^0) = \mathbf{E}I(\xi_0^{1}, \eta/\xi^0). \tag{7.1.9}$$

Equations (7.1.8) and (7.1.9) show that $\vec{I}(\xi, \eta)$ is always defined, and satisfies relation (7.1.1).

(2), (3) follow from the definition of the information rate and the properties of information.

(4) According to (7.1.1) and (3.6.6)

$$\vec{I}(\xi, (\eta, \zeta)) = \mathbf{E}I(\xi_0^{1}, (\eta, \zeta)/\xi^0) = \mathbf{E}I(\xi_0^{1}, \eta/\xi^0)$$
$$+ \mathbf{E}I(\xi_0^{1}, \zeta/(\eta, \xi^0)) = \vec{I}(\xi, \eta) + \mathbf{E}I(\xi_0^{1}, \zeta/(\eta, \xi^0)). \tag{7.1.10}$$

But since ξ, η, ζ form a Markov chain, $\mathbf{E}I(\xi, \zeta/\eta) = 0$ and a fortiori

$\mathbf{E}I(\xi_0^1, \zeta/(\eta, \xi^0)) = 0$, i.e., in the present case formula (7.1.10) goes over into (7.1.4).

(5) By the definition of regularly subordinate, there exist numbers $S_1, S_2 > 0$ such that for any T the random variable ζ^T is subordinate to the random variable ξ^{T+S_1} and the random variable ξ^T is subordinate to ζ^{T+S_2}. Therefore

$$\mathbf{E}I(\zeta_0^T, \eta/\zeta^0) \leqslant \mathbf{E}I(\xi^{T+S_1}, \eta/\zeta^0) \tag{7.1.10$'$}$$

and

$$\begin{aligned} &\mathbf{E}I(\xi^{T+S_1+S_2}, \eta/\xi^0) = \mathbf{E}I((\xi^{T+S_1+S_2}, \zeta^{S_2}), \eta/\xi^0) = \mathbf{E}I(\zeta^{S_2}, \eta/\xi^0) \\ &+ \mathbf{E}I(\xi^{T+S_1+S_2}, \eta/(\xi^0, \zeta^{S_2})) \geqslant \mathbf{E}I(\xi^{T+S_1+S_2}, \eta/(\xi^0, \zeta^{S_2})) \\ &= \mathbf{E}I(\xi^{T+S_1+S_2}, \eta/\zeta^{S_2}) = \mathbf{E}I(\xi^{T+S_1}, \eta/\zeta^0). \end{aligned} \tag{7.1.11}$$

Comparing (7.1.10$'$) and (7.1.11), we find that

$$\mathbf{E}I(\xi_0^T, \eta/\zeta^0) \leqslant \mathbf{E}I(\xi^{T+S_1+S_2}, \eta/\xi^0).$$

It follows that

$$\vec{I}(\zeta, \eta) = \lim_{T\to\infty} \frac{1}{T} \mathbf{E}I(\zeta_0^T, \eta/\zeta^0) \leqslant \lim_{T\to\infty} \frac{T + S_1 + S_2}{T} \frac{1}{T + S_1 + S_2}$$
$$\times\ \mathbf{E}I(\xi_0^{T+S_1+S_2}, \eta/\xi^0) = \vec{I}(\xi, \eta),$$

i.e.,

$$\vec{I}(\zeta, \eta) \leqslant \vec{I}(\xi, \eta).$$

Interchanging ξ and ζ, it follows that $\vec{I}(\xi, \eta) \leqslant \vec{I}(\zeta, \eta)$, from which we conclude (7.1.5).

(6) The proof of this property differs only slightly from the proof of the corresponding property for discrete-parameter finite-state processes (Section 6.2) and therefore will not be carried through.

7.2. PROPERTIES OF $\bar{I}^{(g)}(\xi, \eta)$

THEOREM 7.2.1. Let ξ, η, ζ, ν and θ be as in the preceding section; then the information rate $\bar{I}^{(g)}(\xi, \eta)$ is always defined, and has the following properties;

(1) $$\bar{I}^{(g)}(\xi, \eta_1) \geqslant 0. \tag{7.2.1}$$

(2) $$\bar{I}^{(g)}(\xi, \eta) = \bar{I}^{(g)}(\eta, \xi). \tag{7.2.2}$$

(3) If the pair (ξ, η) is independent of the pair (ζ, ν), then

$$\bar{I}^{(g)}((\xi, \zeta), (\eta, \nu)) = \bar{I}^{(g)}(\xi, \eta) + \bar{I}^{(g)}(\zeta, \nu). \tag{7.2.3}$$

If the processes ξ *and* η *are continuous-parameter processes with finite-state spaces (i.e.,* $\xi(t)$ *and* $\eta(t)$ *take on only finitely many values), then*

$$\bar{I}^{(g)}(\xi, \eta) = \lim_{h \to +0} \frac{1}{h} \bar{I}(\xi^{(h)}, \eta^{(h)}). \tag{7.2.4}$$

(We recall that $\xi^{(h)} = \{\xi^{(h)}(n)\}$ *and* $\eta^{(h)} = \{\eta^{(h)}(n)\}$ *are discrete-parameter processes, formed by the random variables* $\xi^{(h)}(n) = \xi(nh)$ *and* $\eta^{(h)}(n) = \eta(nh)$*). Moreover, in the general case, where* ξ *and* η *are processes with arbitrary state spaces,*

$$\bar{I}^{(g)}(\xi, \eta) = \lim_{h \to +0} \frac{1}{h} \bar{I}^{(g)}(\xi^{(h)}, \eta^{(h)}). \tag{7.2.5}$$

(5) Let (X, S_x) *and* (Y, S_y) *be the value spaces of the variables* ξ, η; $\{E_i'\}$ *and* $\{F_j'\}$ *- arbitrary finite measurable partitions of* X, Y *respectively,* $\beta'(t)$ *and* $\gamma'(t)$ *- random variables with values in the measurable spaces* $(E'(t), S_{e'(t)})$, $(F'(t), S_{f'(t)})$ *respectively, whose "points" consist of the sets* $E_{it}' = U_t E_i'$ *and* $F_{jt}' = U_t F_j'$, *and in which the* σ*-algebras* $S_{e'(t)}$ *and* $S_{f'(t)}$ *consist of all subsets of the spaces in question. Let* $\beta'(t)$ *and* $\gamma'(t)$ *be so defined that* $\beta'(t) = E_{it}'$ *if* $\xi \in E_{it}'$, *and* $\gamma'(t) = F_{jt}'$ *if* $\eta \in F_{jt}'$. *Then* $\beta' = \{\beta'(t)\}$ *and* $\gamma' = \{\gamma'(t)\}$ *are stationary and stationarily correlated finite-state processes, and*

$$\bar{I}^{(g)}(\xi, \eta) = \sup_{\substack{\beta' \in K'_\xi, \gamma' \in K'_\eta \\ 0 < h < \infty}} \frac{1}{h} \bar{I}(\beta'^{(h)}, \gamma'^{(h)}). \tag{7.2.6}$$

in which the upper bound is taken over the families K_ξ' *and* K_η' *of random processes* β' *and* γ', *defined by all possible partitions* $\{E_i'\}$ *and* $\{F_j'\}$ *of* X *and* Y. *We denote by* U_t *the translation operators on* X *and on* Y *without distinction, or we may equivalently consider* U_t *defined on* $X \times Y$, *with the obvious convention for considering sets of* X *or of* Y *as sets of* $X \times Y$.

(6) If the random variables ξ, η, ζ *form a Markov chain, then*

$$\bar{I}^{(g)}(\xi, (\eta, \zeta)) = \bar{I}^{(g)}(\xi, \eta).$$

(7) If the process ζ *is subordinate to the process* ξ, *then*

$$\bar{I}^{(g)}(\xi, \eta) \geq \bar{I}^{(g)}(\zeta, \eta).$$

(8) If the process ξ *is completely singular, then*

$$\bar{I}^{(g)}(\xi, \eta) = 0.$$

If, however, the process ξ *is weakly regular, then* $\bar{I}^{(g)}(\xi,\eta) = 0$ *if and only if* ξ *and* η *are independent. In particular, then, if the process* ξ *is weakly regular and* η *is completely singular,* ξ *and* η *are independent.*

PROOF. Since $\bar{I}^{(g)}(\xi,\eta)$ is defined as the supremum, over a certain class, of the information rate of pairs of stationary discrete-parameter finite-state processes, it is always well defined.

(1), (2), (3). Relations (7.2.1), (7.2.2) and (7.2.3) follow from the definition of $\bar{I}^{(g)}(\xi,\eta)$ and the properties of the information rate for discrete-parameter finite-state processes.

(4) First of all, we show that in this case

$$\lim_{\tau\to+0} I(\xi(t), \xi(t+\tau)) = H(\xi(t)), \quad \lim_{\tau\to+0} I(\eta(t), \eta(t+\tau)) = H(\eta(t)). \tag{7.2.7}$$

Let the space $X(t)$ consist of finitely many points $x_1(t), \ldots, x_k(t)$, i.e., the random variable $\xi(t)$ takes on the values $x_i(t)$, $i = 1, \ldots, k$. Then by formula (2.1.6)

$$I(\xi(t), \xi(t+\tau)) = \sum_{i,j=1}^{k} P\{\xi(t) = x_i(t), \xi(t+\tau) = x_j(t+\tau)\} \log \frac{P\{\xi(t) = x_i(t), \xi(t+\tau) = x_j(t+\tau)\}}{P\{\xi(t) = x_i(t)\}P\{\xi(t+\tau) = x_j(t+\tau)\}}.$$

Since the process ξ is continuous,

$$\lim_{\tau\to+0} P\{\xi(t) = x_i(t), \xi(t+\tau) = x_j(t+\tau)\}$$
$$= P\{\xi(t) = x_i(t), \xi(t) = x_j(t)\} = \begin{cases} P\{\xi(t) = x_j(t)\}, & \text{if } i = j, \\ 0, & \text{if } i \neq j, \end{cases}$$

and consequently

$$\lim_{\tau\to+0} I(\xi(t), \xi(t+\tau)) = \sum_{i=1}^{k} P\{\xi(t) = x_i(t)\} \log P\{\xi(t) = x_i(t)\} = H(\xi(t)),$$

i.e., we obtain (7.2.7). Moreover, for any $h, t > 0$ there exists an integer l such that $t - h < lh \leqslant t$, and it therefore follows from (7.2.7) that for any given $\epsilon > 0$ there is a τ such that for $h \leqslant \tau$, $t \geqslant 0$

$$\begin{gathered} I(\xi(t),(\xi(0), \xi(h), \ldots, \xi(mh))) \geqslant H(\xi(t)) - \epsilon \\ I(\eta(t),(\eta(0), \eta(h), \ldots, \eta(mh))) \geqslant H(\eta(t)) - \epsilon \\ t - mh < \tau. \end{gathered} \tag{7.2.8}$$

Consequently, by Lemma 6.2.1

$$
\begin{aligned}
& I((\xi(0), \ldots, \xi(mh)), (\eta(0), \ldots, \eta(mh))). \\
& \geqslant I((\xi(0), \ldots, \xi(nh')), (\eta(0), \ldots, \eta(mh))) \\
& - n\epsilon \geqslant I((\xi(0), \ldots, \xi(nh')), (\eta(0), \ldots, \eta(nh'))) - 2n\epsilon
\end{aligned} \tag{7.2.9}
$$

for $h \leqslant \tau$, where $T - h < mh$, $nh' \leqslant T$, and T, h' are arbitrary positive numbers. We assume m, n to be the smallest and largest integers, respectively, which satisfy the preceding inequalities. Then, since $\lim_{T\to\infty} T/m = h$ and $\lim_{T\to\infty} T/n = h'$, dividing the left and right sides of (7.2.9) by T and letting $T \to \infty$, we obtain the relation

$$\frac{1}{h}\bar{I}(\xi^{(h)}, \eta^{(h)}) \geqslant \frac{1}{h'}\bar{I}(\xi^{(h')}, \eta^{(h')}) - \frac{2\epsilon}{h'}.$$

Here $\xi^{(h')} = \{\xi^{(h')}(n)\} = \{\xi(nh')\}$ and $\eta^{(h')} = \{\eta^{(h')}(n)\} = \{\eta(nh')\}$ are stationary and stationarily correlated discrete-parameter processes. It follows that

$$\varliminf_{h\to+0} \frac{1}{h}\bar{I}(\xi^{(h)}, \eta^{(h)}) \geqslant \frac{1}{h'}\bar{I}(\xi^{(h')}, \eta^{(h')}) - \frac{2\epsilon}{h'},$$

and since ϵ is arbitrary

$$\varliminf_{h\to+0} \frac{1}{h}I(\xi^{(h)}, \eta^{(h)}) \geqslant \frac{1}{h'}\bar{I}(\xi^{(h')}, \eta^{(h')}). \tag{7.2.10}$$

From (7.2.10) it follows that $\lim_{h\to+0} \frac{1}{h}\bar{I}(\xi^{(h)}, \eta^{(h)})$, exists and that in the case under consideration

$$\bar{I}^{(g)}(\xi, \eta) = \sup_{0<h<\infty} \frac{1}{h}\bar{I}(\xi^{(h)}, \eta^{(h)}) = \lim_{h\to+0} \frac{1}{h}\bar{I}(\xi^{(h)}, \eta^{(h)}).$$

Thus, relation (7.2.4) is proved. It remains to consider the general case, in which ξ and η are processes with arbitrary state spaces. By definition,

$$\bar{I}^{(g)}(\xi, \eta) = \sup_{\substack{\beta\in K_\xi,\ \gamma\in K_\eta \\ 0<h<\infty}} \frac{1}{h}\bar{I}(\beta^{(h)}, \gamma^{(h)}); \tag{7.2.11}$$

$$\frac{1}{h}\bar{I}^{(g)}(\xi^{(h)}, \eta^{(h)}) = \frac{1}{h} \sup_{\beta\in K_\xi,\ \gamma\in K_\eta} \bar{I}(\beta^{(h)}, \gamma^{(h)}); \tag{7.2.12}$$

$$\bar{I}^{(g)}(\beta, \gamma) = \sup_{0<h<\infty} \frac{1}{h}\bar{I}(\beta^{(h)}, \gamma^{(h)}). \tag{7.2.13}$$

Comparing (7.2.12) and (7.2.13) with (7.2.11), we find that

$$\bar{I}^{(g)}(\xi, \eta) = \sup_{\beta\in K_\xi,\, \gamma\in K_\eta} \bar{I}^{(g)}(\beta, \gamma); \tag{7.2.14}$$

$$\bar{I}^{(g)}(\xi, \eta) \geqslant \overline{\lim_{h\to+0}} \frac{1}{h}\bar{I}^{(g)}(\xi^{(h)}, \eta^{(h)}). \tag{7.2.15}$$

On the other hand, we have proved that for processes β and γ, having finite-state spaces,

$$\bar{I}^{(g)}(\beta, \gamma) = \lim_{h\to 0} \frac{1}{h}\bar{I}(\beta^{(h)}, \gamma^{(h)}). \tag{7.2.16}$$

Comparing (7.2.16) with (7.2.12), we see that for any $\beta\in K_\xi$, $\gamma\in K_\eta$

$$\bar{I}^{(g)}(\beta, \gamma) \leqslant \underline{\lim}_{h\to+0} \frac{1}{h}\bar{I}^{(g)}(\xi^{(h)}, \eta^{(h)}). \tag{7.2.17}$$

At the same time, comparing (7.2.14) with (7.2.17), we find that

$$\bar{I}^{(g)}(\xi, \eta) \leqslant \underline{\lim}_{h\to+0} \frac{1}{h}\bar{I}^{(g)}(\xi^{(h)}, \eta^{(h)}). \tag{7.2.18}$$

Combining formulas (7.2.15) and (7.2.18) proves (7.2.5).

(5) By definition

$$\bar{I}^{(g)}(\xi, \eta) = \sup_{\substack{\beta\in K_\xi,\, \gamma\in K_\eta \\ 0<h<\infty}} \frac{1}{h}\bar{I}(\beta^{(h)}, \gamma^{(h)}),$$

where K_ξ and K_η are respectively the classes of stationary and stationarily correlated processes $\beta = \{\beta(t)\}$ and $\gamma = \{\gamma(t)\}$ defined by all possible finite partitions $\{E_i(t)\}$ and $\{F_j(t)\}$, $E_i(t) = E_i(0)$, $F_j(t) = F_j(0)$ of the spaces $X(t)$, $Y(t)$ of values of $\xi(t)$ and $\eta(t)$. Now the partitions $\{E_i(0)\}$ of $X(0)$ and $\{F_j(0)\}$ of $Y(0)$ may in an obvious way be considered partitions of the spaces X and Y, and in the same way it is clear that the sets $E_i(t)$, $F_j(t)$ may be identified with the sets E'_{it} and F'_{jt} respectively, and so the processes β and γ may be identified with processes β' and γ'. Consequently

$$\bar{I}(\beta^{(h)}, \gamma^{(h)}) = \bar{I}(\beta'^{(h)}, \gamma'^{(h)}). \tag{7.2.19}$$

We associate with the process $\beta'^{(h)} = \{\beta'^{(h)}(n)\} = \{\beta'(nh)\}$ a process $\beta'_1{}^{(kh)} = \{\beta'_1{}^{(h')}\} = \{\beta'_1(nh')\}$, $1 < kh = h' < \infty$ such that the two random variables $(\beta'(0), \beta'(h), \ldots, \beta'(kh))$ and $\beta'_1(0)$ are each a function of the other. Similarly, we associate a process γ'_1 with the process γ'. Obviously, for every integer n the two random variables $(\beta'(0), \beta'(h), \ldots, \beta'(nkh))$ and $(\beta'_1(0), \beta'_1(h'), \ldots, \beta'_1(nh'))$ are functions of each other, and similarly with β' replaced by γ'. Therefore

$$I((\beta'(0), \ldots, \beta'(nkh)), (\gamma'(0), \gamma'(h), \ldots, \gamma'(nkh)))$$
$$= I((\beta'_1(0), \ldots, \beta'_1(nh')), (\gamma'_1(0), \ldots, \gamma'_1(nh'))).$$

Dividing both sides by $nkh = nh'$ and letting $n \to \infty$, we obtain

$$\frac{1}{h}\bar{I}(\beta'^{(h)}, \gamma'^{(h)}) = \frac{1}{h'}\bar{I}(\beta_1'^{(h')}, \gamma_1'^{(h')}), \quad 1 < h' < \infty .$$

Since $h > 0$ is arbitrary, as is $\beta' \epsilon K'_\xi$ and $\gamma' \epsilon K'_\eta$, this proves (7.2.28).

It follows from (7.2.28) that for any $\epsilon > 0$ processes $\beta'_1 \epsilon K'_\xi$, $\gamma'_1 \epsilon K'_\eta$ may be chosen so that

$$\sup_{\substack{\beta' \epsilon K'_\xi, \gamma' \epsilon K'_\eta \\ 0<h<\infty}} \frac{1}{h}\bar{I}(\beta'^{(h)}, \gamma'^{(h)}) - \frac{1}{h'}\bar{I}(\beta_1'^{(h')}, \gamma_1'^{(h')}) < \epsilon \; h' > l. \tag{7.2.29}$$

According to (7.2.21) there is a $\beta = \{\beta(t)\} \epsilon K_\xi$ and $h'_1 > 0$ such that for $\bar{h} < h'_1$

$$H(\beta'_1(t)) - I(\beta'_1(t), \beta^{(\bar{h})}) < \epsilon$$

and by Lemma 6.2.1

$$I((\beta'_1(0), \beta'_1(h'), \ldots, \beta'_1(mh')), (\gamma'_1(0), \gamma'_1(h'), \ldots, \gamma'_1(mh'))$$
$$- I(\beta^{(\bar{h})}, (\gamma'_1(0), \gamma'_1(h'), \ldots, \gamma'_1(mh'))) \leqslant \epsilon m \tag{7.2.30}$$

for any admissible h'. Put $\bar{h} = h'/r < h'_1$ where r is an integer. Since the random variable $(\gamma'_1(0), \gamma'_1(h'), \ldots, \gamma'_1(mh'))$ is a function of the random variable $(\gamma'_1(0), \gamma'_1(\bar{h}), \ldots, \gamma'_1(mr\bar{h}))$, it follows from (7.2.30) that

$$I((\beta'_1(0), \beta'_1(h'), \ldots, \beta'_1(mh')), (\gamma'_1(0), \gamma'_1(h'), \ldots, \gamma'_1(mh')))$$
$$- I(\beta^{(\bar{h})}, (\gamma'_1(0), \gamma'_1(\bar{h}), \ldots, \gamma'_1(rm\bar{h}))) \leqslant \epsilon m. \tag{7.2.31}$$

Dividing both sides of (7.2.31) by $mh' = mr\bar{h}$ and letting $m \to \infty$, we obtain

$$\frac{1}{h'}\bar{I}(\beta_1'^{(h')}, \gamma_1'^{(h')}) - \frac{1}{\bar{h}}\bar{I}(\gamma'^{(\bar{h})}, \beta^{(\bar{h})}) < \frac{\epsilon}{h'}, \quad h' > 1. \tag{7.2.32}$$

Comparing this result with (7.2.29), we find that

$$\begin{aligned} \sup_{\substack{\beta' \in K'_\xi, \gamma' \in K'_\eta \\ 0<h<\infty}} \frac{1}{h}\bar{I}(\beta'^{(h)}, \gamma'^{(h)}) &\leqslant \frac{1}{\bar{h}}\bar{I}(\gamma'^{(\bar{h})}, \beta^{(\bar{h})}) + \frac{\epsilon}{h'} + \epsilon \\ &\leqslant \frac{1}{\bar{h}}\bar{I}(\beta^{(\bar{h})}, \gamma'^{(\bar{h})}) + 2\epsilon \end{aligned} \tag{7.2.33}$$

and since ϵ is arbitrary, that

$$\sup \frac{1}{h}\bar{I}(\beta'^{(h)}, \gamma'^{(h)}) \leqslant \sup \frac{1}{h}\bar{I}(\beta^{(h)}, \gamma'^{(h)}), \tag{7.2.34}$$

where both upper bounds are taken over all processes $\beta \in K_\xi$, $\beta' \in K'_\xi$, $\gamma' \in K'_\eta$ and all admissible $h > 0$. Similarly we find that

$$\sup_{\substack{\beta \in K_\xi, \gamma \in K'_\eta \\ 0<h<\infty}} \frac{1}{h}\bar{I}(\beta^{(h)}, \gamma'^{(h)}) \leqslant \sup_{\substack{\beta \in K_\xi, \gamma \in K_\eta \\ 0<h<\infty}} \frac{1}{h}\bar{I}(\beta^{(h)}, \gamma^{(h)}). \tag{7.2.35}$$

Comparing (7.2.34) and (7.2.35), we see that

$$\sup_{\substack{\beta' \in K'_\xi, \gamma' \in K'_\eta \\ 0<h<\infty}} \frac{1}{h}\bar{I}(\beta'^{(h)}, \gamma'^{(h)}) \leqslant \sup_{\substack{\beta \in K_\xi, \gamma \in K_\eta \\ 0<h<\infty}} \frac{1}{h}\bar{I}(\beta^{(h)}, \gamma^{(h)}). \tag{7.2.36}$$

Combining relations (7.2.20) and (7.2.36) proves (7.2.6).

(6) First of all we show that

$$\bar{I}^{(g)}(\xi, \eta) = \sup_{\substack{\beta \in K_\xi \\ 0<h<\infty}} \frac{1}{h}I(\beta^{(h)}, \eta/(\beta^{(h)})^0). \tag{7.2.37}$$

We recall that $(\beta^{(h)})^0$ is the random variable formed by the family of random variables $\beta(nh)$, $n \leqslant 0$. In fact

$$\begin{aligned} \bar{I}^{(g)}(\xi, \eta) &= \sup \frac{1}{h}\bar{I}(\beta^{(h)}, \gamma^{(h)}) = \sup \frac{1}{h}\vec{I}(\beta^{(h)}, \gamma^{(h)}) \\ &= \sup \frac{1}{h}\mathbf{E}I(\beta(h), \gamma^{(h)}/(\beta^{(h)})^0), \end{aligned}$$

where the upper bound is taken over all $\beta \epsilon K_\xi$, $\gamma \epsilon K_\eta$, and all admissible $h > 0$. But γ, and consequently $\gamma^{(h)}$, is a function of η, and therefore

$$\frac{1}{h}\mathbf{E}I(\beta(h), \gamma^{(h)}/(\beta^{(h)})^0) \leqslant \frac{1}{h}\mathbf{E}I(\beta(h), \eta/(\beta^{(h)})^0),$$

$$\bar{I}^{(g)}(\xi, \eta) = \sup_{\substack{\beta \epsilon K_\xi, \gamma \epsilon K_\eta \\ 0<h<\infty}} \frac{1}{h}\mathbf{E}I(\beta(h), \gamma^{(h)}/(\beta^{(h)})^0)$$

$$\leqslant \sup_{\beta \epsilon K_\xi, 0<h<\infty} \frac{1}{h}\mathbf{E}I(\beta(h), \eta/(\beta^{(h)})^0). \tag{7.2.38}$$

It remains to prove the reverse inequality. By formula (3.7.51)

$$\mathbf{E}I(\beta(h), \eta/((\beta^{(h)})^0) = \sup_{\gamma' \epsilon K'_\eta} \mathbf{E}I(\beta(h), \gamma'(0)/(\beta^{(h)})^0),$$

and consequently

$$\mathbf{E}I(\beta(h), \eta/(\beta^{(h)})^0) \leqslant \sup_{\gamma' \epsilon K'_\eta} \mathbf{E}I(\beta(h), \gamma'^{(h)}/(\beta^{(h)})^0).$$

Hence, recalling that

$$\mathbf{E}I(\beta(h), \gamma'^{(h)}/(\beta^{(h)})^0) = \vec{I}(\beta^{(h)}, \gamma'^{(h)}) = \bar{I}(\beta^{(h)}, \gamma'^{(h)}),$$

we see that

$$\mathbf{E}I(\beta(h), \eta/(\beta^{(h)})^0) \leqslant \sup_{\gamma' \epsilon K'_\eta} \bar{I}(\beta^{(h)}, \gamma'^{(h)}).$$

Comparing this result with (7.2.35), we find that

$$\sup_{\beta \epsilon K_\xi, 0<h<\infty} \frac{1}{h}\mathbf{E}I(\beta(h), \eta/(\beta^{(h)})^0) \leqslant \sup_{\substack{\beta \epsilon K_\xi, \gamma \epsilon K_\eta \\ 0<h<\infty}} \frac{1}{h}\bar{I}(\beta^{(h)}, \gamma^{(h)})$$

$$= \bar{I}^{(g)}(\xi, \eta,),$$

which is the reverse of (7.2.38), and therefore proves (7.2.37).

For the two processes ξ, (η, ζ), equation (7.2.37) takes the form

$$\bar{I}^{(g)}(\xi, (\eta, \zeta)) = \sup_{\substack{\beta \epsilon K_\xi, \\ 0<h<\infty}} \frac{1}{h}\mathbf{E}I(\beta(h), (\eta, \zeta)/(\beta^{(h)})^0). \tag{7.2.39}$$

By formula (3.6.6)

$$\mathbf{E}I(\beta(h), (\eta, \zeta)/(\beta^{(h)})^0) = \mathbf{E}I(\beta(h), \eta/(\beta^{(h)})^0) + \mathbf{E}I(\beta(h), \zeta/(\eta, (\beta^{(h)})^0)). \tag{7.2.40}$$

Taking into account that β is a function of ξ,

$$\mathbf{E}I(\xi, \zeta/\eta) \geqslant \mathbf{E}I(\beta^{(h)}, \zeta/\eta) \geqslant \mathbf{E}I((\beta^{(h)})^1, \zeta/\eta) = \mathbf{E}I((\beta^{(h)})^0, \zeta/\eta) + \mathbf{E}I(\beta(h), \zeta/(\eta, (\beta^{(h)})^0)).$$

Since by hypothesis the sequence ξ, η, ζ forms a Markov chain, $\mathbf{E}I(\xi, \zeta/\eta) = 0$, and therefore also $\mathbf{E}I(\beta(h), \zeta/(\eta, (\beta^{(h)})^0)) = 0$. Thus, equation (7.2.40) becomes

$$\mathbf{E}I(\beta(h), (\eta, \zeta)/(\beta^{(h)})^0) = \mathbf{E}I(\beta(h), \eta/(\beta^{(h)})^0),$$

and therefore, according to (7.2.37) and (7.2.39)

$$\bar{I}^{(g)}(\xi, (\eta, \zeta)) = \sup_{\substack{\beta \in K_\xi \\ 0<h<\infty}} \frac{1}{h}\mathbf{E}I(\beta(h), (\eta, \zeta)/(\beta^{(h)})^0)$$

$$= \sup_{\substack{\beta \in K_\xi \\ 0<h<\infty}} \frac{1}{h}\mathbf{E}I(\beta(h), \eta/(\beta^{(h)})^0) = \bar{I}^{(g)}(\xi, \eta).$$

(7) From the definition of the process ζ being subordinate to the process ξ, it follows that for each random variable $\alpha'(0)$, $\alpha' = \{\alpha'(t)\} \in K'_\zeta$, there exists a random variable $\beta'(0)$, $\beta' = \{\beta'(t)\} \in K'_\xi$ such that $\alpha'(0)$ is subordinate to $\beta'(0)$. From this it is obvious that the process $\alpha'^{(h)}$ will be subordinate to the process $\beta'^{(h)}$, $h > 0$. But for the discrete-parameter processes $\alpha'^{(h)}$ and $\beta'^{(h)}$

$$\frac{1}{h}\bar{I}(\alpha'^{(h)}, \gamma'^{(h)}) \leqslant \frac{1}{h}\bar{I}(\beta'^{(h)}, \gamma'^{(h)})$$

by Theorem 6.2.1, and consequently

$$\bar{I}^{(g)}(\zeta, \eta) = \sup_{\substack{\alpha' \in K'_\zeta, \gamma' \in K'_\eta \\ 0<h<\infty}} \frac{1}{h}I(\alpha'^{(h)}, \gamma'^{(h)})$$

$$\leqslant \sup_{\substack{\beta' \in K'_\xi, \gamma' \in K'_\eta \\ 0<h<\infty}} \frac{1}{h}I(\beta'^{(h)}, \gamma'^{(h)}) = \bar{I}^{(g)}(\xi, \eta).$$

(8) The proof of this property follows easily from the definition of weak regularity and $\bar{I}^g(\xi,\eta)$, and the corresponding property for

finite-state discrete-parameter processes. We will not spend further time on this point.

COROLLARY. *From formulas (7.2.5), (7.2.6) and (7.2.28) it follows that*

$$\bar{I}^{(g)}(\xi, \eta) = \sup_{\beta' \in K'_{\xi}, \gamma' \in K'_{\eta}} \bar{I}^{(g)}(\beta', \gamma') = \sup_{\beta' \in K'_{\xi}, \gamma' \in K'_{\eta}} \lim_{h \to +0} \frac{1}{h} \bar{I}(\beta'^{(h)}, \gamma'^{(h)})$$

$$= \sup_{\beta' \in K'_{\xi}, \gamma' \in K'_{\eta}} \frac{1}{h} \bar{I}(\beta'^{(h)}, \gamma'^{(h)}).$$

7.3. PROPERTIES OF $\bar{I}(\xi,\eta)$ AND $\tilde{I}(\xi,\eta)$.

THEOREM 7.3.1. *Let* $\xi = \{\xi(t)\}$, $\eta = \{\eta(t)\}$, $\zeta = \{\zeta(t)\}$, $\nu = \{\nu(t)\}$ *and* $\theta = \{\theta(t)\} = \{(\xi(t), \eta(t), \zeta(t), \nu(t))\}$ *be stationary random processes. Then the information rates* $\bar{I}(\xi,\eta)$ *and* $\tilde{I}(\xi,\eta)$, *whenever they exist, have the following properties:*

$$(1)\ 0 \leqslant \bar{I}(\xi,\eta) \leqslant \tilde{I}(\xi,\eta) \leqslant \infty. \tag{7.3.1}$$

$$(2)\ \bar{I}(\xi,\eta) = \bar{I}(\eta,\xi). \tag{7.3.2}$$

(3) If the random variable (ξ,η) *is independent of the random variable* (ζ,ν), *then*

$$\bar{I}((\xi,\zeta),(\eta,\nu)) = \bar{I}(\xi,\eta) + \bar{I}(\zeta,\nu),\quad \tilde{I}((\xi,\zeta)(\eta,\nu)) = \tilde{I}(\xi,\eta) + \tilde{I}(\zeta,\nu).$$

(4) If the random variables ξ, η, ζ *form a Markov chain, then*

$$\tilde{I}(\xi,(\eta,\zeta)) = \tilde{I}(\xi,\eta); \tag{7.3.4}$$

and from the existence of either side of this equation follows the existence of the other side.

(5) If the process ζ *is finitely subordinate to the process* ξ, *then*

$$\bar{I}(\xi,\eta) \geqslant \bar{I}(\zeta,\eta); \tag{7.3.5}$$

$$\tilde{I}(\xi,\eta) \geqslant \tilde{I}(\zeta,\eta). \tag{7.3.6}$$

PROOF. Properties (1), (2), (3) follow from the definitions of the information rates and the corresponding properties of information.

(4) We have by (3.6.3)

$$I(\xi_0^T,(\eta,\zeta)) = I(\xi_0^T,\eta) + \mathbf{E}I(\xi_0^T,\zeta/\eta). \tag{7.3.7}$$

On the other hand, since the sequence ξ, η, ζ is a Markov chain, $I(\xi, \zeta/\eta) = 0$, and therefore $\mathbf{E}I(\xi_0^T, \zeta/\eta) = 0$ and equation (7.3.7) becomes $I(\xi_0^T, (\eta, \zeta)) = I(\xi_0^T, \eta)$. Dividing both sides by T and letting $T \to \infty$, we obtain (7.3.4).

(5) According to the definition of finitely subordinate, there exists a constant $S > 0$ such that for every $T > 0$ the random variable ζ_0^T is subordinate to the random variable ξ_{-S}^{T+S}. Thus, using the fact that ξ and η are stationarily correlated, we have

$$I(\zeta_0^T, \eta_0^T) \leqslant I(\xi_{-S}^{T+S}, \eta_0^T) \leqslant I(\xi_{-S}^{T+S}, \eta_{-S}^{T+S}) = I(\xi_0^{T+2S}, \eta_0^{T+2S});$$
$$I(\zeta_0^T, \eta) \leqslant I(\xi_{-S}^{T+S}, \eta) = I(\xi_0^{T+2S}, \eta).$$

Dividing right and left sides by T and letting $T \to \infty$, we obtain

$$\bar{I}(\zeta, \eta) = \lim_{T\to\infty} \frac{1}{T} I(\zeta_0^T, \eta_0^T) \leqslant \lim_{T\to\infty} \frac{T + 2S}{T} \cdot \frac{1}{T + 2S} I(\xi_0^{T+2S}, \eta_0^{T+2S})$$
$$= \bar{I}(\xi, \eta);$$
$$\tilde{I}(\zeta, \eta) = \lim_{T\to\infty} \frac{1}{T} I(\zeta_0^T, \eta) \leqslant \lim_{T\to\infty} \frac{T + 2S}{T} \frac{1}{T + 2S} I(\xi_0^{T+2S}, \eta)$$
$$= \tilde{I}(\xi, \eta).$$

7.4. RELATIONS AMONG THE VARIOUS DEFINITIONS OF INFORMATION RATE

First of all we prove the following theorem.

THEOREM 7.4.1. Let $\xi = \{\xi(t)\}$ and $\eta = \{\eta(t)\}$ be stationary and stationarily correlated random processes; then

$$\tilde{I}(\xi, \eta) \geqslant \bar{I}(\xi, \eta) \geqslant \bar{I}^{(g)}(\xi, \eta) \geqslant \vec{I}(\xi, \eta). \quad (7.4.1)$$

If not all of the information rates exist, then this chain of inequalities is to be considered as holding only for those terms which are defined.

PROOF. (a) We have already (formula (7.3.1)) established the inequality

$$\tilde{I}(\xi, \eta) \geqslant \bar{I}(\xi, \eta). \quad (7.4.2)$$

(b) We show that

$$\bar{I}(\xi, \eta) \geqslant \bar{I}^{(g)}(\xi, \eta). \quad (7.4.3)$$

In fact, for any $\beta = \{\beta(t)\} \epsilon K_\xi$, $\gamma = \{\gamma(t)\} \epsilon K_\eta$, the random variables $\beta(t)$ and $\gamma(t)$ are measurable functions respectively of $\xi(t)$ and

$\eta(t)$, and consequently the random variables $(\beta(0), \beta(h), \ldots, \beta(mh))$, and $(\gamma(0), \gamma(h), \ldots, \gamma(mh))$, m a positive integer, are functions respectively of the random variables ξ_0^{mh} and η_0^{mh}. Therefore

$$\begin{aligned}\bar{I}(\xi, \eta) &= \lim_{m\to\infty} \frac{1}{mh} I(\xi_0^{mh}, \eta_0^{mh}) \\ &\geqslant \lim_{m\to\infty} \frac{1}{mh} I((\beta(0), \beta(h), \ldots, \beta(mh)), (\gamma(0), \gamma(h), \ldots, \gamma(mh)) \\ &= \frac{1}{h}\bar{I}(\beta^{(h)}, \gamma^{(h)}).\end{aligned} \tag{7.4.4}$$

Recalling that $\bar{I}^{(g)}(\xi, \eta)$ is the upper bound, over all $\beta \in K_\xi$, $\gamma \in K_\eta$ and admissible $h > 0$, of $\frac{1}{h}\bar{I}(\beta^{(h)}, \gamma^{(h)}$, we obtain (7.4.3).

(c) It remains to verify the inequality

$$\bar{I}^{(g)}(\xi, \eta) \geqslant \vec{I}(\xi, \eta). \tag{7.4.5}$$

For this we need a somewhat stronger version of Lemma 6.2.1, namely:

LEMMA 7.4.1. If

$$\mathbf{E}H(\zeta_i/\xi) - \mathbf{E}I(\eta, \zeta_i/\xi) \leqslant \epsilon_i, i = 1, \ldots, n, \tag{7.4.6}$$

then

$$\mathbf{E}I((\zeta, \ldots, \zeta_n), \nu/\xi) - \mathbf{E}I(\eta, \nu/\xi) \leqslant \sum_{i=1}^{n} \epsilon_i. \tag{7.4.7}$$

The proof of this lemma is completely analogous to the proof of Lemma 6.2.1. We will restrict ourselves to the case n = 1, and put $\zeta_1 = \zeta$, $\epsilon_1 = \epsilon$ since we need only this case for the proof of (7.4.5). We have

$$\begin{aligned}\epsilon &\geqslant \mathbf{E}H(\zeta/\xi) - \mathbf{E}I(\eta, \zeta/\xi) = \mathbf{E}I(\zeta, \zeta/\xi) - \mathbf{E}I(\eta, \zeta/\xi) \\ &= \mathbf{E}I(\zeta, (\zeta, \nu)/\xi) - \mathbf{E}I(\eta, \zeta/\xi) \geqslant \mathbf{E}I(\zeta, (\zeta, \nu)/\xi) - \mathbf{E}I(\eta, (\zeta, \nu)/\xi) \\ &= \mathbf{E}I(\zeta, \nu/\xi) + \mathbf{E}I(\zeta, \zeta/(\nu, \xi)) - \mathbf{E}I(\eta, \nu/\xi) - \mathbf{E}I(\eta, \zeta/(\nu, \xi)),\end{aligned}$$

and since $\mathbf{E}I(\zeta, \zeta/(\nu, \xi)) - \mathbf{E}I(\eta, \zeta/(\nu, \xi)) \geqslant 0$, we obtain (7.4.7) for the case n = 1, i.e.,

$$\epsilon \geqslant \mathbf{E}I(\zeta, \nu/\xi) - \mathbf{E}I(\eta, \nu/\xi). \tag{7.4.8}$$

We note, further, that

$$H(\zeta) - I(\eta, \zeta) \geqslant \mathbf{E}H(\zeta/\xi) - \mathbf{E}I(\eta, \zeta/\xi). \tag{7.4.9}$$

Indeed

$$H(\zeta) - I(\eta, \zeta) = I(\zeta, \zeta) - I(\eta, \zeta) = I((\zeta, \xi), \zeta)$$
$$- I(\eta, \zeta) \geqslant I((\zeta, \xi), \zeta) - I((\eta, \xi), \zeta)) = I(\xi, \zeta)$$
$$+ \mathbf{E}I(\zeta, \zeta/\xi) - I(\xi, \zeta) - \mathbf{E}I(\eta, \zeta/\xi)$$
$$= \mathbf{E}I(\zeta, \zeta/\xi) - \mathbf{E}I(\eta, \zeta/\xi) = \mathbf{E}H(\zeta/\xi) - \mathbf{E}I(\eta, \zeta/\xi).$$

We come now to the proof of inequality (7.4.5). According to (7.1.1),

$$\vec{I}(\xi, \eta) = \mathbf{E}I(\xi_0^1, \eta/\xi^0). \tag{7.4.10}$$

At the same time, by formula (3.7.51)

$$\mathbf{E}I(\xi_0^1, \eta/\xi^0) = \sup \mathbf{E}I(\alpha', \eta/\xi^0),$$

where the supremum is taken over all random variables α' which are measurable functions of the random variable ξ_0^1 and which take on only finitely many values. Therefore for any $\epsilon > 0$ there exists a random variable α'' which is a measurable function of ξ_0^1 and takes on only finitely many values, such that

$$\vec{I}(\xi, \eta) = \mathbf{E}I(\xi_0^1, \eta/\xi^0) \leqslant \mathbf{E}I(\alpha'', \eta/\xi^0) + \frac{\epsilon}{2}. \tag{7.4.11}$$

In exactly the same way that (7.2.21) was obtained, it is easy to establish that for any $\epsilon > 0$ there is a $\beta \epsilon K_\xi$ and $h' > 0$ such that for $h = \frac{1}{r} < h'$, r a positive integer

$$I(\alpha'', (\eta, \xi^0)) - I(\alpha'', (\eta, (\beta^{(h)})^0) < \frac{\epsilon}{4}; \tag{7.4.12}$$

$$H(\alpha'') - I(\alpha'', (\beta(0), \beta(h), \dots, \beta(1))) < \frac{\epsilon}{4}. \tag{7.4.13}$$

Moreover, by formula (3.6.3)

$$I(\alpha'', (\eta, \xi^0)) = I(\alpha'', \xi^0) + \mathbf{E}I(\alpha'', \eta/\xi^0);$$
$$I(\alpha'', (\eta, (\beta^{(h)})^0)) = I(\alpha'', (\beta^{(h)})^0) + \mathbf{E}I(\alpha'', \eta/(\beta^{(h)})^0).$$

From this, using the inequality $I(\alpha'', \xi^0) - I(\alpha'', (\beta^{(h)})^0) \geqslant 0$ which holds because $(\beta^{(h)})^0$ is a function of ξ^0, we obtain

$$\mathbf{E}I(\alpha'', \eta/\xi^0) - \mathbf{E}I(\alpha'', \eta/(\beta^{(h)})^0) = [I(\alpha'', (\eta, \xi^0))$$
$$- I(\alpha'', (\eta, (\beta^{(h)})^0))] - [I(\alpha'', \xi^0) - I(\alpha'', (\beta^{(h)})^0)]$$
$$\leqslant I(\alpha'', (\eta, \xi^0)) - I(\alpha'', (\eta, (\beta^{(h)})^0)).$$

Comparing this with (7.4.12), we find that

$$\mathbf{E}I(\alpha'', \eta/\xi^0) - \mathbf{E}I(\alpha'', \eta/(\beta^{(h)})^0) < \frac{\epsilon}{4}. \tag{7.4.14}$$

Finally, in view of (7.4.9) it follows from (7.4.13) that

$$\mathbf{E}H(\alpha''/(\beta^{(h)})^0) - \mathbf{E}I((\beta(0), \beta(h), \ldots, \beta(1)), \alpha''/(\beta^{(h)})^0) < \frac{\epsilon}{4}$$

and by Lemma 7.4.1

$$\mathbf{E}I(\alpha'', \eta/(\beta^{(h)})^0) - \mathbf{E}I((\beta(0), \beta(h), \ldots, \beta(1)), \eta/(\beta^{(h)})^0) < \frac{\epsilon}{4}. \tag{7.4.15}$$

Comparing (7.4.14) and (7.4.15), we see that

$$\mathbf{E}I(\alpha'', \eta/\xi^0) - \mathbf{E}I((\beta(0), \beta(h), \ldots, \beta(1)), \eta/(\beta^{(h)})^0) < \frac{\epsilon}{2}. \tag{7.4.16}$$

But

$$\frac{1}{h} = r \text{ and } \mathbf{E}I((\beta(0), \beta(h), \ldots, \beta(1)), \eta/(\beta^{(h)})^0)$$
$$= r\mathbf{E}I(\beta(h), \eta/(\beta^{(h)})^0) = \frac{1}{h}\mathbf{E}I((\beta(h), \eta/(\beta^{(h)})^0), \tag{7.4.17}$$

and therefore, according to (7.4.16)

$$\mathbf{E}I(\alpha'', \eta/\xi^0) - \frac{1}{h}\mathbf{E}I(\beta(h), \eta/(\beta^{(h)})^0) < \frac{\epsilon}{2}. \tag{7.4.18}$$

Comparing (7.4.18) with (7.4.11), we obtain

$$\vec{I}(\xi, \eta) - \frac{1}{h}\mathbf{E}I(\beta(h), \eta/(\beta^{(h)})^0) \leqslant \epsilon. \tag{7.4.19}$$

Since (c.f. (7.2.37))

$$\bar{I}^{(g)}(\xi, \eta) = \sup_{\substack{\beta\in\mathbf{K}_{\xi},\\ 0<h<\infty}} \frac{1}{h}\mathbf{E}I(\beta(h), \eta/(\beta^{(h)})^0),$$

(7.4.5) follows from (7.4.19) in view of the arbitrariness of ϵ, and the theorem is proved.

Remark. We have in fact proved more than (7.4.1), namely

$$\varliminf_{T\to\infty} \frac{1}{T}I(\xi_0^T, \eta) \geqslant \varliminf_{T\to\infty} \frac{1}{T}I(\xi_0^T, \eta_{0'}^T) \geqslant \bar{I}^{(g)}(\xi, \eta) \geqslant \vec{I}(\xi, \eta), \tag{7.4.20}$$

so that the validity of either inequality

$$\overline{\lim_{T\to\infty}} \frac{1}{T} I(\xi_0^T, \eta) \leqslant I^{(g)}(\xi, \eta), \overline{\lim_{T\to\infty}} \frac{1}{T} I(\xi_0^T, \eta) \leqslant \vec{I}(\xi, \eta) \tag{7.4.21}$$

would imply the existence of $\bar{I}(\xi,\eta)$ and $\tilde{I}(\xi,\eta)$ and $\bar{I}(\xi,\eta) = \tilde{I}(\xi,\eta) = \bar{I}^{(g)}(\xi,\eta)$, and the second inequality would in addition imply that $\vec{I}(\xi,\eta)$ was equal to the three preceding information rates. Similarly, the validity of either of

$$\overline{\lim_{T\to\infty}} \frac{1}{T} I(\xi_0^T, \eta_0^T) \leqslant \bar{I}^{(g)}(\xi, \eta), \overline{\lim_{T\to\infty}} \frac{1}{T} I(\xi_0^T, \eta_0^T) \leqslant \vec{I}(\xi, \eta) \tag{7.4.22}$$

would imply the existence of $\bar{I}(\xi,\eta)$ and $\bar{I}(\xi,\eta) = \bar{I}^{(g)}(\xi,\eta)$, while the second inequality would in addition imply that $\vec{I}(\xi,\eta)$ is equal to the two preceding information rates.

THEOREM 7.4.2. *Let $\xi = \{\xi(t)\}$ and $\eta = \{\eta(t)\}$ be stationary and stationarily correlated random processes, and suppose that for some interval (O, S) and some set $N \in (O, S)$*

$$\lim_{T\to\infty} \frac{1}{T-S} \mathbf{E} I(\xi^0, \xi_S^T/\xi^N) = \lim_{T\to\infty} \frac{1}{T} \mathbf{E} I(\xi^0, \xi_S^T/\xi^N) = 0, \tag{7.4.23}$$

where ξ^N is the random variable consisting of the family $\xi(t)$, $t \in N$. Then: (1) If

$$I(\xi^N, \eta) < \infty \tag{7.4.24}$$

then the information rates $\tilde{I}(\xi,\eta)$ and $\bar{I}(\xi,\eta)$ are defined, and

$$\tilde{I}(\xi, \eta) = \bar{I}(\xi, \eta) = \bar{I}^{(g)}(\xi, \eta) = \vec{I}(\xi, \eta). \tag{7.4.25}$$

(2) If

$$\lim_{T\to\infty} \frac{1}{T} I(\xi^N, \eta_0^T) = 0, \tag{7.4.26}$$

then the information rate $\bar{I}(\xi,\eta)$ is defined, and

$$\bar{I}(\xi, \eta) = \bar{I}^{(g)}(\xi, \eta) = \vec{I}(\xi, \eta). \tag{7.4.27}$$

Before turning to the proof of the theorem, we point out various cases in which condition (7.4.23) is fulfilled.

$$\text{(a) } I(\xi^0, \xi_S) < \infty, \tag{7.4.28}$$

where, as usual, ξ_s, $S > 0$ is the random variable consisting of the family of random variables $\xi(t)$, $t > S$.

Indeed, if (7.4.28) holds, then

$$\lim_{T\to\infty} \frac{1}{T} I(\xi^0, \xi_S^T) \leqslant \lim_{T\to\infty} \frac{1}{T} I(\xi^0, \xi_S) = 0.$$

(b) For some $T > 0$

$$I(\xi^0, \xi_0^T) < \infty. \tag{7.4.29}$$

In fact, applying formula (3.6.6) n-1 times to $I(\xi^0, \eta_0^{nT})$ and using the stationarity of ξ, we obtain

$$\mathbf{E}I(\xi^0, \xi_0^{nT}) = I(\xi^0, \xi_0^T) + \sum_{i=1}^{n-1} \mathbf{E}I(\xi^0, \xi_{iT}^{(i+1)T}/\xi_0^{iT})$$

$$= I(\xi^0, \xi_0^T) + \sum_{i=1}^{n-1} \mathbf{E}I(\xi^{-iT}, \xi_0^T/\xi_{-iT}^0). \tag{7.4.30}$$

By formula (3.6.3)

$$I(\xi^0, \xi_0^T) = I(\xi_{-iT}^0, \xi_0^T) + \mathbf{E}I(\xi^{-iT}, \xi_0^T/\xi_{-iT}^0)$$

and since $\lim_{i\to\infty} I(\xi_{-iT}^0, \xi_0^T) = I(\xi^0, \xi_0^T)$, then

$$\lim_{i\to\infty} \mathbf{E}I(\xi^{-iT}, \xi_0^T/\xi_{-iT}^0) = 0. \tag{7.4.31}$$

Comparing (7.4.30) and (7.4.31), we see that

$$\lim_{n\to\infty} \frac{1}{n} I(\xi^\circ, \xi_0^{nT}) = \lim_{T\to\infty} \frac{1}{T} I(\xi^0, \xi_0^T) = 0. \tag{7.4.32}$$

(c) For some $T > S > 0$

$$\mathbf{E}I(\xi^0, \xi_S^T/\xi_0^S) < \infty. \tag{7.4.33}$$

This case is analagous to case b, and the fact that (7.4.33) implies (7.4.23) is verified exactly as in case b. We note that since in cases a and b the set N is empty, conditions (7.4.24) and (7.4.26) are vacuous.

We come to the proof of the theorem.

(1) Using the stationarity of the process (ξ, η) and formula (3.6.6), we obtain the relations

$$I(\xi_0^{T-S}, \eta) = I(\xi_S^T, \eta) \leqslant I((\xi_S^T, \xi^N), \eta) = I(\xi^N, \eta) + \mathbf{E}I(\xi_S^T, \eta/\xi^N)$$

$$\leqslant I(\xi^N, \eta) + \mathbf{E}I(\xi_S^T, (\eta, \xi^0)/\xi^N) = I(\xi^N, \eta)$$

$$+ \mathbf{E}I(\xi_S^T, \xi^0/\xi^N) + \mathbf{E}I(\xi_S^T, \eta/(\xi^0, \xi^N))$$

and

$$\mathbf{E}I(\xi_s^T, \eta/(\xi^0, \xi^N)) \leqslant \mathbf{E}I((\xi_s^T, \xi^N), \eta/\xi^0) \leqslant \mathbf{E}I(\xi_0^T, \eta/\xi^0).$$

Thus

$$I(\xi_0^{T-s}, \eta) \leqslant I(\xi^N, \eta) + \mathbf{E}I(\xi_s^T, \xi^0/\xi^N) + \mathbf{E}I(\xi_0^T, \eta/\xi^0). \tag{7.4.34}$$

Since by hypothesis $I(\xi^N, \eta) < \infty$ and $\lim_{T\to\infty} \frac{1}{T}\mathbf{E}I(\xi_s^T, \xi^0/\xi^N) = 0$, it follows from (7.4.34) that

$$\overline{\lim_{T\to\infty}} \frac{1}{T} I(\xi_0^T, \eta) = \overline{\lim_{T\to\infty}} \frac{1}{T} I(\xi_0^{T-s}, \eta) \leqslant \overline{\lim_{T\to\infty}} \frac{1}{T} I(\xi_0^T, \eta/\xi^0)$$
$$= \vec{I}(\xi, \eta).$$

According to the remark following the preceding theorem, this implies that $\bar{\mathrm{I}}(\xi, \eta)$ and $\bar{I}(\xi, \eta)$ exist and that (7.4.25) holds.

(2) Using the stationarity of (ξ, η) and formula (3.6.6), we obtain the relations

$$I(\xi_0^{T-s}, \eta_0^{T-s}) = I(\xi_s^T, \eta_s^T) \leqslant I((\xi_s^T, \xi^N), \eta_s^T) = I(\xi^N, \eta_s^T) + \mathbf{E}I(\xi_s^T, \eta_s^T/\xi^N)$$
$$\leqslant I(\xi^N, \eta_s^T) + \mathbf{E}I(\xi_s^T, (\eta_s^T, \xi^0)/\xi^N)$$
$$= I(\xi^N, \eta_s^T) + \mathbf{E}I(\xi_s^T, \xi^0/\xi^N) + \mathbf{E}I(\xi_s^T, \eta_s^T/(\xi^0, \xi^N))$$

and

$$\mathbf{E}I(\xi_s^T, \eta_s^T/(\xi^0, \xi^N)) \leqslant \mathbf{E}I((\xi_s^T, \xi^N), \eta_s^T/\xi^0) \leqslant \mathbf{E}I(\xi_0^T, \eta/\xi^0).$$

Thus

$$I(\xi_0^{T-s}, \eta_0^{T-s}) \leqslant I(\xi^N, \eta_s^T) + \mathbf{E}I(\xi_s^T, \xi^0/\xi^N) + \mathbf{E}I(\xi_0^T, \eta/\xi^0). \tag{7.4.35}$$

Since by hypothesis

$$\lim_{T\to\infty} \frac{1}{T} I(\xi^N, \eta_s^T) = \lim_{T\to\infty} \frac{1}{T}\mathbf{E}I(\xi_s^T, \xi^0/\xi^N) = 0,$$

it follows from (7.4.35) that

$$\overline{\lim_{T\to\infty}} \frac{1}{T} I(\xi_0^T, \eta_0^T) = \overline{\lim_{T\to\infty}} \frac{T-S}{T} \cdot \frac{1}{T-S} I(\xi_0^{T-s}, \eta_0^{T-s}) \leqslant \lim_{T\to\infty} \frac{1}{T}\mathbf{E}I(\xi_0^T, \eta/\xi^0)$$
$$= \vec{I}(\xi, \eta).$$

According to the remark to Theorem 7.4.1, this implies that $\bar{I}(\xi, \eta)$ exists and that (7.4.27) holds.

7.5. PROPERTIES OF THE INFORMATION RATES FOR GENERALIZED RANDOM PROCESSES

The properties of the information rates, as well as their proofs, as they have been formulated in the earlier sections of this chapter, carry over to generalized random processes with only a few minor changes. These changes are called for only because the relation

$$\xi_S^T = (\xi_S^Q, \xi_Q^T), \; S < Q < T, \tag{7.5.1}$$

which is obvious for non-generalized processes, need not hold for generalized random processes. This is due to the fact that not every function φ, which belongs to the class Φ of basic functions and which vanishes outside the interval (S, T), can be represented as the sum of two functions from the class Φ, vanishing outside the intervals (S, Q) and (Q, T) respectively. But on the other hand, any function φ from the class Φ, which vanishes outside the interval (S, T), can always be represented as the sum of two basic functions which vanish respectively outside the intervals $(S, Q + \sigma)$ and (Q, T) where $\sigma > 0$ may be chosen arbitrarily. Therefore, in place of (7.5.1) one can use the fact that the random variables ξ_S^T and $(\xi_S^{Q+\sigma}, \xi_Q^T)$ are mutually subordinate. The reader can easily carry out the infrequent and minor changes, occasioned by the circumstance which we have pointed out, which are needed to derive the properties of the information rates for generalized random processes.

We mention only the more or less essential changes: formulas (7.1.1), (7.4.29), (7.4.33), (7.4.39) and (7.4.40) go over into

$$T\overrightarrow{I}(\xi, \eta) = \mathbf{E}I(\xi_{-\sigma}^T, \eta/\xi^0) = \mathbf{E}I(\xi_0^{T+\sigma}, \eta/\xi^0); \tag{7.5.2}$$

$$I(\xi^\sigma, \xi_0^T) < \infty; \tag{7.5.3}$$

$$\mathbf{E}I(\xi^\sigma, \xi_S^T/\xi_0^{S+\sigma}) < \infty. \tag{7.5.4}$$

7.6. RATE OF CREATION OF ENTROPY OF ONE STATIONARY RANDOM PROCESS WITH RESPECT TO ANOTHER

Without stopping to give the details involved in obtaining the properties of the entropy rate $\overline{H}_\eta(\xi) = \overline{H}_{P_\eta}(P_\xi)$ of one stationary process ξ with respect to another η, we will write down a condition, frequently encountered in applications, under which $\overline{H}_\eta(\xi)$ is defined, and indicate how to evaluate it.

Thus, let $\eta = \{\eta(\cdot)\}$ be a stationary random process with finite memory; i.e., there exists $T > 0$ such that the sequence of random variables $\eta^0, \eta_{-\sigma}^{T+\sigma}, \eta_T, \sigma > 0$ forms a Markov chain, and suppose that for some $\epsilon > 0$ the entropy of the distribution $P_{\xi^{T+\epsilon}}$ with respect to the distribution $P_{\xi^0 \times \eta_0^{T+\epsilon}}$ is finite, i.e.,

$$H_{P_{\xi^0 \times \eta_0^{T+\epsilon}}}(P_{\xi^{T+\epsilon}}) < \infty. \tag{7.6.1}$$

Then the entropy rate $\overline{H}_\eta(\xi)$ is defined and

$$\overline{H}_\eta(\xi) = \frac{1}{\epsilon}(H_{P_{\xi^0 \times \eta_0^{T+\epsilon}}}(P_{\xi^{T+\epsilon}}) - H_{P_{\xi^0 \times \eta_0^T}}(P_{\xi^T})). \tag{7.6.2}$$

In case ξ and η are generalized random processes, condition (7.6.1) goes over into

$$H_{P_{\xi^\sigma \times \eta_0^{T+\epsilon}}}(P_{\xi^\sigma \xi_0^{T+\epsilon}}) < \infty, \tag{7.6.3}$$

and (7.6.2) goes over into

$$\overline{H}_\eta(\xi) = \frac{1}{\epsilon}(H_{P_{\xi^\sigma \times \eta_0^{T+\epsilon}}}(P_{\xi^\sigma \xi_0^{T+\epsilon}}) - H_{P_{\xi^\sigma \times \eta_0^T}}(P_{\xi^\sigma \xi_0^T})). \tag{7.6.4}$$

Condition (7.6.1) generalizes the condition used by Perez [24, 27],

$$H_{P_{\xi^0 \times \eta_0^T}}(P_{\xi^T}) < \infty, \tag{7.6.5}$$

which he considered for random processes ξ and η, with η being memoryless.

Chapter 8 Information stability of stationary random processes

In this chapter a criterion is given for the information stability of random processes, which contains as special cases a number of criteria which are encountered in the literature (cf., for example, [16], [21]).

8.1. RELATIVE INFORMATION STABILITY

THEOREM 8.1.1. Let $\xi = \{\xi(t)\}$ *and* $\eta = \{\eta(t)\}$ *be stationary and stationarily correlated processes. Then the pair* (ξ, η) *will be relatively information stable if one of the following conditions is satisfied:*

(1) The process $(\xi, \eta) = \{(\xi(t), \eta(t))\}$ *is ergodic, and* $0 \leqslant \bar{I}(\xi, \eta) < \infty$.

(2) For some $T \geq 0$ *the measure* $P_{\xi^T \eta}$ *is singular with respect to the measure* $\bar{P}_{\xi_0^T \times \eta/\xi^0}$.

PROOF. (1) Let $t = n$, where n is a positive integer. Applying formula (3.6.5) $n - 1$ times, we obtain

$$\bar{i}(\xi_0^n, \eta/\xi^0) = \sum_{j=1}^{n} \bar{i}(\xi_{j-1}^j, \eta/\xi^{j-1}). \tag{8.1.1}$$

On the other hand, from the stationarity and ergodicity of the process (ξ, η) it follows that the random variables

$$\bar{i}(\xi_{j-1}^j, \eta/\xi^{j-1}), \quad j = \ldots, 1, 0, 1, 2, \ldots$$

form a stationary ergodic process, and therefore by a known ergodic theorem, the ratio

$$\frac{\bar{i}(\xi_0^n, \eta/\xi^0)}{\mathbf{E}I(\xi_0^n, \eta/\xi^0)} = \frac{\sum_{j=1}^{n} \bar{i}(\xi_{j-1}^j, \eta/\xi^{j-1}).}{\sum_{j=1}^{n} \mathbf{E}I(\xi_{j-1}^j, \eta/\xi^{j-1}).} \tag{8.1.2}$$

converges in probability to one. If now t is any admissible positive number, then, taking n so that $n \leqslant t < n+1$, we put

$$\zeta(t) = \begin{cases} \xi_n^{n+1} & \text{for } t \geqslant 0; \\ 0 & \text{for } t < 0. \end{cases} \tag{8.1.3}$$

Obviously

$$\mathbf{E}I(\zeta_0^t, \eta/\xi^0) = \mathbf{E}I(\xi_0^n, \eta/\xi^0); \ \bar{i}(\zeta_0^t, \eta/\xi^0) = \bar{i}(\xi_0^n, \eta/\xi^0), \tag{8.1.4}$$

and consequently the ratio $\frac{i(\zeta_0^t, \eta/\xi^0)}{\mathbf{E}I(\zeta_0^t, \eta/\xi^0)}$ converges in probability to one, i.e., the family of pairs of random variables (ζ_0^t, η), $t \geqslant 0$ is information stable with respect to the family of random variables $\nu(t) = \xi^0$. But the random variable ζ^t is a function of the random variable ξ^t, and

$$\lim_{t\to\infty} \frac{\mathbf{E}I(\xi_0^t, \eta/\xi^0)}{\mathbf{E}I(\zeta_0^t, \eta/\xi^0)} = \lim_{t\to\infty} \frac{\mathbf{E}I(\xi_0^t, \eta/\xi^0)}{\mathbf{E}I(\xi_0^n, \eta/\xi^0)} = \lim_{t\to\infty} \frac{t\vec{I}(\xi, \eta)}{n\vec{I}(\xi, \eta)} = 1. \tag{8.1.5}$$

Then by Theorem 4.2.1, the family of random variables (ξ_0^t, η) is information stable with respect to the family of random variables $\nu(t) = \xi^0$, i.e., the process (ξ, η) is relatively information stable.

(2) Since the random variable ξ_0^T is a function of the random variable ξ_0^t for $t \geqslant T$, then from the singularity of the measure $P_{\xi^T\eta}$ with respect to the measure $\overline{P}_{\xi_0^T \times \eta/\xi^0}$ follows (see Section 4.2) the singularity of $P_{\xi^t\eta}$ with respect to $\overline{P}_{\xi_0^t \times \eta/\xi^0}$. Thus the process (ξ, η) is relatively information stable.

Remark 1. In the case where $\vec{I}(\xi, \eta) = \infty$ and the pair (ξ, η) is ergodic, either $\lim_{t\to\infty} P_{\xi\eta}(N^t) = 0$, where N^t is the set of absolute continuity of $P_{\xi^t\eta}$ with respect to $\overline{P}_{\xi_0^t \times \eta/\xi^0}$, or for some $c > 0$

$$\lim_{t\to\infty} P\left\{\frac{\bar{i}(\xi_0^t, \eta/\xi^0)}{ct} - 1 < \epsilon\right\} = 0.$$

Remark 2. The proof of the first part of the theorem actually reduces to the proof of the following ergodic theorem. Let $\zeta = \{\zeta(t)\}$

be a continuous random process with stationary increments such that for every τ the stationary process $\theta_\tau = \{\theta_\tau(t)\}$ (where $\theta_\tau(t) = \zeta(t+\tau) - \zeta(t)$) is ergodic and $\mathbf{E}\zeta(0) = 0$. Then the random variable $\zeta(t)/\mathbf{E}\zeta(t)$ converges in probability (or with probability one, or in the mean, and so on) to one.

8.2. INFORMATION STABILITY

THEOREM 8.2.1. Let $\xi = \{\xi(t)\}$ *and* $\eta = \{\eta(t)\}$ *be stationary and stationarily correlated random processes. Then the pair* (ξ, η) *will be information stable if one of the following conditions is satisfied:*

(1) The process (ξ, η) *is ergodic and*

$$0 \leqslant \bar{I}^{(g)}(\xi, \eta) = \bar{I}(\xi, \eta) < \infty. \tag{8.2.1}$$

(2) For some $T > 0$ *the measure* $P_{\xi_0^T \eta_0^T}$ *is singular with respect to the measure* $P_{\xi_0^T \times \eta_0^T}$.

PROOF. (1) Recalling the definition of $\bar{I}^{(g)}(\xi, \eta)$, (8.2.1) implies that for any $\delta > 0$ there exist stationary and stationarily correlated processes $\beta^{(h)} = \{\beta^{(h)}(n)\} = \{\beta(nh)\}$ and $\gamma^{(h)} = \{\gamma^{(h)}(n)\} = \{\gamma(nh)\}$, $\beta \epsilon K_\xi$, $\gamma \epsilon K_\eta$ (with discrete parameter n) such that

$$\frac{\frac{1}{h}\bar{I}(\beta^{(h)}, \gamma^{(h)})}{\bar{I}(\xi, \eta)} > 1 - \delta. \tag{8.2.2}$$

Since the random process $(\beta, \gamma) = \{(\beta(t), \gamma(t))\}$ is stationarily correlated with the process $(\xi, \eta) = \{(\xi(t), \eta(t))\}$ and is also a function of it, the ergodicity of (ξ, η) implies that of (β, γ) and therefore that of $(\beta^{(h)}, \gamma^{(h)})$ for suitable h. We put $(\beta^{(h)})_0^n = (\beta(0), \beta(h), \ldots, \beta(nh))$, $(\gamma^{(h)})_0^n = (\gamma(0), \gamma(h), \ldots \gamma(nh)$. By Theorem 6.4.1 the process $(\beta^{(h)}, \gamma^{(h)})$ or, what is the same thing, the sequence of pairs $((\beta^{(h)})_0^n, (\gamma^{(h)})_0^n)$, n = 1, 2, ... is information stable. We introduce the random variables $\bar{\beta}(t) = \beta(nh)$ and $\bar{\gamma}(t) = \gamma(nh)$ for $nh \leqslant t < (n+1)h$, and $\bar{\beta} = \{\bar{\beta}(t)\}$, $\bar{\gamma} = \{\bar{\gamma}(t)\}$. Obviously

$$I(\bar{\beta}_0^t, \bar{\gamma}_0^t) = I((\beta^{(h)})_0^n, (\gamma^{(h)})_0^n);$$

$$i(\bar{\beta}_0^t, \bar{\gamma}_0^t) = i((\beta^{(h)})_0^n, (\gamma^{(h)})_0^n);$$

$$\lim_{t\to\infty} \frac{1}{t} I(\bar{\beta}_0^t, \bar{\gamma}_0^t) = \lim_{t\to\infty} \frac{nh}{t} \cdot \frac{1}{nh} I((\beta^{(h)})_0^n, (\gamma^{(h)})_0^n) = \frac{1}{h}\bar{I}(\beta^{(h)}, \gamma^{(h)}). \tag{8.2.3}$$

Therefore from the information stability of the family of pairs $((\beta^{(h)})_0^n, (\gamma^{(h)})_0^n)$ follows the information stability of the family of pairs $(\overline{\beta}_0^t, \overline{\gamma}_0^t)$. Comparing (8.2.2) and (8.2.3), we see that

$$\lim_{t\to\infty} \frac{\frac{1}{t} I(\overline{\beta}_0^t, \overline{\gamma}_0^t)}{\frac{1}{t} I(\xi_0^t, \eta_0^t)} = \frac{\frac{1}{h}\overline{I}(\beta^{(h)}, \gamma^{(h)})}{\overline{I}(\xi, \eta)} > 1 - \delta. \tag{8.2.4}$$

Since $\delta > 0$ is arbitrary, and since the random variables $\overline{\beta}_0^t, \overline{\gamma}_0^t$ are functions respectively of the variables β_0^t and γ_0^t and therefore of ξ_0^t and η_0^t, it follows (see Remarks) that the family (ξ_0^t, η_0^t) is information stable, in other words, that the process (ξ, η) is information stable.

(2) For $t \geqslant T$ the random variables ξ_0^T, η_0^T are functions respectively of ξ_0^t, η_0^t. Therefore the singularity of $P_{\xi_0^T \eta_0^T}$ with respect to $P_{\xi_0^T \times \eta_0^T}$ implies that of $P_{\xi_0^t \eta_0^t}$ with respect to $P_{\xi_0^t \times \eta_0^t}$ for all $t \geqslant T$, and therefore the information stability of the process (ξ, η), which proves the theorem.

8.3. INFORMATION STABILITY OF GENERALIZED STATIONARY RANDOM PROCESSES

From the discussion in Chapter 7 it can be seen that both the statements and the proofs of the theorems of Sections 8.1 and 8.2 carry over in their entirety to generalized stationary random processes.

8.4. ENTROPY STABILITY OF GENERALIZED AND NON-GENERALIZED STATIONARY RANDOM PROCESSES

The following result holds:

If the stationary process ξ is ergodic, and if the stationary process η has finite memory and satisfies conditions (7.6.1) or (7.6.3) respectively, then the process (ξ, η) is entropy stable.

TRANSLATOR'S REMARKS TO CHAPTER 8

The following is intended as a clarification of a few points in the proof of Theorem 8.2.1.

(a) Let $\{\xi(t)\}$ be a continuous finite-state stationary and ergodic continuous-parameter process. Then the process $\{\xi^{(h)}\}$ is ergodic for all but at most countably many values of h. We will give only the ingredients of a proof; the details are not difficult to supply.

Since $\{\xi(t)\}$ is continuous and finite-state, the Hilbert space H generated by all the $\xi(t)$ is separable. Now to each value of h for which $\{\xi^{(h)}\}$ is non-ergodic there corresponds at least one jump in the spectral family corresponding to the process $\{\xi(t)\}$. Since these jumps are distinct for non-commensurable values of h, the separability of H shows that there can be only countable many such h, and hence only countably many h for which $\{\xi^{(h)}\}$ is non-ergodic.

(b) Theorem 4.2.2 is not immediately applicable, nor is a repeated use of it, since all of the β and γ processes depend upon δ. However, the reader should have no trouble in constructing, along the lines of the proof of Theorem 4.2.2, a theorem whose assertion is just what is required to complete the proof of Part 1 of Theorem 8.2.1.

PART III

Information, information rate, and information stability of gaussian random variables and processes

This third part occupies a central position in our work. Here we establish formulas which enable one to compute the information and information rate of gaussian variables and processes in every case encountered in practice, both one-dimensional and multi-dimensional. We give necessary and sufficient conditions for the information stability of such random variables and processes. It is shown that the distribution of the information density almost always converges to a normal distribution. Furthermore, we write down formulas for computing the entropy and entropy rate of gaussian random variables and processes with respect to other such variables and processes respectively, and state conditions for the entropy stability of such variables and processes. In the course of developing these results a number of facts will be established concerning the correlation theory of random variables and processes.

Certain of the results of this part are contained in the author's notes and thesis [28, 29, 31, 32], and also in the paper of Gelfand and Yaglom [9].

Chapter 9 Information and information stability of gaussian random variables

In this chapter various formulas are obtained which enable one to compute the information of one gaussian variable with respect to another in terms of the correlation coefficients. Necessary and sufficient conditions are established for the information stability of gaussian random variables and for the convergence of the distribution of the information density to a normal distribution. It is proved that the joint distribution $\mathbf{P}_{\xi\eta}$ and the product distribution $P_{\xi\times\eta}$ of gaussian variables ξ, η are either mutually absolutely continuous or singular, according to whether the information of the pair (ξ, η) is finite or infinite.

We consider the corresponding generalizations of these results to the entropy and entropy density of one gaussian variable with respect to another.

9.1. THE NORMAL DISTRIBUTION

Let $\xi = \{\xi_\tau\}$ ($\tau \in N$, N some set) be a random variable consisting of the one-dimensional complex or real random variables ξ_τ. If for every $\tau \in N, D\xi_\tau = \mathbf{E}|\xi_\tau - \mathbf{E}\xi_\tau|^2 < \infty$, we call ξ a random variable **with finite variance.**

Everywhere in Part III except for those sections concerned with entropy, whenever we consider such random variables we will assume that ξ_τ has **mean zero.** Otherwise we can replace ξ_τ by the random variable $\xi'_\tau = \xi_\tau - \mathbf{E}\xi_\tau$ which is everywhere dense in ξ_τ. The random variable $\xi = \{\xi_\tau\}, \tau \in N$ is called **gaussian** if ξ consists of one-dimensional real random variables ξ_τ and if the joint distribution of any family $\xi_{\tau_1}, \ldots, \xi_{\tau_n}, \tau_1, \ldots, \tau_n \in N$ is normal (i.e., gaussian).

Let $\xi = \{\xi_\tau\}, \tau \in N$ be a random variable with finite variance.

We denote by B_ξ the real or complex Hilbert space* whose vectors consist of classes of equivalent (i.e., equal to each other with probability one) random variables η, which are finite linear combinations of random variables ξ_τ or limits in mean square of such linear combinations, in which the scalar product is given by $\rho_{\eta_1\eta_2} = \mathbf{E}\eta_1\eta_2$.

Since every random variable of an equivalence class is everywhere dense in the random variable consisting of all members of this class, it follows from the results of earlier chapters that in any expressions containing informations, we may replace any random variable, and even an entire class of random variables, by equivalent random variables. Therefore, from the point of view of information we may (and frequently will) identify a random variable ξ with any class of random variables which are equivalent to it.

We will denote by $\{B_\xi\}$ the random variable consisting of all the random variables belonging to B_ξ. Obviously ξ is everywhere dense in $\{B_\xi\}$. If ξ is gaussian, then $\{B_\xi\}$ will also be gaussian.

Any one-dimensional complex or real-valued random variable which has finite variance may be represented as the sum of two one-dimensional random variables $\hat{\zeta}$ and $\check{\zeta}, \zeta = \hat{\zeta} + \check{\zeta}$ which are uncorrelated (i.e., $\mathbf{E}\hat{\zeta}\check{\zeta} = 0$) and such that $\check{\zeta} \in B_\xi, \mathbf{E}\hat{\zeta}\xi_\tau = 0, \tau \in N$. The variables $\hat{\zeta}$ and $\check{\zeta}$ are defined by these properties up to a set of probability zero. We call $\hat{\zeta}$ the **perpendicular** from ζ onto B_ξ, and $\check{\zeta}$ the **projection** of ζ onto B_ξ. If ξ and ζ are real, then $\hat{\zeta}$ and $\check{\zeta}$ will be real, and if (ξ, ζ) is a gaussian random variable, then $(\hat{\zeta}, \check{\zeta}, \xi)$ will also be gaussian. If $\hat{\zeta} = 0$, then $\zeta = \check{\zeta} \in B_\xi$ and ζ is subordinate to $\xi = \{\xi_\tau\}$. Moreover, ζ may be represented as the limit in mean square of finite linear combinations of the ξ_τ. In this case we will say that ζ is **linearly subordinate** to ξ.

9.2. INFORMATION OF GAUSSIAN RANDOM VARIABLES

THEOREM 9.2.1. Let $\xi = (\xi_1, \ldots, \xi_n), \eta = (\eta_1, \ldots, \eta_m) = (\xi_{n+1}, \ldots, \xi_{n+m}), (\xi, \eta) = (\xi_1, \ldots, \xi_{n+m})$ *be gaussian random variables, taking values respectively in the measurable spaces* $X = X_1 \times \ldots \times X_n$, $Y = Y_1 \times \ldots \times Y_m = X_{n+1} \times \ldots \times X_{n+m}$, $Z = X \times Y$, *and let* $A_\xi = \| \rho_{\xi_i\xi_j} \|_{i,j=1,\ldots,n}, A_\eta = \| \rho_{\xi_i\xi_j} \|_{i,j=n+1,\ldots,n+m}, A_\zeta = A_{\xi\eta} = \| \rho_{\xi_i\xi_j} \|_{i,j=1,\ldots,n+m}$ *be the matrices of second moments* $\rho_{\xi_i\xi_j} = E\xi_i\xi_j, i, j = 1, \ldots, n+m$ *(we recall that* $E\xi_i = 0$*).*

---

* It will be clear from the text whether we are considering the real or complex Hilbert space.

Then: (1) If the determinant $\det A_\zeta = \det A_{\xi\eta}$ *is different from zero, then the determinants* $\det A_\xi$ *and* $\det A_\eta$ *are likewise different from zero, and*

$$I(\xi, \eta) = \frac{1}{2} \log \frac{\det A_\xi \cdot \det A_\eta}{\det A_\zeta}. \tag{9.2.1}$$

If, however $\det A_\zeta = 0$, *but* $\det A_\xi \neq 0$ *and* $\det A_\eta \neq 0$, *then*

$$I(\xi, \eta) = +\infty. \tag{9.2.2}$$

For $n = m = 1$, *formula (9.2.1) takes the form*

$$I(\xi, \eta) = -\frac{1}{2} \log (1 - r_{\xi\eta}^2), \tag{9.2.3}$$

where

$$r_{\xi\eta}^2 = \frac{(\mathbf{E}\xi\eta)^2}{\mathbf{E}\xi^2\mathbf{E}\eta^2} \tag{9.2.4}$$

is the correlation coefficient of the variables ξ *and* η.

(2) If $\det A_\xi \cdot \det A_\eta = 0$, *then, denoting by* $\det A_{\bar{\xi}} = \det \| \rho_{\xi_i\xi_j} \|_{i, j = i_1, \ldots, i_s}$, $\det A_{\bar{\eta}} = \det \| \rho_{\xi_i \xi_j} \|_{i, j = i_{s+1}, \ldots, i_{s+r}}$ *any highest order non-vanishing principal minors of* $\det A_\xi$ *and* $\det A_\eta$ *respectively, and by* $\det A_{\bar{\xi}\bar{\eta}} = \det \| \rho_{\xi_i\xi_j} \| i, j = i_1, \ldots, i_{s+r}$ *the principal minor of order* $s + r$ *of* $\det A_\zeta$, *which contains the minors* $\det A_{\bar{\xi}}$ *and* $\det A_{\bar{\eta}}$, *we have*

$$I(\xi, \eta) = \begin{cases} \dfrac{1}{2} \log \dfrac{\det A_{\bar{\xi}} \det A_{\bar{\eta}}}{\det A_{\bar{\xi}\bar{\eta}}} & \text{for } \det A_{\bar{\xi}\bar{\eta}} \neq 0 \\ +\infty & \text{for } \det A_{\bar{\xi}\bar{\eta}} = 0. \end{cases} \tag{9.2.5}$$

PROOF. (1) If $\det A_\zeta \neq 0$, then the normal distributions $P_{\xi\eta}(\cdot) = P_\zeta(\cdot), P_\xi(\cdot), P_\eta(\cdot)$ have densities of the form

$$p_{\xi\eta}(x, y) = p_\zeta(z) = \frac{1}{(2\pi)^{\frac{n+m}{2}} (\det A_\zeta)^{\frac{1}{2}}} e^{-\frac{1}{2}(A_\zeta^{-1}z, z)};$$

$$p_\xi(x) = \frac{1}{(2\pi)^{\frac{n}{2}}(\det A_\xi)^{\frac{1}{2}}} e^{-\frac{1}{2}(A_\xi^{-1}x, x)};$$

$$p_\eta(y) = \frac{1}{(2\pi)^{\frac{m}{2}}(\det A_\eta)^{\frac{1}{2}}} e^{-\frac{1}{2}(A_\eta^{-1}y, y)}.$$

Substituting these expressions for the densities into formula (2.1.8), we obtain

$$I(\xi, \eta) = \int \left\{ \frac{1}{2} \log \frac{\det A_\xi \det A_\eta}{\det A_\zeta} - \frac{1}{2}[(A_\zeta^{-1}z, z) - A_\xi^{-1}x, x) - (A_\eta^{-1}y, y)] \right\} p_\zeta(z)dz = \frac{1}{2} \log \frac{\det A_\xi \det A_\eta}{\det A_{\xi\eta}} - \frac{1}{2} \int (A_\zeta^{-1}z, z)p_\zeta(z)dz + \frac{1}{2} \int (A_\xi^{-1}x, x)p_\xi(x)dx + \frac{1}{2} \int (A_\eta^{-1}y, y)p_\eta(y)dy. \tag{9.2.6}$$

Since the matrix A_ζ has elements

$$\int x_i x_j p_\zeta(z)\, dz = \mathbf{E}\xi_i\xi_j = \rho_{\xi_i\xi_j},\ i, j = 1, \ldots, n + m,$$

it follows that

$$\int (A_\zeta^{-1}z, z)p_\zeta(z)\, dz = S^P(A_\zeta^{-1}A_\zeta) = n + m \tag{9.2.7}$$

where $S^P A$ stands for the trace of A, i.e., the sum of its diagonal elements. Similarly

$$\int (A_\xi^{-1}x, x)p_\xi(x)\, dx = n; \tag{9.2.8}$$

$$\int (A_\eta^{-1}y, y)p_\eta(y)\, dy = m. \tag{9.2.9}$$

Comparing equations (9.2.6)–(9.2.9), we obtain (9.2.1).

If now $\det A_\zeta = \det A_{\xi\eta} = 0$ and $\det A_\xi \neq 0, \det A_\eta \neq 0$, then the distribution $P_\zeta = P_{\xi\eta}$ does not have a density (it is degenerate) while the distribution $P_{\xi\times\eta} = P_\xi \times P_\eta$ has a density (it is non-degenerate), i.e., $P_\zeta = P_{\xi\eta}$ is singular with respect to $P_{\xi\times\eta}$. By the theorem of Gelfand, Yaglom and Perez, $I(\xi, \eta) = \infty$.

(2) For any $\xi_i, i = 1, \ldots, n$ and $n_j, j = 1, \ldots, m$ there exist linear combinations of the random variables $\xi_{i_1}, \ldots, \xi_{i_s}$ and $\xi_{i_{s+1}}, \ldots, \xi_{i_{s+r}}$ respectively

$$\check{\xi}_i = \sum_{k=1}^{s} c_{ki}\xi_{i_k} \text{ and } \check{\eta}_j = \sum_{k=s+1}^{s+r} c_{kj}\ \xi_{i_k} \text{ such that}$$

$$\mathbf{E}|\xi_i - \check{\xi}_i|^2 = 0, \qquad \mathbf{E}|\eta_j - \check{\eta}_j|^2 = 0,$$

i.e., the random variables $\tilde{\xi} = (\xi_{i_1}, \ldots, \xi_{i_s})$ and $\tilde{\eta} = (\xi_{i_{s+1}}, \ldots, \xi_{i_{s+r}})$ are everywhere dense respectively in the random variables ξ and

η, so that

$$I(\xi, \eta) = I(\tilde{\xi}, \tilde{\eta}). \tag{9.2.10}$$

By part 1 of the theorem

$$I(\tilde{\xi}, \tilde{\eta}) = \begin{cases} \frac{1}{2}\log \frac{\det A_{\tilde{\xi}} \det A_{\tilde{\eta}}}{\det A_{\tilde{\xi}\tilde{\eta}}} & \text{for } \det A_{\tilde{\xi}\tilde{\eta}} \neq 0; \\ +\infty & \text{for } \det A_{\tilde{\xi}\tilde{\eta}} = 0. \end{cases} \tag{9.2.11}$$

Comparing (9.2.10 and (9.2.11) proves (9.2.5).

Remark. Formula (9.2.2) may be considered a particular case of (9.2.1), if we put $\log \frac{\alpha}{0} = \infty$ for $\alpha > 0$.

We give now a geometric interpretation of the results of the theorem. Obviously the determinants $\det A_{\xi\eta}$, $\det A_\xi$ and $\det A_\eta$ are respectively the Gramians of the random variables $\xi_1, \ldots, \xi_{n+m}$; $\xi_1, \ldots, \xi_n$; $\eta_1 = \xi_{n+1}, \ldots, \eta_m = \xi_{n+m}$. For each gaussian random variable $\xi_i, i = 1, \ldots, n$, the perpendicular $\hat{\xi}_i$ and the projection $\check{\xi}_i$ onto the space B_η are defined up to a set of probability zero, and $\check{\xi}_i$ is equal with probability one to a linear combination of the random variables $\eta_k = \xi_{n+k}, k = 1, \ldots, m$. If $\det A_{\xi\eta} \neq 0$, then, as is known,

$$\det A_{\hat{\xi}(\eta)} = \frac{\det A_{\xi\eta}}{\det A_\eta}. \tag{9.2.12}$$

Here $\det A_{\hat{\xi}(\eta)}$ is the Gramian of the random variables $\hat{\xi}_i, i = 1, \ldots, n$. Suppose that $\det A_{\xi\eta} = 0$ and $\det A_\xi . \det A_\eta \neq 0$. Then there exists a non-trivial linear combination of the variables ξ_i, $i = 1, \ldots, n + m$ such that with probability one $\sum_{i=1}^{n+m} c_i \xi_i = 0$. Since $\det A_\xi \neq 0$ and $\det A_\eta \neq 0$, the sums $\sum_{i=1}^{n} c_i \xi_i$ and $\sum_{i=n+1}^{n+m} c_i \xi_i = -\sum_{i=1}^{n} c_i \xi_i$ cannot vanish with probability one, i.e., there exists a non-null vector which belongs simultaneously to the spaces B_ξ and B_η. Conversely, if some non-null vector belongs simultaneously to the spaces B_ξ and B_η, then $\det A_{\xi\eta} = 0$.

When $\det A_\xi \det A_\eta = 0$, the same considerations hold for the random variables $\tilde{\xi} = (\tilde{\xi}_1, \ldots, \tilde{\xi}_s) = (\xi_{i_1}, \ldots, \xi_{i_s})$, $\tilde{\eta} = (\tilde{\eta}_1, \ldots, \tilde{\eta}_r) = (\xi_{i_{s+1}}, \ldots, \xi_{i_{s+r}})$ and $B_{\tilde{\xi}} = B_\xi, B_{\tilde{\eta}} = B_\eta$. Formula (9.2.12) goes over into

$$\det A_{\hat{\tilde{\xi}}(\eta)} = \frac{\det A_{\tilde{\xi}\tilde{\eta}}}{\det A_{\tilde{\eta}}}, \tag{9.2.13}$$

where $\det A_{\hat{\xi}(\eta)}$ is the Gramian of the random variables $\hat{\hat{\xi}}_k = \hat{\xi}_{i_k}$, $k = 1, \ldots, s$ which are the perpendiculars from the $\tilde{\xi}_k$ onto the space $B_{\tilde{\eta}} = B_\eta$.

Finally, $\det A_{\tilde{\xi}\tilde{\eta}} = 0$ if and only if there exists a non-null vector which belongs simultaneously to the spaces $B_{\tilde{\xi}} = B_\xi$ and $B_{\tilde{\eta}} = B_\eta$, i.e., $I(\xi, \eta) = I(\tilde{\xi}, \tilde{\eta}) = \infty$ if and only if the spaces B_ξ and B_η have a common non-null vector. Formula (9.2.13) permits us to write (9.2.5) in the form

$$I(\xi, \eta) = I(\tilde{\xi}, \tilde{\eta}) = \frac{1}{2} \log \frac{\det A_{\tilde{\xi}}}{\det A_{\hat{\xi}(\eta)}}, \tag{9.2.13'}$$

which remains valid even when $\det A_{\tilde{\xi}\tilde{\eta}} = 0$, for, in this case, since the spaces $B_{\tilde{\xi}}$ and $B_{\tilde{\eta}}$ have a common non-null vector, the vectors $\hat{\hat{\xi}}_k = \hat{\xi}_{i_k}$, $k = 1, \ldots, s$, perpendicular to $B_{\tilde{\eta}} = B_\eta$, will be linearly dependent, so that $\det A_{\hat{\xi}(\eta)} = 0$.

Formula (9.2.13′) enables us to write down an expression for the quantity of information in the case where the gaussian random variables consist of an infinite number of one-dimensional random variables. Let $\xi = (\xi_1, \ldots, \xi_n)$, $\eta = (\eta_1, \eta_2, \ldots)$.
We have

$$I(\xi, \eta) = \lim_{m \to \infty} I(\xi, (\eta_1, \ldots, \eta_m)) = \lim_{m \to \infty} \frac{1}{2} \log \frac{\det A_{\tilde{\xi}}}{\det A_{\hat{\xi}(\eta_1, \ldots, \eta_m)}}.$$

Obviously $\det A_{\hat{\xi}(\eta_1, \ldots, \eta_m)}$ converges for $m \to \infty$ to $\det A_{\hat{\xi}(\eta)}$, the Gramian of the random variables $\hat{\hat{\xi}}_k = \hat{\xi}_{i_k}$, where $\hat{\xi}_{i_k}$, $k = 1, \ldots, s$ is the perpendicular from ξ_{i_k} onto B_η. Thus

$$I(\xi, \eta) = \frac{1}{2} \log \frac{\det A_{\tilde{\xi}}}{\det A_{\hat{\xi}(\eta)}}. \tag{9.2.14}$$

When ξ is a one-dimensional random variable, formula (9.2.14) takes the form

$$I(\xi, \eta) = \frac{1}{2} \log \frac{\rho_{\xi\xi}}{\rho_{\hat{\xi}\hat{\xi}}}, \tag{9.2.15}$$

where $\rho_{\xi\xi} = \mathbf{E}\xi^2, \rho_{\hat{\xi}\hat{\xi}} = \mathbf{E}\hat{\xi}^2$. Let now $\xi = (\xi_1, \xi_2, \ldots)$, $\eta = (\eta_1, \eta_2 \ldots)$, $\xi_{l} = (\xi_1, \ldots, \xi_l)$. Then

$$I(\xi, \eta) = \lim_{l \to \infty} I((\xi_1, \ldots, \xi_l), \eta) = \lim_{l \to \infty} \frac{1}{2} \log \frac{\det A_{\tilde{\xi}}^{(l)}}{\det A_{\hat{\xi}}^{(l)}(\eta)} \cdot \tag{9.2.16}$$

Formulas (9.2.15) and (9.2.16) remain valid in the case where $\eta = \{\eta_\tau\}, \tau \in N$, $N -$ an arbitrary set.

Kolmogorov [18] has proposed a different method for computing the information for gaussian random variables $\xi = (\xi_1, \ldots, \xi_n)$, $\eta = (\eta_1, \ldots, \eta_m)$, (ξ, η). As is known [13, 22, 23], if the ξ_i and also the η_j are linearly independent, then there exist non-singular linear transformations of the variables $\xi_1, \ldots, \xi_n$ and $\eta_1, \ldots, \eta_m$

$$\xi'_j = \sum_{i=1}^{n} c_{ji}\xi_i, \qquad \eta'_l = \sum_{i=1}^{m} d_{li}\eta_i \tag{9.2.17}$$

and an integer $k \leqslant \min(n, m)$ such that any subset of the set $\xi_1, \ldots, \xi_n, \eta_1, \ldots, \eta_m$ which does not contain a pair (ξ_j, η_j), $j \leqslant k$ consists of independent random variables. Since the random variables ξ and $\xi' = (\xi'_1, \ldots, \xi'_n)$, η and $\eta' = (\eta'_1, \ldots, \eta'_m)$ are mutually subordinate, it follows easily that

$$I(\xi, \eta) = I(\xi', \eta') = \sum_{j=1}^{k} I(\xi'_j, \eta'_j).$$

According to (9.2.3)

$$I(\xi, \eta) = \sum_{j=1}^{k} I(\xi'_j, \eta'_j) = -\frac{1}{2}\sum_{j=1}^{k} \log\,(1 - r^2_{\xi'_j\eta'_j}). \tag{9.2.18}$$

This method of computing the information was developed by Gelfand and Yaglom in [9], in which they introduced the self-adjoint operators $\Pi_{\xi\eta\xi} = \overline{\Pi}_\xi\overline{\Pi}_\eta\overline{\Pi}_\xi$, $\Pi_{\eta\xi\eta} = \overline{\Pi}_\eta\overline{\Pi}_\xi\Pi_\eta$, where $\overline{\Pi}_\xi$ and $\overline{\Pi}_\eta$ are respectively the projection operators on the spaces B_ξ and B_η, and proved that for a gaussian random variable (ξ, η), $I(\xi, \eta) < \infty$ if and only if at least one of the operators $\Pi_{\xi\eta\xi}$ and $\Pi_{\eta\xi\eta}$ is completely continuous and has finite trace (by trace we mean the sum of its characteristic values). In this case the second operator will satisfy the same conditions, and

$$I(\xi, \eta) = -\frac{1}{2}\log\det\,(E - \Pi_{\xi\eta\xi}) = -\frac{1}{2}\log\det\,(E - \Pi_{\eta\xi\eta}), \tag{9.2.19}$$

where $\mathbf{E}$ is the identity operator and $\det\,(\mathbf{E} - \Pi_{\xi\eta\xi}) = \det\,(\mathbf{E} - \Pi_{\eta\xi\eta})$ is the product of the characteristic values of the operator $\mathbf{E} - \Pi_{\xi\eta\xi}$. This result can also be formulated in the following way.

The quantity of information $I(\xi, \eta)$ is finite if and only if there exists a finite or denumerable sequence of gaussian random variables $\xi'_1, \xi'_2, \ldots; \eta'_1, \eta'_2, \ldots; \xi' = (\xi'_1, \xi'_2, \ldots), \eta' = (\eta'_1, \eta'_2, \ldots)$, $\xi'_j \in B_\xi, \eta'_j \in B_\eta, j = 1, 2, \ldots$ such that the random variables (ξ'_j, η'_j),

$j = 1, 2, \ldots$ are mutually independent, and the sequence ξ, ξ', η', η forms a Markov chain. In this case

$$I(\xi, \eta) = \sum_j I(\xi'_j, \eta'_j) = -\frac{1}{2}\sum_j \log(1 - r^2_{\xi'_j \eta'_j}) = -\frac{1}{2}\sum_j \log(1 - \lambda_j). \tag{9.2.20}$$

The random variables $\xi'_1, \xi'_2, \ldots; \eta'_1, \eta'_2, \ldots$ will be those characteristic vectors respectively of the operators $\Pi_{\xi\eta\xi}$ and $\Pi_{\eta\xi\eta}$ whose characteristic values $\lambda_j = r^2_{\xi'_j \eta'_j}$ are different from zero.

9.3. CONDITIONAL INFORMATION OF GAUSSIAN RANDOM VARIABLES

Let $\xi = \{\xi_t\}, t \in N$, $\eta = \{\eta_\tau\}, \tau \in K$, $\zeta = \{\zeta_s\}, s \in S$ (N, K, S are arbitrary sets) and (ξ, η, ζ) be gaussian random variables. By Kolmogorov's formula (3.6.3), the average conditional information $\mathbf{E}I(\eta, \zeta/\xi)$ can be expressed in terms of unconditional informations, which can be computed by the formulas of the preceding section. We will simplify somewhat the method of computation. For this purpose we now obtain a relation establishing the connection between the average conditional information $\mathbf{E}I(\eta, \zeta/\xi)$ and the unconditional information $I(\hat{\eta}, \hat{\zeta})$ of a certain pair of gaussian random variables $(\hat{\eta}, \hat{\zeta})$ defined by the random variable (ξ, η, ζ).

Each random variable η_τ, ζ_s may be represented as a sum of random variables*

$$\eta_\tau = \hat{\eta}_\tau + \check{\eta}_\tau, \qquad \zeta_s = \hat{\zeta}_s + \check{\zeta}_s, \tag{9.3.1}$$

where $\check{\eta}_\tau$ and $\check{\zeta}_s$ are the projections of η_τ and ζ_s onto the space B_ξ, and $\hat{\eta}_\tau$ and $\hat{\zeta}_s$ are the perpendiculars from η_τ and ζ_s to B_ξ. The random variables $\check{\eta}_\tau$ and $\check{\zeta}_s$ are subordinate to the random variable ξ, and hence the variables $\check{\eta} = \{\check{\eta}_\tau\}$ and $\check{\zeta} = \{\check{\zeta}_s\}$ are also. The random variables $\hat{\eta}_\tau$ and $\hat{\zeta}_s$, $\tau \in K, s \in S$ are uncorrelated with the random variables $\xi_t, t \in N$, and therefore, since (ξ, η, ζ) is gaussian, the random variables $\hat{\eta} = \{\hat{\eta}_\tau\}, \hat{\zeta} = \{\hat{\zeta}_s\}, (\hat{\eta}, \hat{\zeta})$ are independent of ξ. Since the random variable $\check{\eta}$ is subordinate to the random variable ξ, by Corollary 2 to Theorem 3.7.2

$$\mathbf{E}I(\eta, \zeta/\xi) = \mathbf{E}I((\eta, \check{\eta}), \zeta/\xi) \tag{9.3.2}$$

and

$$\bar{i}(\eta, \zeta/\xi) = \bar{i}((\eta, \check{\eta}), \zeta/\xi). \tag{9.3.3}$$

---

* Recall that we omit the phrase "with probability one" wherever it is inessential to the argument.

From (9.3.1) it is seen that $(\eta_\tau, \check{\eta}_\tau)$ and $(\hat{\eta}_\tau, \check{\eta}_\tau)$, $\tau \in K$ are mutually subordinate, and therefore the variables $(\eta, \check{\eta})$ and $(\hat{\eta}, \check{\eta})$ are mutually subordinate. By the corollary to Theorem 3.7.1

$$\mathbf{E}I((\eta, \check{\eta}), \zeta/\xi) = \mathbf{E}I((\hat{\eta}, \check{\eta}), \zeta/\xi) \tag{9.3.4}$$

and

$$\bar{i}((\eta, \check{\eta}), \zeta/\xi) = \bar{i}((\hat{\eta}, \check{\eta}), \zeta/\xi). \tag{9.3.5}$$

Since $\check{\eta}$ is subordinate to ξ, by Corollary 2 to Theorem 3.7.2

$$\mathbf{E}I((\hat{\eta}, \check{\eta}), \zeta/\xi) = \mathbf{E}I(\hat{\eta}, \zeta/\xi) \tag{9.3.6}$$

and

$$\bar{i}((\hat{\eta}, \check{\eta}), \zeta/\xi) = \bar{i}((\hat{\eta}, \zeta/\xi). \tag{9.3.7}$$

Comparing (9.3.2), (9.3.4) and (9.3.6), (9.3.3), (9.3.5) and (9.3.7) we find that

$$\mathbf{E}I(\eta, \zeta/\xi) = \mathbf{E}I(\hat{\eta}, \zeta/\xi)$$

and

$$\bar{i}(\eta, \zeta/\xi) = \bar{i}(\hat{\eta}, \zeta/\xi).$$

In a completely analogous way it can be shown that

$$\mathbf{E}I(\hat{\eta}, \zeta/\xi) = \mathbf{E}I(\hat{\eta}, \hat{\zeta}/\xi)$$

and

$$\bar{i}(\hat{\eta}, \zeta/\xi) = \bar{i}(\hat{\eta}, \hat{\zeta}/\xi),$$

and consequently

$$\mathbf{E}I(\eta, \zeta/\xi) = \mathbf{E}I(\hat{\eta}, \hat{\zeta}/\xi) \tag{9.3.8}$$

and

$$\bar{i}(\eta, \zeta/\xi) = \bar{i}(\hat{\eta}, \hat{\zeta}/\xi). \tag{9.3.9}$$

Since the random variable $(\hat{\eta}, \hat{\zeta})$ is independent of ξ,

$$I(\hat{\eta}, \hat{\zeta}) = I(\hat{\eta}, (\hat{\zeta}, \xi)) = I(\hat{\eta}, \xi) + \mathbf{E}I(\hat{\eta}, \hat{\zeta}/\xi) = \mathbf{E}I(\hat{\eta}, \hat{\zeta}/\xi) \tag{9.3.10}$$

and

$$i(\hat{\eta}, \hat{\zeta}) = i(\hat{\eta}, (\hat{\zeta}, \xi)) = i(\hat{\eta}, \xi) + \bar{i}(\hat{\eta}, \hat{\zeta}/\xi) = \bar{i}(\hat{\eta}, \hat{\zeta}/\xi). \tag{9.3.11}$$

Comparing (9.3.8) with (9.3.10) and (9.3.9) with (9.3.11), we obtain

$$\mathbf{E}I(\eta, \zeta/\xi) = I(\hat{\eta}, \hat{\zeta}), \tag{9.3.12}$$

$$\bar{i}(\eta, \zeta/\xi) = \bar{i}(\hat{\eta}, \hat{\zeta}). \tag{9.3.13}$$

Thus, the average conditional information $EI(\eta, \zeta/\xi)$ *and the conditional information density* $\bar{i}(\eta, \zeta/\xi)$ *of a gaussian random variable* (ξ, η, ζ) *are respectively equal and equal with probability one to the unconditional information* $I(\hat{\eta}, \hat{\zeta})$ *and the unconditional information density* $i(\hat{\eta}, \hat{\zeta})$ *of the gaussian random variable* $(\hat{\eta}, \hat{\zeta}) = \{(\hat{\eta}_\tau, \hat{\zeta}_s)\}$ *consisting of the perpendiculars respectively from* η_τ, ζ_s *to* B_ξ.

As a corollary of the foregoing, we obtain the following result: If $\xi = \{\xi_t\}, \eta = \{\eta_\tau\}, \zeta = \{\zeta_s\}$ $(t \in N, \tau \in K, s \in S)$, (ξ, η, ζ) is gaussian, and the perpendiculars $\hat{\eta}_\tau$ from η_τ onto B_ξ are uncorrelated with the random variables ζ_s, then the sequence η, ξ, ζ forms a Markov chain. In fact, since the random variable (ξ, η, ζ) is gaussian, the absence of correlation of $\hat{\eta}_\tau$ with ξ_t and ζ_s implies that $\hat{\eta} = \{\hat{\eta}_\tau\}$ is independent of (ξ, ζ), and a fortiori of $\hat{\zeta}$, and hence

$$\mathbf{E}I(\eta, \zeta/\xi) = I(\hat{\eta}, \hat{\zeta}) = 0$$

which implies that η, ξ, ζ forms a Markov chain.

9.4. THE ENTROPY OF ONE GAUSSIAN RANDOM VARIABLE WITH RESPECT TO ANOTHER

Let $\xi = (\xi_1, \ldots, \xi_n)$ and $\eta = (\eta_1, \ldots, \eta_n)$ be n-dimensional non-degenerate gaussian random variables. The following expression for the entropy $H_\eta(\xi) = \mathbf{E}h_\eta(\xi)$ can easily be obtained by means of simple calculations:

$$H_\eta(\xi) = H_{P_\eta}(P_\xi) = \frac{1}{2}\sum_{j,k=1}^{n} \rho^{(-1)}_{\eta_j\eta_k}\rho_{\xi_k\xi_j} - \frac{n}{2} + \frac{1}{2}\sum_{j,k=1}^{n} \rho^{(-1)}_{\eta_j\eta_k}(m_{\xi_j} - m_{\eta_j}) \times (m_{\xi_k} - m_{\eta_k}) - \frac{1}{2}\log\frac{\det\|\rho_{\xi_j\xi_k}\|_{j,k=1,\ldots,n}}{\det\|\rho_{\eta_j\eta_k}\|_{j,k=1,\ldots,n}}, \tag{9.4.1}$$

where

$$\rho_{\xi_j\xi_k} = \mathbf{E}(\xi_j - m_{\xi_j})(\xi_k - m_{\xi_k}),\ \rho_{\eta_j\eta_k} = \mathbf{E}(\eta_j - m_{\eta_j})(\eta_k - m_{\eta_k}),$$

$$m_{\xi_j} = \mathbf{E}\xi_j,\ m_{\eta_j} = \mathbf{E}\eta_j,$$

and $\rho^{(-1)}_{\eta_j\eta_k}$ are the elements of the inverse of the matrix

$$\|\rho_{\eta_j\eta_k}\| j, k = 1, \ldots, n.$$

Hajek has proposed another method for computing $H_\eta(\xi)$. In [11] he considered non-singular linear transformations of the random variables $\xi_1, \ldots, \xi_n$ and $\eta_1, \ldots, \eta_n$

$$\xi'_j = \sum_{k=1}^{n} c_{jk}\xi_k,\ \eta'_j = \sum_{k=1}^{n} c_{jk}\xi_k \tag{9.4.2}$$

such that the sets $(\xi'_1, \ldots, \xi'_n)$ and $(\eta'_1, \ldots, \eta'_n)$ consist of independent random variables. Then

$$H_\eta(\xi) = H_{P_\eta}(P_\xi) = H_{P_{\eta'}}(P_{\xi'}) = \sum_{j=1}^{n} H_{P_{\eta'_j}}(P_{\xi'_j}) = \sum_{j=1}^{n} H_{\eta'_j}(\xi'_j). \tag{9.4.3}$$

If $\mathbf{E}\xi_j = \mathbf{E}\eta_j = 0$, then

$$\mathbf{E}\xi'_j = \mathbf{E}\eta'_\eta = 0. \tag{9.4.4}$$

It is easily verified that

$$H_{\eta'_j}(\xi'_j) = H_{P_{\eta'_j}}(P_{\xi'_j}) = \frac{1}{2}\left(\frac{\sigma^{2\prime}_{\xi_j}}{\sigma^{2\prime}_{\eta_j}} - 1 - \log\frac{\sigma^{2\prime}_{\xi_j}}{\sigma^{2\prime}_{\eta_j}}\right), \tag{9.4.5}$$

where

$$\sigma^{2\prime}_{\xi_j} = D\xi'_j = \mathbf{E}\xi'^2_j, \qquad \sigma^{2\prime}_{\eta_j} = D\eta'_j = \mathbf{E}\eta'^2_j. \tag{9.4.6}$$

In the general case, where $\mathbf{E}\xi_j \neq 0$ or $\mathbf{E}\eta_j \neq 0$, transformations of the form (9.4.2) still lead to independent random variables $\xi'_1, \ldots, \xi'_n$ and $\eta'_1, \ldots, \eta'_n$, but condition (9.4.4) need not hold. In this case

$$H_{\eta'_j}(\xi'_j) = \frac{1}{2}\left(\frac{\sigma^{2\prime}_{\xi_j} + (m_{\xi'_j} - m_{\eta'_j})^2}{\sigma^{2\prime}_{\eta_j}} - 1 - \log\frac{\sigma^{2\prime}_{\xi_j}}{\sigma^{2\prime}_{\eta_j}}\right), \tag{9.4.7}$$

where $m_{\xi'_j} = \mathbf{E}\xi'_j$, $m_{\eta'_j} = \mathbf{E}\eta'_j$. Combining (9.4.3) with 9.4.7), we obtain

$$H_\eta(\xi) = \frac{1}{2}\sum_{j=1}^{n}\left[\frac{\sigma^{2\prime}_{\xi_j} + (m_{\xi'_j} - m_{\eta'_j})^2}{\sigma^{2\prime}_{\eta_j}} - 1 - \log\frac{\sigma^{2\prime}_{\xi_j}}{\sigma^{2\prime}_{\eta_j}}\right]. \tag{9.4.8}$$

For computing the entropy it is useful to observe that

$$\sum_{j=1}^{n}\log\frac{\sigma^{2\prime}_{\xi_j}}{\sigma^{2\prime}_{\eta_j}} = \log\frac{\det A_\xi}{\det A_\eta}. \tag{9.4.9}$$

Substituting (9.4.9) into (9.4.8), we obtain

$$H_\eta(\xi) = \frac{1}{2}\left[\sum_{j=1}^{n}\left(\frac{\sigma^{2\prime}_{\xi_j} + (m_{\xi'_j} - m_{\eta'_j})^2}{\sigma^{2\prime}_{\eta_j}} - 1\right) - \log\frac{\det A_\xi}{\det A_\eta}\right]. \tag{9.4.10}$$

If $\xi_1, \ldots, \xi_n$, as well as $\eta_1, \ldots, \eta_m$, are independent, then

$$\sum_{j=1}^{n}\frac{\sigma^{2\prime}_{\xi_j}}{\sigma^{2\prime}_{\eta_j}} = \sum_{j=1}^{n}\frac{\sigma^{2}_{\xi_j}}{\sigma^{2}_{\eta_j}} \text{ and } \sum_{j=1}^{n}\frac{(m_{\xi'_j} - m_{\eta'_j})^2}{\sigma^{2\prime}_{\eta_j}} = \sum_{j=1}^{n}\frac{(m_{\xi_j} - m_{\eta_j})^2}{\sigma^{2}_{\eta_j}} \tag{9.4.11}$$

and (9.4.10) becomes

$$H_\eta(\xi) = \frac{1}{2}\left[\sum_{j=1}^{n}\left(\frac{\sigma^{2}_{\xi_j} + (m_{\xi_j} - m_{\eta_j})^2}{\sigma^{2}_{\eta_j}} - 1\right) - \log\frac{\det A_\xi}{\det A_\eta}\right]. \tag{9.4.12}$$

In the case where one of the variables ξ, η is degenerate, (9.4.2), (9.4.3) and (9.4.8) remain valid if we agree that $0/0 = 1$ and that if any term in (9.4.8) is undefined, then $H_\eta(\xi) = \infty$. If $\mathbf{E}\xi_j = \mathbf{E}\eta_j = 0$, then $H_n(\xi) < \infty$ if and only if corresponding principal minors of the matrices A_ξ and A_η are simultaneously zero or different from zero. In this case

$$H_{\tilde\eta}(\tilde\xi) = H_\eta(\xi), \tag{9.4.13}$$

where $\tilde\xi = (\xi_{j_1}, \ldots, \xi_{j_k})$, $\tilde\eta = (\eta_{j_1}, \ldots, \eta_{j_k})$ and $\det A_{\tilde\xi}$ and $\det A_{\tilde\eta}$ are the highest order non-vanishing principal minors of A_ξ and A_η. In order to compute $H_\eta(\xi)$, we can use the formulas already derived above, applied to $\tilde\xi$ and $\tilde\eta$.

Just as in the case of information, the methods for computing the entropy which we have developed can be generalized to arbitrary gaussian random variables. Let $\xi = \{\xi_t\}$ and $\eta = \{\eta_t\}$ ($t \in \mathbf{N}$, **N** an arbitrary set) be gaussian random variables. To any random variable $\beta \in B_\eta$ which is a finite linear combination

$$\beta = \sum_{j=1}^{m} c_j \eta_{t_j} \tag{9.4.14}$$

of random variables $\eta_t, t \in N$, we associate the random variable $\alpha \in B_\xi$ given by

$$\alpha = \sum_{j=1}^{m} c_j \xi_{t_j}, \tag{9.4.15}$$

and introduce the notation

$$\alpha = \theta(\beta). \tag{9.4.16}$$

The entropy $H_{P_\eta}(P_\xi) = H_\eta(\xi)$ is finite if and only if the following conditions are satisfied.

(1) If a sequence of random variables $\beta_1, \beta_2, \ldots \in B_\eta$ converges in the mean square to the variable $\beta \in B_\eta$, then the sequence $\alpha_1 = \theta(\beta_1)$, $\alpha_2 = \theta(\beta_2), \ldots$ also converges in mean square to a variable $\alpha \in B_\xi$, and putting $\alpha = \theta(\beta)$ yields an extension of the mapping (9.4.16) which is a one to one mapping of B_η onto B_ξ.

(2) There exists a finite or denumerable sequence of mutually independent random variables $\eta'_1, \eta'_2, \ldots \in B_\eta$ such that:

(a) The sequence $\xi'_1 = \theta(\eta'_1), \xi'_2 = \theta(\eta'_2), \ldots$ is a set of independent random variables.

(b) If $\beta \in B_\eta$ is any random variable which is independent of $\eta' = (\eta'_1, \eta'_2, \ldots)$, then $\alpha = \theta(\beta) \in B_\xi$ is independent of $\xi' = (\xi'_1, \xi'_2, \ldots)$.

(c) $$\mathbf{E}\beta = \mathbf{E}\alpha, D\beta = D\alpha. \tag{9.4.17}$$

In this case

$$H_\eta(\xi) = H_{\eta'}(\xi') = \frac{1}{2}\sum_j \left(\frac{\sigma^2_{\xi'_j} + (m_{\xi'_j} - m_{\eta'_j})^2}{\sigma^2_{\eta'_j}} - 1 - \log\frac{\sigma^2_{\xi'_j}}{\sigma^2_{\eta'_j}}\right). \tag{9.4.18}$$

A similar expression holds for $H_\xi(\eta)$.

In [11] the sum of entropies

$$H_{\xi\eta} = H(P_\xi, P_\eta) = H_{P_\eta}(P_\xi) + H_{P_\xi}(P_\eta) = H_\eta(\xi) + H_\xi(\eta) \tag{9.4.19}$$

is considered. Using (9.4.18), simple calculations lead to

$$H_{\xi\eta} = \frac{1}{2}\sum_j \frac{(\sigma^{2\prime}_{\xi j} - \sigma^{2\prime}_{\eta j})^2 + (m_{\xi j}' - m_{\eta j}')^2(\sigma^{2\prime}_{\xi j} + \sigma^{2\prime}_{\eta j})}{\sigma^{2\prime}_{\xi j}\sigma^{2\prime}_{\eta j}} . \tag{9.4.20}$$

From these expressions it follows that the quantities $H_{\xi\eta}, H_\eta(\xi)$ and $H_\xi(\eta)$ are either simultaneously finite or infinite.

9.5. SOME PROPERTIES OF COMPLEX-VALUED RANDOM VARIABLES

This section is supplementary in nature. The facts which are derived here will be used to study the properties of stationary random properties. Actually, the results of this section can be considered generalizations and stronger versions of certain results which have been obtained in earlier sections for gaussian random variables. In Section 9.2. we asserted that for any non-degenerate gaussian random variables $\xi = (\xi_1, \ldots, \xi_n)$ and $\eta = (\eta_1, \ldots, \eta_m)$ there exist non-singular linear transformations

$$\xi_j' = \sum_{s=1}^{n} c_{js}\xi_s \text{ and } \eta_j' = \sum_{s=1}^{m} d_{js}\eta_s \tag{9.5.1}$$

such that the random variables $\xi_1', \ldots, \xi_n', \eta_1', \ldots, \eta_m'$ are all independent except for pairs $(\xi_j', \eta_j'), j = 1, \ldots, k \leqslant \min(n, m)$.

This result remains valid for arbitrary multi-dimensional complex valued random variables; however, we must replace the word " independent" by "uncorrelated." Precisely, let $\xi = (\xi_1, \ldots, \xi_n)$ and $\eta = (\eta_1, \ldots, \eta_m)$ be respectively n and m-dimensional complex valued random variables with finite variance;* then [22] there exist non-singular linear transformations of the form (9.5.1) such that all pairs from $\xi_1', \ldots, \xi_n', \eta_1', \ldots, \eta_m'$ are uncorrelated except for the pairs $(\xi_j', \eta_j'), j = 1, \ldots, k,$ where k is some integer not exceeding $\min(n, m)$. Moreover, the coefficients c_{js} and d_{js} may always be chosen so that $\rho_{\xi_j'\eta_j'} = \mathbf{E}\xi_j'\overline{\eta_j'} \geqslant 0; j = 1, \ldots, k \leqslant \min(n, m)$. If ξ and η are real, then $\xi_1', \ldots, \xi_n', \eta_1', \ldots, \eta_m'$ may also be taken as real.

Just as was done for the case of gaussian random variables, given a pair (ξ, η) of random variables $\xi = \{\xi_t\}, \eta = \{\eta_\tau\}, t \in N, \tau \in K$(N, K are arbitrary sets) consisting of one-dimensional complex

---

* The $\xi_j, j = 1, \ldots, n$ as well as the $\eta_i, i = 1, \ldots, m$ must also be assumed linearly independent, as elements of B_ξ and B_η.Tr.

valued random variables ξ_t, η_τ with finite variance, we can introduce the self-adjoint operators

$$\Pi_{\xi\eta\xi} = \overline{\Pi}_\xi \overline{\Pi}_\eta \overline{\Pi}_\xi \qquad \text{and} \qquad \Pi_{\eta\xi\eta} = \overline{\Pi}_\eta \overline{\Pi}_\xi \overline{\Pi}_\eta,$$

where $\overline{\Pi}_\xi$ and $\overline{\Pi}_\eta$ are respectively the projection operators on the spaces B_ξ and B_η.

If one of the operators $\Pi_{\xi\eta\xi}$ *or* $\Pi_{\eta\xi\eta}$ *is completely continuous, the other is also, and* $\Pi_{\xi\eta\xi}$ *and* $\Pi_{\eta\xi\eta}$ *have the same proper values* λ_j, *which are non-negative and not greater than one. We have in this case*

$$\lambda_j = \frac{|\mathbf{E}\xi_j'\overline{\eta}_j'|}{\sqrt{\mathbf{E}|\xi_j'|^2\mathbf{E}|\eta_j'|^2}} = |r_{\xi_j'\eta_j'}|^2, \tag{9.5.2}$$

where ξ_j' *and* η_j' *are the proper vectors respectively of the operators* $\Pi_{\xi\eta\xi}$ *and* $\Pi_{\eta\xi\eta}$ *corresponding to the proper value* λ_j. *In the case where* $\xi = (\xi_1, \ldots, \xi_n)$, $\eta = (\eta_1, \ldots, \eta_m)$, *the proper vectors of the operators* $\Pi_{\xi\eta\xi}$ *and* $\Pi_{\eta\xi\eta}$ *coincide respectively with the random variables* $\xi_j', \eta_l', j = 1, \ldots, n, l = 1, \ldots, m$ *occurring in the representation (9.5.1).*

We say that the random variable ξ is linearly subordinate to the random variable η, if each of the random variables ξ_t is either a finite linear combination of random variables $\eta_\tau, \tau \in K$, or is a limit in mean square of finite linear combinations, i.e., if $B_\xi \subseteq B_\eta$.

LEMMA 9.5.1. Let $\xi = \{\xi_t\}, \eta = \{\eta_\tau\}, \zeta = \{\zeta_s\}, t \in N, \tau \in K, s \in S$ *(N, K, S are arbitrary sets) be random variables consisting respectively of the one-dimensional complex-valued random variables* $\xi_t, \eta_\tau, \zeta_s$ *with finite variance. Suppose that* $B_\zeta \subseteq B_\eta$ *and that the operator* $\Pi_{\eta\xi\eta}$ *is completely continuous and* $\lambda_1 \geqslant \lambda_2 \geqslant \ldots$ *are its non-zero proper values in non-increasing order.* Then the operator* $\Pi_{\zeta\xi\zeta} = \overline{\Pi}_\zeta \overline{\Pi}_\xi \overline{\Pi}_\zeta$ *is also completely continuous, and its j-th proper value* λ_j' *does not exceed* λ_j, *i.e.,* $\lambda_1' \leqslant \lambda_1, \lambda_2' \leqslant \lambda_2, \ldots$.

PROOF. We have to show that if there exist normalized families $\alpha_1, \ldots, \alpha_l \in B$ and $\gamma_1, \ldots, \gamma_l \in B$ which are pairwise orthogonal except for pairs $(\alpha_j, \gamma_j), j = 1, \ldots, l$ (i.e., $\mathbf{E}|\alpha_j|^2 = \mathbf{E}|\gamma_j|^2 = 1$ and $\mathbf{E}\alpha_j\overline{\alpha}_r = \mathbf{E}\gamma_j\overline{\alpha}_r = \mathbf{E}\gamma_j\overline{\gamma}_r = 0$ for $j \neq r$) and

$$\mathbf{E}\alpha_j\bar{\gamma}_j \geqslant 0,\ r^2_{\alpha_j\gamma_j} = \frac{(\mathbf{E}\alpha_j\bar{\gamma}_j)^2}{\mathbf{E}|\alpha_j|^2\mathbf{E}|\gamma_j|^2} = \mathbf{E}(\alpha_j\bar{\gamma}_j)^2 > \lambda, \tag{9.5.3}$$

---

* Each value is taken as many times as its multiplicity.

then there are at least l proper vectors (random variables) $\beta_1, \ldots, \beta_l \in B$ of the operator $\Pi_{\eta\xi\eta}$ with proper values greater than λ. Indeed, on the one hand, for any random variable $\gamma \in B_\zeta \subseteq B_\eta$, orthogonal to every proper vector of the operator $\Pi_{\eta\xi\eta}$ whose proper values exceeds λ, and for any $\alpha \in B_\xi$

$$|r_{\alpha\gamma}|^2 = \frac{|\mathbf{E}\alpha\bar{\gamma}|^2}{\mathbf{E}|\alpha|^2\mathbf{E}|\gamma|^2} \leqslant \lambda, \tag{9.5.4}$$

while on the other hand, if the number of proper vectors of $\Pi_{\eta\xi\eta}$ whose proper values exceed λ is less than l, then in the space $B_{\gamma_1 \ldots \gamma_l}$ whose dimension is l there is a vector γ which is orthogonal to the aforementioned proper vectors and such that $\mathbf{E}|\gamma|^2 = 1$. The random variable γ will be a linear combination of $\gamma_1, \ldots, \gamma_l$ i.e., $\gamma = \sum_{j=1}^{l} c_j\gamma_j$ and

$$1 = \mathbf{E}|\gamma|^2 = \mathbf{E}\left|\sum_{j=1}^{l} c_j\gamma_j\right|^2 = \sum_{j=1}^{l}|c_j|^2\mathbf{E}|\gamma_j|^2 = \sum_{j=1}^{l}|c_j|^2. \tag{9.5.5}$$

Putting $\alpha = \sum_{j=1}^{l} c_j\alpha_j$, we have according to (9.5.5) and (9.5.4)

$$\mathbf{E}|\alpha|^2 = \mathbf{E}\left|\sum_{j=1}^{l} c_j\alpha_j\right|^2 = \sum_{j=1}^{l}|c_j|^2\mathbf{E}|\alpha_j|^2 = \sum_{j=1}^{l}|c_j|^2 = 1;$$

$$|r_{\alpha\gamma}|^2 = \frac{|\mathbf{E}\alpha\bar{\gamma}|^2}{\mathbf{E}|\alpha|^2\mathbf{E}|\gamma|^2} = \left|\mathbf{E}\left(\sum_{j=1}^{l} c_j\alpha_j\right)\left(\sum_{j=1}^{l}\bar{c}_j\bar{\gamma}_j\right)\right|^2 = \left|\sum_{j=1}^{l}|c_j|^2\mathbf{E}\alpha_j\bar{\gamma}_j\right|^2$$

$$\geqslant \left(\sum_{j=1}^{l}|c_j|^2\right)^2 \min_{j=1,\ldots,l}(\mathbf{E}\alpha_j\bar{\gamma}_j)^2 = \min_{j=1,\ldots,l}(\mathbf{E}\alpha_j\bar{\gamma}_j)^2 > \lambda \tag{9.5.6}$$

in contradiction with (9.5.4), which shows that the number of proper vectors of $\Pi_{\eta\xi\eta}$ with proper value greater than λ is not less than l, and proves the lemma.

COROLLARY. If ξ, η, ζ are finite-dimensional complex valued random variables, then the operators $\Pi_{\eta\xi\eta}$ and $\Pi_{\zeta\xi\zeta}$ are completely continuous and the lemma always applies.

LEMMA 9.5.2. Let $\xi = \{\xi_t\}, \eta = \{\eta_\tau\}, \zeta = \{\zeta_s\}$ be as in the preceding lemma, and let $\hat{\eta} = \{\hat{\eta}_\tau\}, \hat{\zeta} = \{\hat{\zeta}_s\}, \tau \in K, s \in S$ be random variables consisting of the perpendiculars $\hat{\eta}_\tau, \hat{\zeta}_s$ respectively from η_τ, ζ_s onto B_ξ. Then if the operator $\Pi_{\eta(\zeta\xi)\eta} = \overline{\Pi}_\eta\overline{\Pi}_{(\zeta\xi)}\overline{\Pi}_\eta$ is completely continuous, so is the operator $\Pi_{\hat{\eta}\hat{\zeta}\hat{\eta}}$, and its j-th proper value λ_j' does not exceed the j-th proper value of the operator $\Pi_{\eta(\zeta\xi)\eta}$, i.e., $\lambda_1' \leqslant \lambda_1, \lambda_2' \leqslant \lambda_2, \ldots$.

PROOF. We must show that if there exist families of vectors (random variables) $\beta_1, \ldots, \beta_l \in B_{\hat{\eta}}$ and $\gamma_1, \ldots, \gamma_l \in B_{\hat{\xi}}$ which are normalized and pairwise orthogonal except for pairs (β_j, γ_j), $j = 1, \ldots, l$ and

$$\mathbf{E}\beta_j\bar{\gamma}_j \geqslant 0, \; r^2_{\beta_j\gamma_j} = \frac{(\mathbf{E}\beta_j\bar{\gamma}_j)^2}{\mathbf{E}|\beta_j|^2\mathbf{E}|\gamma_j|^2} = (\mathbf{E}\beta_j\bar{\gamma}_j)^2 > \lambda, \tag{9.5.7}$$

then there are at least l proper vectors of the operator $\Pi_{\eta(\zeta\xi)\eta}$ with proper values greater than λ.

By definition of $B_{\hat{\eta}}$ there exist vectors $a_1, \ldots, a_l \in B_\xi$ such that $\nu_j = a_j + \beta_j \in B_\eta$. Now since the vectors $\beta_1, \ldots, \beta_l$ are orthogonal, they are linearly independent, from which it is at once seen that $\nu_1, \ldots, \nu_l$ are linearly independent, so that the dimensionality of $B_{\nu_1 \ldots \nu_l} \subseteq B_\eta$ is l. Thus, if the number of proper vectors of the operator $\Pi_{\eta(\zeta\xi)\eta}$, with proper values exceeding λ, is less than l, the space $B_{\nu_1 \ldots \nu_l}$ contains a random variable ν which is orthogonal to these proper vectors. Now the random variable ν is a linear combination of $\nu_1, \ldots, \nu_l$, i.e.,

$$\nu = \sum_{j=1}^{l} c_j\nu_j = \sum_{j=1}^{l} c_j\alpha_j + \sum_{j=1}^{l} c_j\beta_j = \alpha + \sum_{j=1}^{l} c_j\beta_j, \tag{9.5.8}$$

where $\alpha = \sum_{j=1}^{l} c_j\alpha_j \in B_\xi$, and we can of course assume that

$$\sum_{j=1}^{l} |c_j|^2 = 1. \tag{9.5.9}$$

Putting $\vartheta = \alpha + \sum_{j=1}^{l} c_j\gamma_j \in B_{\zeta\xi}$, we have, according to (9.5.9) and (9.5.7)

$$\begin{aligned} \mathbf{E}|\nu|^2 &= \mathbf{E}|\alpha + \sum_{j=1}^{l} c_j\beta_j|^2 = \mathbf{E}|\alpha|^2 + \sum_{j=1}^{l} |c_j|^2\mathbf{E}|\beta_j|^2 \\ &= \mathbf{E}|\alpha|^2 + \sum_{j=1}^{l} |c_j|^2 = \mathbf{E}|\alpha|^2 + 1; \end{aligned}$$

$$\mathbf{E}|\vartheta|^2 = \mathbf{E}|\alpha + \sum_{j=1}^{l} c_j\gamma_j|^2 = \mathbf{E}|\alpha|^2 + \sum_{j=1}^{l}|c_j|^2\mathbf{E}|\gamma_j|^2 = |\alpha|^2 + 1;$$

$$\mathbf{E}\nu\bar{\vartheta} = \mathbf{E}\,|\alpha + \sum_{j=1}^{l} c_j\beta_j)(\bar{\alpha} + \sum_{j=1}^{l} \bar{c}_j\bar{\gamma}_j) = \mathbf{E}|\alpha|^2 + \sum_{j=1}^{l} |c_j|^2\mathbf{E}\beta_j\bar{\gamma}_j;$$

$$r^2_{\nu\vartheta} = \frac{(\mathbf{E}\nu\bar{\vartheta})^2}{\mathbf{E}|\nu|^2\mathbf{E}|\vartheta|^2} = \frac{(\mathbf{E}|\alpha|^2 + \sum_{j=1}^{l} |c_j|^2\mathbf{E}\beta_j\bar{\gamma}_j)^2}{(\mathbf{E}|\alpha|^2 + 1)(\mathbf{E}|\alpha|^2 + 1)} \tag{9.5.10}$$

$$\geqslant \left(\sum_{j=1}^{l} |c_j|^2\mathbf{E}\beta_j\bar{\gamma}_j\right)^2 \geqslant \left(\sum_{j-1}^{l} \left| c_j \right|^2\right)^2 \min_{s=1,\ldots,l} (\mathbf{E}\beta_s\bar{\gamma}_s)^2 = \min_j(\mathbf{E}\beta_j\bar{\gamma}_j)^2 > \lambda.$$

On the other hand, for any random variable $\nu \in B_\eta$ which is orthogonal to every proper vector of the operator $\Pi_{\eta(\zeta\xi)\eta}$ whose proper value exceeds λ, and for any $\vartheta \in B_{\zeta\xi}$

$$|\gamma_{\nu\vartheta}|^2 = \frac{(\mathbf{E}\nu\bar{\vartheta})^2}{\mathbf{E}|\nu|^2\mathbf{E}|\vartheta|^2} \leqslant \lambda, \tag{9.5.11}$$

which contradicts (9.5.10) and shows, therefore, that the number of proper vectors of $\Pi_{\eta(\zeta\xi)\eta}$ whose proper values exceed λ is not less than l, which proves the lemma.

COROLLARY. If ξ, η, ζ are finite-dimensional complex-valued random variables with finite variance, then $\Pi_{\eta(\zeta\xi)\eta}$ is completely continuous, so that the lemma is always applicable.

Lemma 9.5.3 is proved in analogous fashion.

LEMMA 9.5.3. Let $\xi = (\xi_1, \ldots, \xi_n), \eta = (\eta_1, \ldots, \eta_m); \eta^{(1)} = (\eta_1^{(1)}, \ldots, \eta_m^{(1)}), \eta^{(2)} = (\eta_1^{(2)}, \ldots, \eta_m^{(2)}), \ldots$ be finite-dimensional complex-valued random variables with finite variance. If

$$\lim_{i\to\infty} \mathbf{E}\eta_j\bar{\eta}_j^{(i)} = \lim_{i\to\infty} \mathbf{E}|\eta_j^{(i)}|^2 = \mathbf{E}|\eta_j|^2, \tag{9.5.12}$$

then

$$(1) \quad \lim_{i\to\infty} \lambda_j^{(i)} = \lambda_j, \tag{9.5.13}$$

where $\lambda_k^{(i)}$ and λ_k are the k-th proper values respectively of the operators $\Pi_{\eta(i)\xi\eta(i)}$ and $\Pi_{\eta\xi\eta}$.

(2) In the representations of the form (9.5.1) for the pairs $(\xi, \eta^{(i)})$ and (ξ, η)

$$(\xi^{(i)})'_j = \sum_{s=1}^{n} c_{js}^{(i)}\xi_s, \quad (\eta_1^{(i)})'_l = \sum_{s=1}^{m} d_{ls}^{(i)}\eta_s^{(i)}; \tag{9.5.14}$$

$$\xi'_j = \sum_{s=1}^{n} c_{js}\xi_s, \quad \eta'_l = \sum_{s=1}^{m} d_{ls}\eta_s; \tag{9.5.15}$$

the constants $c_{js}^i, d_{js}^i, c_{js}, d_s$ may be taken so that

$$\lim_{i\to\infty} c_{js}^{(i)} = c_{js}, \quad \lim_{i\to\infty} d_{ls}^{(i)} = d_{ls}. \tag{9.5.16}$$

LEMMA 9.5.4. Let $\xi = (\xi_1, \ldots, \xi_n) = (\eta_{m+1}, \ldots, \eta_{m+n})$, $\eta = (\eta_1, \ldots, \eta_m), \zeta = (\zeta_1, \ldots, \zeta_l)$ be multi-dimensional random variables with finite variance, suppose that η and ζ are mutually *linearly subordinate, and let* $\alpha = (\alpha_1, \ldots, \alpha_n)$ *consist of the perpendiculars* $\alpha_j, j = 1, \ldots, n$ *from the* ξ_j *onto* B_η. *Then:*

(1) The value of $\det A_\alpha$, *where* $A_\alpha = \|\rho_{\alpha_j\alpha_k}\|_{j,k=1,\ldots,n}$, $\rho_{\alpha_j\alpha_k} = E\alpha_j\alpha_k$ *is given by*

$$\det A_\alpha = \frac{\det A_{\xi\bar{\eta}}}{\det A_{\bar{\eta}}}, \qquad (9.5.17)$$

where $\det A_{\bar{\eta}} = \det \|\rho_{\eta_j\eta_k}\|\ j, k = j_1, \ldots, j_r$ *is a highest order non-vanishing principal minor of* $\det A_\eta$, *and* $\det A_{\xi\bar{\eta}}$ *is the (principal) minor of order* $(r + n)$ *of* $\det A_{\xi\eta}$ *which contains both* $\det A_\xi$ *and* $\det A_{\bar{\eta}}$. *In case every principal minor of* A_η *equals zero, we put* $\det A_{\bar{\eta}} = 1$, $\det A_{\xi\bar{\eta}} = \det A_\xi$, *and formula (9.5.17) takes the form*

$$\det A_\alpha = \det A_\xi. \qquad (9.5.18)$$

(2)

$$\frac{\det A_{\bar{\xi}\bar{\eta}}}{\det A_{\bar{\xi}} \det A_{\bar{\eta}}} = \frac{\det A_{\bar{\xi}\bar{\zeta}}}{\det A_{\bar{\xi}} \det A_{\bar{\zeta}}}. \qquad (9.5.19)$$

PROOF. (1) Let us first assume that $r = m$, i.e., $A_{\bar{\eta}} = A_\eta$. The random variable ξ_j can be represented as an orthogonal sum $\xi_j = \alpha_j + \beta_j$, where $\beta_j \in B_\eta$ is a linear combination of the random variables $\eta_1, \ldots, \eta_m$, i.e., $\beta_j = \sum_{p=1}^{m} c_{jp}\eta_p$, and

$$\rho_{\xi_j\xi_k} = \overline{\rho}_{\xi_k\xi_j} = \mathbf{E}\xi_j\overline{\xi}_k = \mathbf{E}(\alpha_j + \sum_{p=1}^{m} c_{jp}\eta_p)(\overline{\alpha}_k + \sum_{p=1}^{m} \overline{c}_{kp}\overline{\eta}_p) = \mathbf{E}\alpha_j\overline{\alpha}_k$$

$$+ \sum_{p,s=1}^{m} c_{jp}\overline{c}_{ks}\mathbf{E}\eta_p\overline{\eta}_s = \rho_{\alpha_j\alpha_k} + \sum_{p,s=1}^{m} c_{jp}c_{ks}\rho_{\eta_p\eta_s},\ j, k = 1, \ldots, n.$$

Replacing, in $\det A_{\xi\eta}$, $\rho_{\xi_j\xi_k}$ by these expressions, we obtain

$$\det A_{\xi\eta} = \det \|\rho_{\eta_j\eta_k}\|_{j,k=1,\ldots,m+n} = \det \begin{Vmatrix} \rho_{\alpha_p\alpha_s} & 0 \\ 0 & \rho_{\eta_j\eta_k} \end{Vmatrix}_{p,s=1,\ldots,n;\ j,k=1,\ldots,m}$$

$$= \det \|\rho_{\alpha_p\alpha_s}\|_{p,s=1,\ldots,n} \det \|\rho_{\eta_j\eta_k}\|_{j,k=1,\ldots,m} = \det A_\alpha \det A_\eta,$$

i.e.,

$$\det A_\alpha = \frac{\det A_{\xi\eta}}{\det A_\eta}. \qquad (9.5.20)$$

If $r < m$, it follows that each random variable $n_j, j = 1, \ldots, m$ is a linear combination of $\eta_{j_1}, \ldots, \eta_{j_r}$, and consequently $B_\eta = B_{\tilde{\eta}}$ where $\tilde{\eta} = (\eta_{j_1}, \ldots, \eta_{j_r})$. Therefore the perpendiculars from the $\xi_j, j = 1, \ldots, n$ onto $B_{\tilde{\eta}}$ coincide with the perpendiculars from the ξ_j onto $B_{\tilde{\eta}}$, and by (9.5.20)

$$\det A_\alpha = \frac{\det A_{\xi\tilde{\eta}}}{\det A_{\tilde{\eta}}}$$

which proves (9.5.17).

(2) Since by hypothesis $B_\eta = B_\zeta$, the perpendiculars from the ξ_j onto B_η coincide with those from the ξ_j onto B_ζ, and therefore, according to the first part of the lemma

$$\det A_\alpha = \frac{\det A_{\xi\tilde{\eta}}}{\det A_{\tilde{\eta}}} = \frac{\det A_{\xi\tilde{\zeta}}}{\det A_{\tilde{\zeta}}}.$$

In order to prove (9.5.19) it is enough to replace the random variable ξ by $\tilde{\xi}$ and divide both sides of the resulting equation by $\det A_{\tilde{\xi}}$.

COROLLARY 1. Let $\xi = (\xi_1, \ldots, \xi_n)$ *and* $\eta = (\eta_1, \ldots, \eta_m)$ *be multi-dimensional complex-valued random variables with finite variance. Then*

$$\frac{\det A_{\tilde{\xi}\tilde{\eta}}}{\det A_{\tilde{\xi}} \det A_{\tilde{\eta}}} = \prod_{j=1}^{k} (1 - \lambda_j), \ k \leqslant \min(n, m), \tag{9.5.21}$$

where λ_j *are the non-zero proper values of* $\Pi_{\eta\xi\eta}$.

For the proof, we consider the random variables $\xi' = (\xi_1', \ldots, \xi_n')$, $\eta' = (\eta_1', \ldots, \eta_m')$ occurring in the representation (9.5.1) for the pair (ξ, η), i.e., random variables such that ξ and ξ', as well as η and η', are mutually linearly subordinate, and the variables $\xi_1', \ldots, \xi_n', \eta_1', \ldots, \eta_m'$ are pairwise uncorrelated (orthogonal) except for pairs $(\xi_j', \eta_j'), j = 1, \ldots, k \leqslant \min(n, m)$. By (9.5.19)

$$\frac{\det A_{\tilde{\xi}\tilde{\eta}}}{\det A_{\tilde{\xi}} \det A_{\tilde{\eta}}} = \frac{\det A_{\tilde{\xi}'\tilde{\eta}'}}{\det A_{\tilde{\xi}'} \det A_{\tilde{\eta}'}}. \tag{9.5.22}$$

But

$$\det A_{\tilde{\xi}'} = c_1 \prod_{j=1}^{k} \rho_{\xi_j'\xi_j'}; \qquad \det A_{\tilde{\eta}'} = c_2 \prod_{j=1}^{k} \rho_{\eta_j'\eta_j'};$$

$$\det A_{\tilde{\xi}\tilde{\eta}} = c_1 c_2 \prod_{j=1}^{k} \begin{vmatrix} \rho_{\xi_j'\xi_j'} & \bar{\rho}_{\xi_j'\eta_j'} \\ \rho_{\xi_j'\eta_j'} & \rho_{\eta_j'\eta_j'} \end{vmatrix} = c_1 c_2 \prod_{j=1}^{k} (\rho_{\xi_j'\xi_j'}\rho_{\eta_j'\eta_j'} - |\rho_{\xi_j'\eta_j'}|^2)$$

and consequently

$$\frac{\det A_{\tilde{\xi}'\tilde{\eta}'}}{\det A_{\tilde{\xi}'}\,\det A_{\tilde{\eta}'}} = \frac{\prod_{j=1}^{k}(\rho_{\xi'_j\xi'_j}\rho_{\eta'_j\eta'_j} - |\rho_{\xi'_j\eta'_j}|^2)}{\prod_{j=1}^{k}\rho_{\xi'_j\xi'_j}\prod_{j=1}^{k}\rho_{\eta'_j\eta'_j}} = \prod_{j=1}^{k}\left(1 - \frac{|\rho_{\xi'_j\eta'_j}|^2}{\rho_{\xi'_j\xi'_j}\rho_{\eta'_j\eta'_j}}\right)$$

$$= \prod_{j=1}^{k}(1 - |r_{\xi'_j\eta'_j}|^2) = \prod_{j=1}^{k}(1 - \lambda_j). \tag{9.5.23}$$

Comparing (9.5.22) and (9.5.23) proves (9.5.21).

COROLLARY 2. Let $\xi = (\xi_1, \ldots, \xi_n)$, $\eta = (\eta_1, \ldots, \eta_m)$, $\zeta = (\zeta_1, \ldots, \zeta_l)$ *be multi-dimensional complex-valued random variables with finite variance, and suppose that* ζ *is linearly subordinate to* η. *Then*

$$\frac{\det A_{\tilde{\xi}\tilde{\eta}}}{\det A_{\tilde{\xi}}\,\det A_{\tilde{\eta}}} \leqslant \frac{\det A_{\tilde{\xi}\tilde{\zeta}}}{\det A_{\tilde{\xi}}\,\det A_{\tilde{\zeta}}}, \tag{9.5.24}$$

and equality holds if and only if

$$|r_{\xi'_j\eta'_j}|^2 = |r_{\xi''_j\zeta''_j}|^2,\ j = 1, \ldots, k \leqslant \min(n, m, l); \tag{9.5.25}$$

where

$$\xi' = (\xi'_1, \ldots, \xi'_n),\ \eta' = (\eta'_1, \ldots, \eta'_m)$$

and

$$\xi'' = (\xi''_1, \ldots, \xi''_n),\ \zeta' = (\zeta'_1, \ldots \zeta'_l)$$

are respectively the random variables occurring in the representation (9.5.1) for the pairs (ξ, η) *and* (ξ, ζ).

In fact, according to Lemma 9.5.1, the proper values of the operator $\Pi_{\zeta\xi\zeta}$ do not exceed the corresponding proper values of the operator $\Pi_{\eta\xi\eta}$, and hence (9.5.24) is a consequence of (9.5.21).

COROLLARY 3. Let $\xi = (\xi_1, \ldots, \xi_n)$, $\eta = (\eta_1, \ldots, \eta_m)$, $\zeta = (\zeta_1, \ldots, \zeta_l)$, $\nu = (\xi, \zeta)$ *be multi-dimensional complex-valued random variables with finite variance, and let* $\beta = (\beta_1, \ldots, \beta_m)$, $\gamma = (\gamma_1, \ldots, \gamma_l)$ *be the random variables consisting of the perpendiculars* β_j, γ_s, $j = 1, \ldots m;\ s = 1, \ldots, l$ *from* η_j, ζ_s *onto* B_ξ. *Then*

$$\frac{\det A_{\tilde{\nu}\tilde{\eta}}}{\det A_{\tilde{\nu}}\,\det A_{\tilde{\eta}}} \leqslant \frac{\det A_{\tilde{\gamma}\tilde{\beta}}}{\det A_{\tilde{\gamma}}\,\det A_{\tilde{\beta}}}, \tag{9.5.26}$$

and equality holds if and only if

$$|r_{\nu'_j \eta'_j}|^2 = |r_{\gamma'_j \beta'_j}|^2, \; j = 1, \ldots, k \leqslant \min(m, n, l), \tag{9.5.27}$$

where $\nu' = (\nu'_1, \ldots, \nu'_{n+l})$, $\eta' = (\eta'_1, \ldots, \eta'_m)$ *and* $\gamma' = (\gamma'_1, \ldots, \gamma'_l)$, $\beta' = (\beta'_1, \ldots, \beta'_m)$ *are respectively the random variables occurring in the representation (9.5.1) applied to the pairs* (ν, η) *and* (γ, β).

In fact, by Lemma 9.5.2 the proper values of the operator $\Pi_{\beta\gamma\beta}$ do not exceed the corresponding proper values of the operator $\Pi_{\eta\nu\eta} = \Pi_{\eta(\xi,\zeta)\eta}$, and so (9.5.26), (9.5.27) follow from (9.5.21).

9.6. INFORMATION STABILITY OF GAUSSIAN RANDOM VARIABLES

The following lemma, which is an assertion concerning the nature of the distribution of the information density, plays an essential role in settling the question of the information stability of gaussian random variables.

LEMMA 9.6.1. Let $\zeta = (\xi, \eta)$ *be a gaussian random variable consisting of the one-dimensional real random variables* ξ, η *whose value spaces we will denote by* X *and* Y (X, Y *the real line). Then the n-th central moment*

$$I^{(n)}_{\xi\eta} = \mathbf{E}(i(\xi, \eta) - I(\xi, \eta))^n \tag{9.6.1}$$

of the information density is given by

$$I^{(n)}_{\xi\eta} = \begin{cases} g(n) r^n_{\xi\eta} & \text{for } n = 2k, \; k = 1, 2, \ldots \\ 0 & \text{for } n = 2k - 1, \end{cases} \tag{9.6.2}$$

where

$$g(n) = \frac{\sum_{k=0}^{n} (-1)^k \cdot 1 \cdot 3 \ldots (2k-1)^* \cdot 1 \cdot 3 \ldots [2(n-k) - 1]^* C^k_n}{2^n} \tag{9.6.3}$$

In particular,

$$I^{(2)}_{\xi\eta} = Di(\xi, \eta) = \mathbf{E}(i(\xi, \eta) - I(\xi, \eta))^2 = r^2_{\xi\eta}. \tag{9.6.4}$$

Here $(2k-1)^* = \begin{cases} 2k-1 & \text{for } k \geqslant 1 \\ 1 & \text{for } k = 0 \end{cases}$, *and* $r_{\xi\eta} = \dfrac{\mathbf{E}\xi\eta}{\sqrt{\mathbf{E}\xi^2 \cdot \mathbf{E}\eta^2_n}}$ *is the* *correlation coefficient of* ξ *and* η *(we recall that* ξ, η *are assumed to have zero mean). The distribution of the information density* $i(\xi, \eta)$ *coincides with the distribution of the random variable*

$$\nu = \frac{1}{2} r_{\xi\eta} (\xi^{*2} - \eta^{*2}) - \frac{1}{2} \log(1 - r_{\xi\eta}^2), \tag{9.6.5}$$

where ξ^* *and* η^* *are independent gaussian random variables with mean zero and unit variance.*

PROOF. The information density $i_{\xi\eta}(x, y)$ is given by

$$i_{\xi\eta}(x, y) = \log \frac{p_{\xi\eta}(x, y)}{(p_\xi(x) p_\eta(y))},$$

where $p_{\xi\eta}(x, y), p_\xi(x)$ and $p_\eta(y)$ are the respective densities of the distributions $P_{\xi\eta}, P_\xi$ and P_η. If we divide ξ and η by σ_ξ and $\sigma_\eta (\sigma_\xi^2 = \mathbf{E}\xi^2, \sigma_\eta^2 = \mathbf{E}\eta^2)$, we obtain random variables $\xi'' = \xi/\sigma_\xi$ and $\eta'' = \eta/\sigma_\eta$ whose variance is one and whose correlation coefficient equals $r_{\xi\eta} = \rho_{\xi''\eta''} = \mathbf{E}\xi''\eta'' = r_{\xi''\eta''}$. Moreover, the variables ξ and ξ'', η and η'' are mutually subordinate, and consequently the information densities $i(\xi'', \eta'')$ and $i(\xi, \eta)$ coincide with probability one. Therefore, in determining the distribution of the information density we can restrict ourselves to the case of random variables ξ and η having unit variance. We will therefore assume in this proof that

$$\mathbf{E}\xi^2 = \mathbf{E}\eta^2 = 1, \text{ i.e., } p_\xi(x) = \frac{1}{\sqrt{2\pi}} e^{-\frac{x^2}{2}}, \; p_\eta(y) = \frac{1}{\sqrt{2\pi}} e^{-\frac{y^2}{2}}.$$

Obviously the information density $i_{\xi\eta}(\cdot)$ is at the same time the entropy density $h_{p_\xi \times p_\eta}(\cdot, P_{\xi\eta})$ of the distribution $P_{\xi\eta}$ with respect to the distribution $P_{\xi \times \eta}$. Let us consider the orthogonal transformation of the space $X \times Y$

$$x'' = x \cos 45^\circ + y \sin 45^\circ;$$

$$y'' = x \sin 45^\circ - y \cos 45^\circ.$$

The random variable $\zeta = (\xi, \eta)$ goes over into (ξ'', η''), where

$$\xi'' = \xi \cos 45^\circ + \eta \sin 45^\circ,$$

$$\eta'' = \xi \sin 45^\circ - \eta \cos 45^\circ$$

are random variables taking values respectively in the spaces X'', Y''. We have

$$\mathbf{E}\xi'' = \mathbf{E}\eta'' = 0;$$

$$D\xi'' = \mathbf{E}\,\xi''^2 = \mathbf{E}(\xi \cos 45^0 + \eta \sin 45^0)^2 = \frac{1}{2} + 2r_{\xi\eta}\frac{1}{2} + \frac{1}{2}$$

$$= 1 + r_{\xi\eta};\ D\eta'' = M\eta''^2 = 1 - r_{\xi\eta};$$

$$\mathbf{E}\xi''\eta'' = \mathbf{E}(\xi \cos 45^\circ + \eta \sin 45^\circ)(\xi \sin 45^\circ - \eta \cos 45^\circ)$$

$$= \mathbf{E}(\xi^2 - \eta^2) = 0,$$

i.e., ξ'' and η'' are independent random variables with mean zero, and variances $1 + r_{\xi\eta}$ and $1 - r_{\xi\eta}$ respectively. From this it follows that the densities $p_{\xi\eta}(x, y)$, and $p_\xi(x)p_\eta(y)$ of the distributions $P_{\xi\eta}$ and $P_{\xi\times\eta}$ are given by

$$p_{\xi\eta}(x, y) = p_{\xi''\eta''}(x'', y'')$$

$$= \frac{1}{\sqrt{2\pi(1 + r_{\xi\eta})}}\exp\left(-\frac{x''^2}{2(1 + r_{\xi\eta})}\right)\frac{1}{\sqrt{2\pi(1 - r_{\xi\eta})}}\exp\left(-\frac{y''^2}{2(1 - r_{\xi\eta})}\right)$$

$$= \frac{1}{2\pi\sqrt{1 - r_{\xi\eta}^2}}\exp\left(-\frac{x''^2}{2(1 + r_{\xi\eta})} - \frac{y''^2}{2(1 - r_{\xi\eta})}\right);$$

$$p_\xi(x)p_\eta(y) = \frac{1}{\sqrt{2\pi}}\exp\left(-\frac{x^2}{2}\right)\frac{1}{\sqrt{2\pi}}\exp\left(-\frac{y^2}{2}\right) = \frac{1}{2\pi}\exp\left(-\frac{x^2}{2} - \frac{y^2}{2}\right)$$

$$= \frac{1}{2\pi}\exp\left(-\frac{x''^2}{2} - \frac{y''^2}{2}\right)$$

and so

$$i_{\xi\eta}(x, y) = \log\frac{p_{\xi\eta}(x, y)}{p_\xi(x)p_\eta(y)} =$$

$$\log\left\{\frac{1}{\sqrt{1 - r_{\xi\eta}^2}}\ \frac{\exp\frac{1}{2}\left(-\frac{x''^2}{1 + r_{\xi\eta}} - \frac{y''^2}{1 - r_{\xi\eta}}\right)}{\exp\left(-\frac{x''^2}{2} - \frac{y''^2}{2}\right)}\right.$$

$$= -\frac{1}{2}\log(1 - r_{\xi\eta}^2) + \frac{r_{\xi\eta}}{2(1 - r_{\xi\eta})}x''^2 - \frac{r_{\xi\eta}}{2(1 - r_{\xi\eta})}y''^2. \qquad (9.6.6)$$

Formula (9.6.5) follows from (9.6.6), whereby $\xi^* = \xi''/\sqrt{1 + r_{\xi\eta}}$, $\eta^* = \eta''/\sqrt{1 - r_{\xi\eta}}$. Furthermore, it follows from (9.6.6) that

$$\mathbf{E}(i(\xi, \eta) - I(\xi, \eta))^n =$$

$$E\left(\tfrac{1}{2}r_{\xi\eta}(\xi^{*2} - \eta^{*2})^n = \sum_{k=0}^{n} C_n^k \frac{r_{\xi\eta}^n}{2^n} E(\xi^{*2})^k E(\eta^{*2})^{n-k} \qquad (9.6.7)$$

But as is known (see, e.g., Cramer [1])

$$\mathbf{E}(\xi^{*2})^k = 1\cdot 3 \ldots (2K-1)^*(D\xi^*)^k = 1\cdot 3 \ldots (2k-1^*)$$

and similarly

$$\mathbf{E}(\eta^{*2})^k = 1\cdot 3 \ldots (2k-1)^*.$$

Substituting these expressions for $\mathbf{E}(\xi^{*2})^k$ and $\mathbf{E}(\eta^{*2})^k$ into (9.6.7), we obtain (9.6.2), which proves the lemma.

In the more general case, where $\zeta = (\xi, \eta) = ((\xi_1, \ldots, \xi_n), (\eta_1, \ldots, \eta_m))$ is a gaussian random variable with values in $X \times Y$ (X, Y respectively n and m-dimensional Euclidean space), and $\xi_1, \ldots, \xi_n, \eta_1, \ldots, \eta_m$ are one-dimensional real random variables, there exist linear transformations of the spaces X and Y under which the random variables ξ and η go over into the form $(\xi_1', \ldots, \xi_n')$ and $(\eta_1', \ldots, \eta_m')$, where the random variables $\xi_1', \ldots, \xi_n', \eta_1', \ldots, \eta_m'$ are pairwise independent with the exception of pairs $(\xi_j', \eta_j'), j = 1, \ldots, k \leqslant \min(n, m)$. This assertion is equivalent to the following, which has been stated earlier: there exist non-singular linear transformations of the $\xi_1, \ldots, \xi_n$ and of the $\eta_1, \ldots, \eta_m$, of the form (9.2.17), such that the random variables $\xi_1', \ldots, \xi_n', \eta_1', \ldots, \eta_m'$ are pairwise independent, with the exception of pairs $(\xi_j', \eta_j'), j = 1, \ldots, k \leqslant \min(n, m)$. Obviously

$$\mathrm{Di}(\xi, \eta) = \mathrm{Di}(\xi', \eta') = \sum_{j=1}^{k} \mathrm{Di}(\xi_j', \eta_j'). \qquad (9.6.8)$$

From this result and the preceding lemma we obtain:

COROLLARY 1. Let $\zeta = (\xi, \eta) = ((\xi_1, \ldots, \xi_n), (\eta_1, \ldots, \eta_m))$ be an $n + m$-dimensional gaussian random variable; then

$$I_{\xi\eta}^{(2)} = Di(\xi, \eta) = \mathbf{E}(i(\xi, \eta) - I(\xi, \eta))^2 = \sum_{j=1}^{k} r^2_{\xi_j'\eta_j'} \qquad (9.6.9)$$

and the distribution of the information density $i(\xi, \eta)$ coincides with the distribution of the random variable

$$\nu = \frac{1}{2} \sum_{j=1}^{k} r_{\xi_j'\eta_j'} (\xi_j^{*2} - \eta_j^{*2}) + I(\xi, \eta), \qquad (9.6.10)$$

where $\xi_1^*, \ldots, \xi_k^*, \eta_1^*, \ldots, \eta_k^*$ are mutually independent gaussian random variables with mean zero and unit variance.

This corollary can be generalized to an arbitrary gaussian random variable $\zeta = (\xi, \eta)$.

As was stated at the end of Section 9.2., $I(\xi, \eta) < \infty$ if and only if the operator $\Pi_{\xi\eta\xi}$ (or $\Pi_{\eta\xi\eta}$) is completely continuous and has finite trace. Let us denote by $\lambda_1 \geqslant \lambda_2 \geqslant \ldots$ the non-zero proper values of $\Pi_{\xi\eta\xi}$ (or of $\Pi_{\eta\xi\eta}$) in non-increasing order, and by $\xi'_1, \xi'_2, \ldots, \eta'_1, \eta'_2, \ldots$. the proper vectors of $\Pi_{\xi\eta\xi}$ and $\Pi_{\eta\xi\eta}$ respectively, corresponding to these proper values. According to the results of [9], which we presented at the end of Section 9.2.

(1) The gaussian random variables $\xi' = (\xi'_1, \xi'_2, \ldots)$ and $\eta' = (\eta'_1, \eta'_2, \ldots)$ are subordinate to ξ and η respectively.

(2) The random variables $\xi'_j, \eta'_j, j = 1, 2, \ldots$ are pairwise independent with the exception of pairs (ξ'_j, η'_j).

(3)

$$\frac{(\mathbf{E}\xi'_j\eta'_j)^2}{\mathbf{E}\xi'^2_j\mathbf{E}\eta'^2_j} = r^2_{\xi'_j\eta'_j} = \lambda_j; \tag{9.6.11}$$

(4)

$$\begin{aligned} I(\xi, \eta) &= I(\xi', \eta') = \sum_j I(\xi'_j, \eta'_j) \\ &= -\frac{1}{2}\sum_j \log(1 - r^2_{\xi'_j\eta'_j}) = -\frac{1}{2}\sum_j \log(1 - \lambda_j) \end{aligned} \tag{9.6.12}$$

(5)

$$i(\xi, \eta) = i(\xi', \eta') = \sum_j i(\xi'_j, \eta'_j). \tag{9.6.13}$$

Starting with these formulas and Lemma 9.6.1, one can obtain a generalization of (9.6.9) and (9.6.10), namely:

$$\begin{aligned} I^{(2)}_{\xi\eta} &= Di(\xi, \eta) = \mathbf{E}(i(\xi, \eta) - I(\xi, \eta))^2 \\ &= \sum_j \mathbf{E}(i(\xi'_j, \eta'_j) - I(\xi'_j, \eta'_j))^2 \\ &= \sum_j r^2_{\xi'_j\eta'_j} = \sum_j \lambda_j, \end{aligned} \tag{9.6.14}$$

and the distribution of the information density $i(\xi, \eta)$ coincides with the distribution of the random variable

$$\nu = \frac{1}{2}\sum_j r_{\xi'_j\eta'_j}(\xi^{*2}_j - \eta^{*2}_j) + I(\xi, \eta), \tag{9.6.15}$$

where $\xi^*_j, \eta^*_j, j = 1, 2, \ldots$ are mutually independent gaussian random variables with mean zero and variance respectively.

Since $-\log(1 - x) > x$ for $0 < x < 1$, comparing (9.6.12) and (9.6.14) shows that

$$2I(\xi, \eta) \geqslant Di(\xi, \eta) = I^{(2)}_{\xi\eta}. \tag{9.6.16}$$

We will call the quantities

$$I\xi^{(n)}_{\eta} = \sum_j \mathbf{E}(i(\xi'_j, \eta'_j) - I(\xi'_j, \eta'_j))^n = \begin{cases} g(n)\sum_j r^n_{\xi'_j\eta'_j} & \text{for } n = 2k \\ 0 & \text{for } n = 2k - 1, \end{cases} \tag{9.6.17}$$

where $g(n)$ is defined by (9.6.3), the derived n-th central moments of the information density $i(\xi, \eta)$. If $n = 2k$, then

$$I_{\xi\eta}^{(n)} = I_{\xi\eta}^{(2k)} = g(2k) \sum_j r_{\xi_j'\eta_j'}^{2k} = g(2k) \sum_j \lambda_j^k. \tag{9.6.18}$$

With the help now of Corollary 1, we prove the following result.

COROLLARY 2. If $(\xi, \eta) = ((\xi_1, \xi_2, \ldots), (\eta_1, \eta_2, \ldots))$ is a gaussian random variable, so that by definition $\xi_1, \xi_2, \ldots, \eta_1, \eta_2, \ldots$ are one-dimensional real random variables whose value spaces we will denote by $X_1, X_2, \ldots, Y_1, Y_2, \ldots$; then if $I(\xi, \eta) = \infty$, the distribution $P_{\xi\eta}$ is singular with respect to $P_{\xi \times \eta}$.

PROOF. We put $\xi^{(n)} = (\xi_1, \ldots, \xi_n), \eta^{(n)} = (\eta_1, \ldots, \eta_n)$ and consider the linear transformations of the spaces $X^n = X_1 \times \ldots \times X_n$ and $Y^n = Y_1 \times \ldots \times Y_n$ such that $\xi^{(n)}$ and $\eta^{(n)}$ go over into $\xi^{(n)} = (\xi_1^{(n)\prime}, \ldots, \xi_n^{(n)\prime})$ and $\eta^{(n)} = (\eta_1^{(n)\prime}, \ldots, \eta_n^{(n)\prime})$, where the one-dimensional gaussian random variables $\xi_1^{(n)\prime}, \ldots, \xi_n^{(n)\prime}, \eta_1^{(n)\prime}, \ldots, \eta_n^{(n)\prime}$ are pairwise independent with the possible exception of pairs $(\xi_j^{(n)\prime}, \eta_j^{(n)\prime}), j = 1, \ldots, n$. If for some n, $I(\xi^{(n)}, \eta^{(n)}) = \infty$, then in the sum $I(\xi^{(n)}, \eta^{(n)}) = -\frac{1}{2} \sum_{j=1}^{n} \log (1 - r^2_{\xi_j^{(n)\prime}\eta_j^{(n)\prime}})$ one of the terms must equal $+\infty$, i.e., $r_{\xi_j^{(n)\prime}\eta_j^{(n)\prime}} = \pm 1$, and with probability one the random variable $\xi_j^{(n)\prime}$ coincides with the random variable $\pm \sqrt{\frac{D\xi_j^{(n)\prime}}{D\eta_j^{(n)\prime}}}\eta_j^{(n)\prime}$. This shows that the distribution $P_{\xi_j^{(n)\prime}\eta_j^{(n)\prime}}$ is singular (degenerate) with respect to the distribution $P_{\xi_j^{(n)\prime} \times \eta_j^{(n)\prime}}$, and a fortiori, that the distributions $P_{\xi^{(n)}\eta^{(n)}}, P_{\xi\eta}$ are singular with respect to $P_{\xi^{(n)} \times \eta^{(n)}}, P_{\xi \times \eta}$. It remains to consider the case when $I(\xi^{(n)}, \eta^{(n)}) < \infty$ for every n.

According to Tchebycheff's inequality,

$$P\{i(\xi^{(n)}, \eta^{(n)}) < (1 - \delta)I(\xi^{(n)}, \eta^{(n)})\} = P\{i(\xi^{(n)}, \eta^{(n)}) - I(\xi^{(n)}, \eta^{(n)}) < -\delta I(\xi^{(n)}, \eta^{(n)})\} \leqslant P\{|i(\xi^{(n)}, \eta^{(n)}) - I(\xi^{(n)}, \eta^{(n)})| > \delta I(\xi^{(n)}, \eta^{(n)})\} \leqslant \frac{Di(\xi^{(n)}, \eta^{(n)})\}}{(\delta I(\xi^{(n)}, \eta^{(n)}))^2}, \delta > 0. \tag{9.6.19}$$

In view of (9.6.16), it follows from (9.6.19) that

$$\lim_{n\to\infty} P\{i(\xi^{(n)}, \eta^{(n)}) < (1 - \delta)I(\xi^{(n)}, \eta^{(n)})\} = 0, \delta > 0 \tag{9.6.20}$$

and so, for arbitrarily large $\Gamma > 0$

$$\lim_{n\to\infty} P\{i(\xi^{(n)}, \eta^{(n)}) > \log \Gamma\} = 1. \tag{9.6.21}$$

From (9.6.21) it follows in turn, that for any $\Gamma > 0$ and $\epsilon > 0$ there exists a set

$$E_\Gamma = E = E^{(n)} \times X_{n+1} \times \dots \times Y_{n+1} \times \dots, \quad \text{where}$$

$E^{(n)} \in S_{x_1} \times \dots \times S_{x_n} \times S_{y_1} \times \dots \times S_{y_n}$, consisting of those points $(x_1, x_2, \dots, y_1, y_2, \dots)$ for which

$$\begin{gathered} i_{\xi^{(n)}\eta^{(n)}}(x_1, \dots, x_n, y_1, \dots, y_n) > \log \Gamma, \\ P_{\xi\eta}(E) = P_{\xi^{(n)}\eta^{(n)}}(E^{(n)}) > 1 - \epsilon. \end{gathered} \tag{9.6.22}$$

Inequality (9.6.22) permits us to write down the relation

$$P_{\xi\eta}(E) = P_{\xi^{(n)}\eta^{(n)}}(E^{(n)}) = \int_{E^{(n)}} \alpha_{\xi^{(n)}\eta^{(n)}}(x^{(n)}, y^{(n)}) P_{\xi^{(n)}\times\eta^{(n)}}(dx^{(n)}dy^{(n)})$$

$$= \int_{E^{(n)}} e^{i_{\xi^{(n)}\eta^{(n)}}(x^{(n)}, y^{(n)})} P_{\xi^{(n)}\times\eta^{(n)}}(dx^{(n)}dy^{(n)})$$

$$\geqslant \int_{E^{(n)}} \Gamma P_{\xi^{(n)}\times\eta^{(n)}}(dx^{(n)}dy^{(n)}) = \Gamma P_{\xi^{(n)}\times\eta^{(n)}}(E^{(n)}) = \Gamma P_{\xi\times\eta}(E).$$

Comparing the right and left sides of this relation, we see that

$$P_{\xi\times\eta}(E) \leqslant \frac{P_{\xi\eta}(E)}{\Gamma} \leqslant \frac{1}{\Gamma}. \tag{9.6.23}$$

Denoting by $E_{(l)} \in S_x \times S_y$ the set E which satisfies (9.6.22) and (9.6.23) for $\Gamma = 2^l$ and $\epsilon = 2^{-l}$, and setting

$$F = \bigcup_{k=1}^{\infty} \bigcap_{l=k}^{\infty} E_{(l)},$$

we find that

$$P_{\xi\eta}(F) = 1, \; P_{\xi\times\eta}(F) = 0,$$

which shows that $P_{\xi\eta}$ is singular with respect to $P_{\xi\times\eta}$.

It is clear, from the proof, that the corollary remains valid when one or both of the random variables ξ and η consists of only finitely many random variables ξ_j, η_j.

Remark. In the considerations of Corollary 2 we have limited somewhat the class of gaussian random variables, in that we have restricted ourselves to classes which consist of at most countably many one-dimensional random variables. This is completely inessential, and in fact, if $\zeta = (\zeta, \eta)$ is a gaussian random variable and $\xi = \{\xi_t\}, \eta = \{\eta_\tau\}, t \in N, \tau \in K,$ where N and K are arbitrary sets, then if $I(\xi, \eta) = \infty$, the measure $P_{\xi\eta}$ will be singular with respect to the measure $P_{\xi \times \eta}$. For the proof of this generalization, we note that

$$I(\xi, \eta) = \sup I((\xi_{t_1}, \ldots, \xi_{t_n}), (\eta_{\tau_1}, \ldots, \eta_{\tau_m})) \tag{9.6.24}$$

where the supremum is taken over every finite collection of the random variables ξ_t and η_τ, and it suffices now to repeat verbatim the proof of Corollary 2.

We proceed to the formulation of the main result of this section—a theorem concerning the information stability of a family of gaussian random variables.

THEOREM 9.6.1. In order that the family $\{\nu^t\} = \{(\xi^t, \eta^t)\}$, $0 < t < \infty$, *of gaussian random variables* (ξ^t, η^t) *depending upon an integer-valued or continuous parameter* t, *be information stable, it is necessary and sufficient that*

$$\lim_{t\to\infty} I(\xi^t, \eta^t) = \infty. \tag{9.6.25}$$

Moreover, if for all t *sufficiently large*

$$I(\xi^t, \eta^t) < \infty \quad \text{and} \quad \lim_{t\to\infty} Di(\xi^t, \eta^t) = \infty. \tag{9.6.26}$$

then the distribution of the information density converges to a normal distribution, i.e.,

$$\lim_{t\to\infty} P\left\{a \leqslant \frac{i(\xi^t, \eta^t) - I(\xi^t, \eta^t)}{\sqrt{Di(\xi^t, \eta^t)}} \leqslant b\right\} = \frac{1}{\sqrt{2\pi}} \int_a^b e^{-\frac{x^2}{2}} dx. \tag{9.6.27}$$

PROOF. (a) Sufficiency. Divide the range of the parameter t into two parts N_1 and N_2 such that $I(\xi^t, \eta^t) < \infty$ for $t \in N_1$, and $I(\xi^t, \eta^t) = \infty$ for $t \in N_2$. By Corollary 2 to Lemma 9.6.1, $I(\xi^t, \eta^t) = \infty$ implies that $P_{\xi^t\eta^t}$ will be singular with respect to $P_{\xi^t \times \eta^t}$, and therefore in order to establish the information stability of the family $\{(\xi^t, \eta^t)\}$ it remains to show that for any $\epsilon > 0$

$$\lim_{t\to\infty,\, t\in N_1} P\left\{\left|\frac{i(\xi^t, \eta^t)}{I(\xi^t, \eta^t)} - 1\right| \geqslant \epsilon\right\} = 0. \tag{9.6.28}$$

According to Tchebycheff's inequality and (9.6.16)

$$P\left\{\left|\frac{i(\xi^t, \eta^t)}{I(\xi^t, \eta^t)} - 1\right| \geqslant \epsilon\right\} \leqslant \frac{D\left(\frac{i(\xi^t, \eta^t)}{I(\xi^t, \eta^t)}\right)}{\epsilon^2} \leqslant \frac{2I(\xi^t, \eta^t)}{\epsilon^2 I^2(\xi^t, \eta^t)} = \frac{2}{\epsilon^2 I(\xi^t, \eta^t)}.$$

In view of (9.6.25), (9.6.28) follows.

(b) Necessity. We have to show that if (9.6.25) does not hold, then we do not have information stability. The violation of (9.6.25) implies that there exists a sequence $t_1, t_2, \ldots$ of values of t and a constant $c > 0$ such that

$$\lim_{k\to\infty} t_k = \infty \text{ and } I(\xi^t, \eta^t) < c, \; t = t_1, t_2, \ldots . \tag{9.6.29}$$

According to (9.6.13)

$$i(\xi^t, \eta^t) = \sum_j i((\xi^t)'_j, (\eta^t)'_j) = \sum_j i(\alpha^t_j, \beta^t_j); \; (\xi^t)'_j = \alpha^t_j, \; (\eta^t)'_j = \beta^t_j, \tag{9.6.30}$$

where the random variables $i(\alpha^t_j, \beta^t_j), j = 1, 2, \ldots$ are mutually independent. We will distinguish two possible cases.

(1) As $t \to \infty, t = t_1, t_2, \ldots$

$$\frac{Di(\alpha^t_j, \beta^t_j)}{I(\xi^t, \eta^t)} = \frac{r^2_{\alpha^t_j \beta^t_j}}{-\frac{1}{2}\sum_k \log(1 - r^2_{\alpha^t_k \beta^t_k})} \to 0, \tag{9.6.31}$$

uniformly in j.

(2) There exists a subsequence $s_1, s_2, \ldots$ of the sequence $t_1, t_2, \ldots$ such that for some j depending upon $s_1, s_2, \ldots$

$$\frac{Di(\alpha^s_j, \beta^s_j)}{I(\xi^s, \eta^s)} > \delta_1 > 0, \quad s = s_1, s_2, \ldots, \tag{9.6.32}$$

where $i(\alpha^s_j, \beta^s_j)$ is a term in the decomposition (9.6.30) of $i(\xi^s, \eta^s)$. Let us consider these cases.

(1) First of all we show that the distribution of the random variable

$$\frac{i(\xi^t, \eta^t)}{\sqrt{I(\xi^t, \eta^t)}} = \sum_j \frac{i(\alpha^t_j, \beta^t_j)}{\sqrt{I(\xi^t, \eta^t)}}$$

converges, as $t \to \infty, t = t_1, t_2, \ldots$ to a normal distribution with variance equal to two. From (9.6.29) and (9.6.31) it follows that for $t \to \infty, t = t_1, t_2, \ldots, r^2_{\alpha_j{}^t \beta_j{}^t} \to 0$, and therefore

$$\frac{Di(\alpha^t_j, \beta^t_j)}{I(\alpha^t_j, \beta^t_j)} = \frac{r^2_{\alpha^t_j \beta^t_i}}{-\frac{1}{2}\log(1 - r^2_{\alpha^t_j \beta^t_j})} \to 2 \tag{9.6.33}$$

uniformly in j. From (9.6.33) it follows that as $t \to \infty, t = t_1, t_2, \ldots$

$$\frac{Di(\xi^t, \eta^t)}{I(\xi^t, \eta^t)} = \frac{\sum_j r^2_{\alpha_j^t \beta_j^t}}{-\frac{1}{2}\sum_j \log(1 - r^2_{\alpha_j^t \beta_j^t})} \to 2 \tag{9.6.34}$$

In order to prove the convergence of the distribution of the random variables $\frac{i(\xi^t, \eta^t)}{\sqrt{I(\xi^t, \eta^t)}}, t = t_1, t_2 \ldots,$ to a normal distribution, it suffices to verify that Liapunov's theorem is applicable to the sequence of series*

$$\gamma_1^t, \gamma_2^t, \ldots, \tag{9.6.35}$$

where

$$\gamma_j^t = \frac{i(\alpha_j^t, \beta_j^t)}{\sqrt{I(\xi^t, \eta^t)}}.$$

The fourth central moment of the random variable γ_j^t can be derived from formula (9.6.2)

$$\mathbf{E}(\gamma_j^t - \mathbf{E}\gamma_j^t)^4 = \frac{9r^4_{\alpha_j^t \beta_j^t}}{I^2(\xi^t, \eta^t)}$$

and consequently

$$\frac{\sum_j \mathbf{E}(\gamma_j^t - \mathbf{E}\gamma_j^t)^4}{(\sum_j \mathbf{E}(\gamma_j^t - \mathbf{E}\gamma_j^t)^2)^2} = \frac{9\sum_j r^4_{\alpha_j^t \beta_j^t}}{I^2(\xi^t, \eta^t)} \Bigg/ \left(\frac{\sum_j r^2_{\alpha_j^t \beta_j^t}}{I(\xi^t, \eta^t)}\right)^2. \tag{9.6.36}$$

Let us estimate the numerator and denominator of the right side. Comparing (9.6.34) with the denominator, we see that the latter converges to 4 as $t \to \infty, t = t_1, t_2, \ldots.$ We estimate the numerator

---

* Here there may be an infinite number of terms in the series. Usually Liapunov's theorem is formulated for series consisting of a finite number of terms; however, it is obvious that its proof does not depend upon this restriction.

by means of the inequality

$$\frac{9\sum_j r^4_{\alpha_j^t\beta_j^t}}{I^2(\xi^t,\eta^t)} \leqslant \frac{9\max_j r^2_{\alpha_j^t\beta_j^t}\sum_k r^2_{\alpha_k^t\beta_k^t}}{I^2(\xi^t,\eta^t)}$$

$$= \frac{9\max_j r^2_{\alpha_j^t\beta_j^t}}{I^2(\xi^t,\eta^t)}\cdot\frac{\sum_j r^2_{\alpha_j^t\beta_j^t}}{I^2(\xi^t,\eta^t)} = \frac{9\max_j r^2_{\alpha_j^t\beta_j^t}}{I^2(\xi^t,\eta^t)}\cdot\frac{\mathrm{Di}(\xi^t,\eta^t)}{I(\xi^t,\eta^t)}. \tag{9.6.36.1}$$

Since, as $t \to \infty, t = t_1, t_2, \ldots$, according to (9.6.31) $\dfrac{9\max_j r^2_{\alpha_j^t\beta_j^t}}{I(\xi^t,\eta^t)} \to 0$,

the last term in (9.6.36.1) converges to zero. Thus, as $t \to \infty$, $t = t_1, t_2, \ldots$, the numerator of the right side of (9.6.36) converges to zero and the denominator converges to 4, hence the whole term converges to zero and we have verified the condition which permits us to apply Liapunov's theorem. Hence the distribution of the sequence of random variables $\dfrac{i(\xi^t,\eta^t)}{\sqrt{I(\xi^t,\eta^t)}}$, $t = t_1, t_2, \ldots$, converges to a normal distribution with variance equal to 2, and so the distribution of the sequence $\dfrac{i(\xi^t,\eta^t)}{I(\xi^t,\eta^t)}$, $t = t_1, t_2, \ldots$ converges to a normal distribution with variance equal to $\dfrac{2}{I(\xi^t,\eta^t)} > \dfrac{2}{c}$, so that the sequence of random variables cannot converge to one with probability one, which rules out the information stability of the family of pairs (ξ^t,η^t).

(2) Relabeling, if necessary, the random variables $\nu_j^s = (\alpha_j^s, \beta_j^s) = ((\xi^s)'_j, (\eta^s)'_j)$, $j = 1, 2\ldots$, we may assume that (9.6.32) holds for $j = 1$, i.e.,

$$\frac{r^2_{\alpha_1^s\beta_1^s}}{I(\xi^s,\eta^s)} = \frac{\mathrm{Di}(\alpha_1^s,\beta_1^s)}{I(\xi^s,\eta^s)} > \delta_1 > 0. \tag{9.6.37}$$

According to (9.6.5), the random variable $i(\alpha_j^s,\beta_j^s) - I(\alpha_j^s,\beta_j^s)$ can be represented as the difference of two independent random variables, each of which obeys a one-dimensional χ^2 distribution with mean $|r_{\alpha_j^s\beta_j^s}|$. Therefore $\dfrac{i(\alpha_1^s,\beta_1^s) - I(\alpha_1^s,\beta_t^s)}{\sqrt{I(\xi^s,\eta^s)}}$ can be represented as the difference of two independent random variables ν_s and υ_s, each of which is governed by a one-dimensional χ^2 distribution with mean

$$\frac{\left|r_{\alpha_1^s\beta_1^s}\right|}{\sqrt{I(\xi^s,\eta^s)}} = c_s.$$

The quantity c_s can be estimated with the help of (9.6.37): $c_s > \sqrt{\delta_1}$, and in view of the properties of the χ^2 distribution, the quantity $T(\delta, \nu_s)$, defined by the equation

$$P\{\nu_s \geqslant T(\delta, \nu_s)\} = P\{\upsilon_s \geqslant T(\delta, \nu_s)\} = \delta , \tag{9.6.38}$$

is a monotonic decreasing function of δ, and as $\delta \to 0, T(\delta, \nu_s) \to \infty$ uniformly in $s = s_1, s_2, \ldots$. Moreover, from the monotonicity of the density of the χ^2 distribution it follows that

$$P\{\nu_s \leqslant T\left(\frac{\delta}{2}, \nu_s\right) - T(\delta, \nu_s)\} \geqslant \frac{\delta}{2}. \tag{9.6.39}$$

From (9.6.38) and (9.6.39), and using the independence of ν_s and υ_s, we obtain

$$P\left\{\frac{i(\alpha_1^s, \beta_1^s) - I(\alpha_1^s, \beta_1^s)}{\sqrt{I(\xi^s, \eta^s)}} \geqslant T(\delta, \nu_s)\right\} = P\{(\nu_s - \upsilon_s) \geqslant T(\delta, \nu_s)\}$$

$$\geqslant P\{\nu_s \geqslant T\left(\frac{\delta}{2}, \nu_s\right), \upsilon_s \leqslant T\left(\frac{\delta}{2}, \nu_s\right) - T(\delta, \nu_s)\} \geqslant \frac{\delta}{2}\cdot\frac{\delta}{2} = \frac{\delta^2}{4}. \tag{9.6.40}$$

Setting

$$\alpha^s = (\alpha_2^s, \alpha_3^s, \ldots), \beta^s = (\beta_2^s, \beta_3^s, \ldots)$$

we have

$$i(\xi^s, \eta^s) = \sum_j i(\alpha_j^s, \beta_j^s) = i(\alpha_1^s, \beta_1^s) + i(\alpha^s, \beta^s);$$

$$I(\xi^s, \eta^s) = I(\alpha_1^s, \beta_1^s) + I(\alpha^s, \beta^s), \tag{9.6.41}$$

and, according to (9.6.16)

$$Di(\alpha^s, \beta^s) \leqslant 2I(\alpha^s, \beta^s) \leqslant 2I(\xi^s, \eta^s).$$

Combining this inequality with Tchebycheff's inequality, we find that

$$P\left\{\left|\frac{i(\alpha^s, \beta^s) - I(\alpha^s, \beta^s)}{\sqrt{I(\xi^s, \eta^s)}}\right| \leqslant \tau\right\} \geqslant 1 - \frac{\frac{Di(\alpha^s, \beta^s)}{\sqrt{I(\xi^s, \eta^s)}^2}}{\tau^2}$$

$$\geqslant 1 - \frac{2I(\xi^s, \eta^s)}{\tau^2 I(\xi^s, \eta^s)} = 1 - \frac{2}{\tau^2}. \tag{9.6.42}$$

Using inequality (9.6.29), equation (9.6.41) and the independence of the random variables $i(\alpha_1^s, \beta_1^s)$ and $i(\alpha^s, \beta^s)$, we can write down the following chain of relations:

$$P\left\{\left|\frac{i(\xi^s, \eta^s)}{I(\xi^s, \eta^s)} - 1\right| \geqslant \epsilon\right\} = P\left\{\left|\frac{i(\xi^s, \eta^s) - I(\xi^s, \eta^s)}{I(\xi^s, \eta^s)}\right| \geqslant \epsilon\right\}$$

$$= P\left\{\left|\frac{i(\xi^s, \eta^s) - I(\xi^s, \eta^s)}{\sqrt{I(\xi^s, \eta^s)}}\right| \geqslant \epsilon \sqrt{I(\xi^s, \eta^s)}\right\}$$

$$\geqslant P\left\{\left|\frac{i(\xi^s, \eta^s) - I(\xi^s, \eta^s)}{\sqrt{I(\xi^s, \eta^s)}}\right| \geqslant \epsilon \sqrt{c}\right\}$$

$$= P\left\{\left|\frac{i(\alpha_1^s, \beta_1^s) + i(\alpha^s, \beta^s) - I(\alpha_1^s, \beta_1^s) - I(\alpha^s, \beta^s)}{\sqrt{I(\xi^s, \eta^s)}}\right| \geqslant \epsilon \sqrt{c}\right\}$$

$$\geqslant P\left\{\left|\frac{i(\alpha_1^s, \beta_1^s) - I(\alpha_1^s, \beta_1^s)}{\sqrt{I(\xi^s, \eta^s)}}\right| - \left|\frac{i(\alpha^s, \beta^s) - I(\alpha^s, \beta^s)}{\sqrt{I(\xi^s, \eta^s)}}\right| \geqslant \epsilon \sqrt{c}\right\}$$

$$\geqslant P\left\{\left|\frac{i(\alpha_1^s, \beta_1^s) - I(\alpha_1^s, \beta_1^s)}{\sqrt{I(\xi^s, \eta^s)}}\right| \geqslant \tau + \epsilon \sqrt{c}, \left|\frac{i(\alpha^s, \beta^s) - I(\alpha^s, \beta^s)}{\sqrt{I(\xi^s, \eta^s)}}\right| \leqslant \tau\right\}$$

$$= P\left\{\left|\frac{i(\alpha_1^s, \beta_1^s) - I(\alpha_1^s, \beta_1^s)}{\sqrt{I(\xi^s, \eta^s)}}\right| \geqslant \tau + \epsilon \sqrt{c}\right\} P\left\{\left|\frac{i(\alpha^s, \beta^s) - I(\alpha^s, \beta^s)}{\sqrt{I(\xi^s, \eta^s)}}\right| \leqslant \tau\right\}.$$

Choosing τ and δ so that $1 - \frac{2}{\tau^2} \geqslant \frac{1}{2}$, $T(\delta, \nu_s) \geqslant \tau + \epsilon\sqrt{c}$, $s = s_1, s_2, \ldots$ (this can always be done, since $T(\delta, \nu_s) \to \infty$ uniformly in $s = s_1, s_2, \ldots$ as $\delta \to +0$), and applying the estimates (9.6.40) and (9.6.42) to the last expression in the chain,we obtain

$$P\left\{\left|\frac{i(\xi^s, \eta^s)}{I(\xi^s, \eta^s)} - 1\right| \geqslant \epsilon\right\} \geqslant \frac{\delta^2}{4} \cdot \frac{1}{2} = \frac{\delta^2}{8}, \qquad (9.6.43)$$

where δ is a positive number not depending upon $s = s_1, s_2, \ldots$. This inequality at once rules out the information stability of the family $\{(\xi^t, \eta^t)\}$. Thus the necessity of condition (9.6.25) is proved, and it remains to prove (9.6.27).

Let us consider the family of series of independent random variables

$$i(\alpha_1^t, \beta_1^t), i(\alpha_2^t, \beta_2^t), \ldots, \qquad (9.6.44)$$

where $i(\alpha_j^t, \beta_j^t) = i((\xi^t)'_j, (\eta^t)'_j)$ is the random variable occurring in the expansion (9.6.30). According to formula (9.6.2)

$$d(t) = \frac{\sum_j \mathbf{E}(i(\alpha_j^t, \beta_j^t) - I(\alpha_j^t, \beta_j^t))^4}{(\mathbf{D}i(\xi^t, \eta^t))^2} = \frac{9 \sum_j r^4_{\alpha_j^t \beta_j^t}}{\left(\sum_j r^2_{\alpha_j^t \beta_j^t}\right)^2}.$$

Since $r^2_{\alpha_j^t\beta_j^t} \leqslant 1$ and $\lim_{t\to\infty} Di(\xi^t, \eta^t) = \lim_{t\to\infty} \sum_j r^2_{\alpha_j^t\beta_j^t} = \infty$, then $\lim_{t\to\infty} d(t) = 0$, i.e., the family of sequences (9.6.44) satisfies the conditions of Liapunov's theorem, which completes the proof of the theorem.

Remark. From the proof of the theorem it follows that a necessary and sufficient condition for the convergence of the distribution of the information density to a normal distribution is the following: For any family of pairs (ζ_t, ν_t) of one-dimensional random variables $\zeta_t \in B_{\xi^t}$, $\nu_t \in B_{\eta^t}$

$$\lim_{t\to\infty} \frac{Di(\zeta_t, \nu_t)}{Di(\xi^t, \eta^t)} = 0. \tag{9.6.45}$$

The following theorem is obtained as a consequence of the theorem just proved.

THEOREM 9.6.2. Let $\nu^t = (\xi^t, \eta^t, \zeta^t)$, $0 \leqslant t < \infty$ be a gaussian random variable depending upon a positive integer or real-valued parameter t. In order that the family of pairs (η^t, ζ^t) be information stable relative to the family $\{\xi^t\}$, it is necessary and sufficient that the condition

$$\lim_{t\to\infty} \mathbf{E}I(\eta^t, \zeta^t/\xi^t) = \infty \tag{9.6.46}$$

be fulfilled. Moreover, if

$$\mathbf{E}I(\eta^t, \zeta^t/\xi^t) < \infty \quad \textit{and} \quad \lim_{t\to\infty} D\bar{i}(\eta^t, \zeta^t/\xi^t) = \infty, \tag{9.6.47}$$

then the distribution of the conditional information density $\bar{i}(\eta^t, \zeta^t|\xi^t)$ converges to a normal distribution, i.e.

$$\lim_{t\to\infty} P\left\{a \leqslant \frac{\bar{i}(\eta^t, \zeta^t/\xi^t) - \mathbf{E}I(\eta^t, \zeta^t/\xi^t)}{\sqrt{D\bar{i}(\eta^t, \zeta^t/\xi^t)}} \leqslant b\right\} = \frac{1}{\sqrt{2\pi}} \int_a^b e^{\frac{-x^2}{2}} dx. \tag{9.6.48}$$

In order to relate the proof of this theorem to the results of the preceding theorem, it suffices to remark that, as was shown in Section 9.3, the conditional information density $\bar{i}(\eta^t, \zeta^t/\xi^t)$ coincides with the information density $i(\hat{\eta}^t, \hat{\zeta}^t)$ of a certain pair of gaussian random variables $\hat{\eta}^t, \hat{\zeta}^t$.

As a final remark, we point out that the theorems which have been proved also enable us to decide on the information stability of random variables which, while not themselves gaussian, are functions of gaussian random variables.

9.7. ENTROPY STABILITY OF GAUSSIAN RANDOM VARIABLES

An extremely important result for the study of the entropy stability of a family of pairs of distributions of gaussian random variables (or simply, of a family of pairs of gaussian random variables) is the following,* which was obtained by Hajek [11]. If $\xi = \{\xi_T\}$ and $\eta = \{\eta_T\}$ are arbitrary gaussian random variables, then the following two alternatives are the only ones possible: either the distributions P_ξ and P_η are mutually singular, or the entropies $H_\eta(\xi) = \mathbf{E}h_\eta(\xi)$ and $H_\xi(\eta) = \mathbf{E}h_\xi(\eta)$ are both finite. It follows from this, in particular, that the entropy density $h_\eta(\xi)$ exists only when $H_\eta(\xi) < \infty$. Thus, once we have determined the value of the entropy, in order to investigate the entropy stability we need focus our attention only on those pairs of gaussian random variables whose entropy is finite.

We now write down a formula which permits us to judge the nature of the distribution of the entropy density of one gaussian random variable with respect to another, and to obtain the higher moments of the entropy density.

Let ξ and η be one-dimensional random variables. Then the distribution of the entropy density $h_\eta(\xi)$ coincides with the distribution of the random variable

$$\frac{1}{2}\left[\frac{(\xi - m_\eta)^2}{\sigma_n^2} - \frac{(\xi - m_\xi)^2}{\sigma_\xi^2}\right] - \frac{1}{2}\log\frac{\sigma_\xi^2}{\sigma_\eta^2}, \tag{9.7.1}$$

where

$$m_\xi = \mathbf{E}\xi,\ m_\eta = \mathbf{E}\eta,\ \sigma_\xi^2 = D\xi = \mathbf{E}(\xi - \mathbf{E}\xi)^2,\ \sigma_\eta^2 = D\eta = \mathbf{E}(\eta - \mathbf{E}\eta)^2.$$

Simple calculations easily lead to the second central moment (i.e., variance) of the entropy density:

$$Dh_\eta(\xi) = \mathbf{E}(h_\eta(\xi) - H_\eta(\xi))^2 = \frac{1}{2}\left[\left(\frac{\sigma_\xi^2}{\sigma_\eta^2} - 1\right)^2 + \frac{2(m_\xi - m_\eta)^2\sigma_\xi^2}{\sigma_\eta^4}\right]. \tag{9.7.2}$$

In the case where $m_\xi = m_\eta$, a very compact formula obtains for any central moment of the entropy density $h_\eta(\xi)$:

$$\mathbf{E}(h_\eta(\xi) - H_\eta(\xi))^n = \ni(n)\left(\frac{\sigma_\xi^2}{\sigma_\eta^2} - 1\right)^n, \tag{9.7.3}$$

---

* See also Yu. A. Rozanov, "On the density of one Gaussian measure with respect to another," Theory of Probability and Its Applications, Vol. VII, No. 1, 82-87 (1962). Tr.

where

$$\vartheta(n) = \frac{1}{2^n} \sum_{j=0}^{n} (-1)^j C_n^j \cdot 1 \cdot 3 \ldots (2j-1)^*. \tag{9.7.4}$$

If $\xi = (\xi_1, \ldots, \xi_n)$ and $\eta = (\eta_1, \ldots, \eta_n)$ are n-dimensional non-singular gaussian random variables, then the distribution of the entropy density $h_\eta(\xi)$ coincides with the distribution of the random variable

$$-\frac{1}{2}\sum_{j,k=1}^{n} \rho_{\xi_j\xi_k}^{(-1)}(\xi_j - m_{\xi_j})(\xi_k - m_{\xi_k}) + \frac{1}{2}\sum_{j,k=1}^{n} \rho_{\eta_j\eta_k}^{(-1)}(\xi_j - m_{\eta_j})(\xi_k - m_{\eta_k})$$
$$-\frac{1}{2}\log\frac{\det A_\xi}{\det A_\eta}, \tag{9.7.5}$$

where

$$m_{\xi_j} = \mathbf{E}\xi_j,\ m_{\eta_j} = \mathbf{E}\eta_j,\ \rho_{\xi_j\xi_k} = \mathbf{E}(\xi_j - m_{\xi_j})(\xi_k - m_{\xi_k}),$$
$$\rho_{\eta_j\eta_k} = \mathbf{E}(\eta_j - m_{\eta_j})(\eta_k - m_{\eta_k})$$

and $\rho_{\xi_j\xi_k}^{(-1)}, \rho_{\eta_j\eta_k}^{(-1)}$ are the elements of the inverses of the correlation matrices $A_\xi = \|\rho_{\xi_j\xi_k}\|$, $A_\eta = \|\rho_{\eta_j\eta_k}\|$. When $h_\eta(\xi)$ is written in this form, the expression for the variance $\mathbf{D}h_\eta(\xi)$ is extremely cumbersome. Without stopping to write down this expression, we will go on to the case of arbitrary gaussian random variables.

Let $\xi = \{\xi_\tau\}$ and $\eta = \{\eta_\tau\}$, $\tau \in N$ be gaussian random variables for which $H_\eta(\xi) < \infty$, and let $\xi_1', \xi_2', \ldots \in B_\xi$, $\eta_1', \eta_2', \ldots \in B_\eta$ be sequences of independent one-dimensional gaussian random variables which satisfy conditions 2 and 3, which appear in Section 9.4. Then with probability one

$$h_\eta(\xi) = h_{\eta'}(\xi') = \sum_j h_{\eta_j'}(\xi_j') \tag{9.7.6}$$

and the distribution of the entropy density coincides with the distribution of the sum of independent random variables $h_{\eta_j'}(\xi_j')$, $j = 1, 2, \ldots,$ i.e., with the distribution of the random variable

$$h_\eta(\xi) = \frac{1}{2}\sum_j \left\{\left[\frac{(\xi_j' - m_{\eta_j}')^2}{\sigma_{\eta_j}^{2\prime}} - \frac{(\xi_j' - m_{\xi_j}')^2}{\sigma_{\xi_j}^{2\prime}}\right] - \log\frac{\sigma_{\xi_j}^{2\prime}}{\sigma_{\eta_j}^{2\prime}}\right\} \tag{9.7.7}$$

and consequently

$$\mathbf{D}h_\eta(\xi) = \frac{1}{2}\sum_j \left[\left(\frac{\sigma_{\xi_j}^{2\prime}}{\sigma_{\eta_j}^{2\prime}} - 1\right)^2 + \frac{2(m_{\xi_j}' - m_{\eta_j}')^2\sigma_{\xi_j}^{2\prime}}{\sigma_{\eta_j}^{4\prime}}\right]. \tag{9.7.8}$$

From formulas (9.7.1) and (9.7.8) it can be seen that for any $r > 0$ there are gaussian random variables for which

$$H_\eta(\xi) \geqslant rDh_\eta(\xi). \tag{9.7.9}$$

It follows that we cannot obtain a simple criterion for entropy stability, as we did for information stability. Nevertheless, one can still give a general criterion for entropy stability, namely:

In order that the family $\{(P_{\xi^t}, P_{\eta^t})\}$ *of pairs of distributions of gaussian random variables* ξ^t, η^t *be entropy stable, it is necessary and sufficient that it be decomposable into two subfamilies, such that for the first of these* $H_{\eta^t}(\xi^t) = H_{P_{\eta^t}}(P_{\xi^t}) = \infty$, *and for the second*

$$\lim_{t\to\infty} \frac{Dh_{\eta^t}(\xi^t)}{(H_{\eta^t}(\xi^t))^2} = 0. \tag{9.7.10}$$

Furthermore, if (9.7.10) is satisfied for some family and $Eh_{\eta^t}(\xi^t) \to \infty$ *then as* $t \to \infty$ *the distribution of the entropy density* $h_{\eta^t}(\xi^t)$ *converges to a normal distribution, i.e.,*

$$\lim_{t\to\infty} P\left\{a \leqslant \frac{h_{\eta^t}(\xi^t) - H_{\eta^t}(\xi^t)}{\sqrt{(Dh_{\eta^t}(\xi^t)}} \leqslant b\right\} = \frac{1}{\sqrt{2\pi}} \int_a^b e^{\frac{-x^2}{2}} dx. \tag{9.7.11}$$

TRANSLATOR'S REMARKS TO CHAPTER 9

A proof of the opening remarks of Section 9.5 is sufficiently simple to warrant inclusion here, as the references are not too easily come by. In essence, the assertion to be proved is the following:

Let M and N be two linear manifolds in a finite-dimensional Hilbert space H which together span H; i.e., H is the smallest linear manifold containing both M and N. Then we can find an orthonormal basis $\varphi_1, \ldots, \varphi_m$ of M, an orthonormal basis $\psi_1, \ldots, \psi_n$ of N and an integer k, $0 \leqslant k \leqslant \min(m, n)$ such that $(\varphi_i, \psi_j) = 0$ for all pairs (i, j) except $(1,1), (2,2), \ldots, (k,k)$.

The proof is as follows. Let P_1, P_2 be the projections onto M and N respectively; then $E_1 = P_1P_2P_1$ and $E_2 = P_2P_1P_2$ are clearly self-adjoint operators, and therefore have complete sets of eigenvectors. Evidently the ranges of E_1 and E_2 lie in M and N respectively. Let φ be an eigenvector of E_1 with eigenvalue $\lambda \neq 0$. Then $\varphi \in M$, and $\lambda\varphi = E_1\varphi = P_1P_2P_1\varphi = P_1P_2\varphi$, so $P_2\varphi \neq 0$, while

$$E_2(P_2\varphi) = P_2P_1P_2P_2\varphi = P_2(P_1P_2\varphi) = P_2(\lambda\varphi) = \lambda(P_2\varphi).$$

From this we see that E_1 and E_2 have the same set of non-zero eigenvalues, with the same multiplicities for them. Now let $\varphi_1, \ldots, \varphi_k$ be a maximal orthonormal set of eigenvectors of E_1 whose corresponding eigenvalues $\lambda_1, \ldots, \lambda_k$ are different from zero. Then

$$\lambda_i(P_2\varphi_i, P_2\varphi_j) = \lambda_i(\varphi_i, P_2\varphi_j) = (P_1P_2\varphi_i, P_2\varphi_j) = (P_1P_2\varphi_i, P_1P_2\varphi_j)$$
$$= \lambda_i\lambda_j(\varphi_i, \varphi_j) = 0 \quad \text{if} \quad i \neq j.$$

Thus $\{P_2\varphi_1, \ldots, P_2\varphi_k\}$ is an orthogonal set of elements in N. Hence $(\varphi_i, P_2\varphi_j) = (P_2\varphi_i, P_2\varphi_j) = 0$ if $i \neq j$. Finally, if $\varphi \epsilon M$ and $E_1\varphi = 0$, then

$$(P_2\varphi, P_2\varphi) = (P_2\varphi, \varphi) = (P_2\varphi, P_1\varphi) = (P_1P_2\varphi, \varphi) = (E_1\varphi, \varphi) = 0,$$

or $P_2\varphi = 0$. This shows that any eigenvector of E_1, lying in M and with eigenvalue zero, is orthogonal to N, with a similar statement holding for zero eigenvectors of E_2 lying in N. Now let $\varphi_1, \ldots, \varphi_m$ be a complete orthonormal basis of M, consisting of eigenvectors of E_1 with the corresponding eigenvalues $\lambda_1, \ldots, \lambda_k \neq 0$ and $\lambda_{k+1} = \ldots = \lambda_m = 0$. Let $\psi_1, \ldots, \psi_k$ be $P_2\varphi_1, \ldots, P_2\varphi_k$ normalized, and let $\psi_{k+1}, \ldots, \psi_n$ be an orthonormal set of eigenvectors of E_2 which lie in N and whose eigenvalues are zero, such that $\psi_1, \ldots, \psi_n$ is a basis for N. Then the preceding results show at once that $(\varphi_i, \psi_j) = 0$ for all pairs (i, j) except $(1, 1), \ldots, (k, k)$.

Chapter 10 Calculation of the information rate of gaussian random processes

In this chapter we derive formulas which enable us to express the information rate of one-dimensional or multi-dimensional stationary gaussian processes in terms of the derivatives of the spectral function or joint spectral function (spectral matrix) of the process. A number of results, of independent interest, are given concerning the theory of stationary random processes. The corresponding generalizations of the formulas derived here to the case of the entropy rate of one gaussian process with respect to another are given. Certain of the results of this chapter have been published in the author's notes [28, 32].

10.1. RANDOM PROCESSES, STATIONARY IN THE WIDE SENSE

In considering the information rate of a stationary gaussian process, it will be worthwhile first to become familiar with certain results of the correlation theory of complex or real-valued random processes. Some of our results are apparently new. These we will state as lemmas or theorems. From the point of view of correlation theory, any information which we may desire concerning a complex-valued process $\xi = \{\xi(t)\} = \{(\xi_1(t), \ldots, \xi_n(t))\}$ is determined by a knowledge of the matrix $\|\rho_{\xi_j\xi_k}(t, \tau)\|_{j,k=1,\ldots,n}$ of correlation functions

$$\rho_{\xi_j\xi_k}(t, \tau) = \mathbf{E}(\xi_j(t + \tau) - \mathbf{E}\xi_j(t + \tau))\overline{(\xi_k(t) - \mathbf{E}\xi_k(t))}.$$

As stated earlier, we will assume everywhere, with the exception of those sections dealing with entropy, that $\mathbf{E}\xi_j(t) = 0$, and consequently

$$\rho_{\xi_j\xi_k}(t, \tau) = \mathbf{E}\xi_j(t + \tau)\overline{\xi_k(t)}.$$

If ξ is a gaussian random variable, then, as is known, the correlation matrix $\|\rho_{\xi_j \xi_k}(t, \tau)\|$ completely defines the distribution of the process (or variable) ξ, and therefore the theory of gaussian random processes is intimately related with correlation theory.

If $\xi = \{\xi(t)\} = \{(\xi_1(t), \ldots, \xi_n(t))\}$ is a stationary complex-valued n-dimensional process with finite variance (i.e., the random variables $\xi_j(t)$, $j = 1, \ldots, n$, $-\infty < t < \infty$ have finite variance), then the functions

$$\rho_{\xi_j \xi_k}(t, \tau) = \rho_{\xi_j \xi_k}(\tau) \tag{10.1.1}$$

are defined and do not depend upon t. The converse, of course, need not be true; but since in correlation theory we deal only with $\rho_{\xi_j \xi_k}(t, \tau)$, then from the point of view of correlation theory it is natural to call those processes stationary, for which (10.1.1) holds. More precisely, a complex-valued random process ξ with finite variance, for which $\rho_{\xi_j \xi_k}(t, \tau)$ does not depend upon t, is generally called **stationary in the wide sense**.

A generalized n-dimensional complex-valued random process $\xi = \{\xi(\varphi)\} = \{(\xi_1(\varphi_1), \ldots, \xi_n(\varphi_n))\}$, $\varphi = (\varphi_1, \ldots, \varphi_n)$ with finite variance is called stationary in the wide sense if $\rho_{\xi_j \xi_k}(\varphi_j, \varphi_k) = \mathbf{E}\xi_j(\varphi_j)\xi_k(\varphi_k)$, $\varphi_j \epsilon \Phi_j$ does not change value if the functions $\varphi_j(t)$, $\varphi_k(t)$ are replaced by the functions $\varphi_j(t + h)$, $\varphi_k(t + h)$. We remark that when ξ is a generalized or non-generalized gaussian random process, the notions of stationary and stationary in the wide sense coincide.

Two random processes $\xi = (\xi_1, \ldots, \xi_n) = \{(\xi_1(\cdot), \ldots, \xi_n(\cdot))\}$ and $\eta = (\eta_1, \ldots, \eta_m) = \{(\eta_1(\cdot), \ldots, \eta_m(\cdot))\}$ which are stationary in the wide sense are said to be **stationarily correlated in the wide sense** if (ξ, η) is stationary in the wide sense. Let $\xi = \{(\xi_1(\cdot), \ldots, \xi_n(\cdot))\}$ be an n-dimensional complex-valued wide-sense stationary process. We consider the correspondence (mapping) $U_\tau \xi_j(t) = \xi_j(t + \tau)$, $j = 1, \ldots, n$, $-\infty < t, \tau < \infty$ when ξ is a non-generalized process stationary in the wide sense, and $U_\tau \xi_j(\varphi_j(t)) = \xi_j(\varphi_j(t + \tau))$, $j = 1, \ldots, n$, $\varphi_j \epsilon \Phi_j$ when ξ is a generalized process stationary in the wide sense. This mapping can be extended to a unitary mapping U_τ of the space B_ξ onto itself, such that if $\alpha_1, \alpha_2 \epsilon B_\xi$ and $\alpha_1(t) = U_t \alpha_1$, $\alpha_2(t) = U_t \alpha_2$, then

(a) $U_t(U_\tau \alpha_1) = U_{t+\tau}\alpha_1$;

(b) $U_t(c_1\alpha_1 + c_2\alpha_2) = c_1 U_t \alpha_1 + c_2 U_t \alpha_2$;

(c) $\mathbf{E}\alpha_1\alpha_2 = \mathbf{E}\alpha_1(t)\overline{\alpha_2(t)}$,

i.e., **the operators** U_t **are unitary and form a group.** If ξ is a discrete-parameter process, then t takes on integer values, and if ξ is a continuous-parameter process or a generalized random process, then t takes all real values, in which case the group U_t

is called **one-parameter**. In what follows, when we speak of the group U_t we will mean the group of unitary operators corresponding to the wide-sense stationary process ξ.

Let us proceed to the discussion of those facts which we need from the spectral theory of wide-sense stationary random processes. The **correlation functions** $\rho_{\xi_j \xi_k}(t)$, $j, k = 1, \ldots, n$, $-\infty < t < \infty$ of a wide-sense stationary process $\xi = \{(\xi_1(t), \ldots, \xi_n(t))\}$ can always be represented as follows:

$$\rho_{\xi_j \xi_k}(t) = \int e^{it\lambda} dF_{\xi_j \xi_k}(\lambda), \tag{10.1.2}$$

and the process itself can be represented as

$$\xi_j(t) = \int e^{it\lambda} dz_{\xi_j}(\lambda), \tag{10.1.3}$$

where the limits of integration are $-\pi$ and π if ξ is a discrete-parameter process, and $-\infty$ and $+\infty$ if ξ is a continuous-parameter process. The functions $F_{\xi_j \xi_j}(\lambda)$, $j = 1, \ldots, n$, which are non-negative and non-decreasing functions of bounded variation, are called the spectral functions of the processes $\xi_j = \{\xi_j(t)\}$. The functions $F_{\xi_j \xi_k}(\lambda)$, $j \neq k$, $j, k = 1, \ldots, n$, which are functions of bounded variation, are called the **joint spectral functions** of the processes $\xi_j = \{\xi_j(t)\}$ and $\xi_k = \{\xi_k(t)\}$. When the functions $F_{\xi_j \xi_k}(\lambda)$, $j, k = 1, \ldots, n$ are absolutely continuous, their derivatives $f_{\xi_j \xi_k}(\lambda) = F'_{\xi_j \xi_k}(\lambda)$ are called the **spectral** and **joint spectral densities** respectively.

$z_{\xi_j} = \{z_{\xi_j}(\lambda)\}$ is a one-dimensional complex-valued random process for which

$$E(z_{\xi_j}(\lambda' + \Delta\lambda') - z_{\xi_j}(\lambda'))(\overline{z_{\xi_k}(\lambda'' + \Delta\lambda'')} - \overline{z_{\xi_k}(\lambda'')}) = 0 \tag{10.1.4}$$

if the intervals $(\lambda', \lambda' + \Delta\lambda')$ and $(\lambda'', \lambda'' + \Delta\lambda'')$ are non-intersecting

$$\begin{aligned} &E(z_{\xi_j}(\lambda + \Delta\lambda) - z_{\xi_j}(\lambda))(\overline{z_{\xi_k}(\lambda + \Delta\lambda)} - \overline{z_{\xi_k}(\lambda)}) \\ &= F_{\xi_j \xi_k}(\lambda + \Delta\lambda) - F_{\xi_j \xi_k}(\lambda), \end{aligned} \tag{10.1.5}$$

and $z_{\xi_j}(\lambda) \epsilon B_{\xi_j}$, $B_{\xi_j} = B_{z_j}$, i.e., the processes $z_{\xi_j} = \{z_{\xi_j}(\lambda)\}$ and $\xi_j = \{\xi_j(t)\}$ are mutually linearly subordinate. If the process ξ is real valued, then

$$\begin{aligned} &F_{\xi_j \xi_k}(\lambda + \Delta\lambda + 0) - F_{\xi_j \xi_k}(\lambda - 0) \\ &= \overline{F_{\xi_j \xi_k}(-\lambda + 0)} - \overline{F_{\xi_j \xi_k}(-\lambda - \Delta\lambda - 0)}; \end{aligned} \tag{10.1.6}$$

$$f_{\xi_j\xi_k}(\lambda) = \overline{f_{\xi_j\xi_k}(-\lambda)},\ f_{\xi_j\xi_k}(\lambda) = F'_{\xi_j\xi_k}(\lambda) \tag{10.1.7}$$

and with probability one

$$z_{\xi_j}(\lambda + \Delta\lambda + 0) - z_{\xi_j}(\lambda - 0) = \overline{z_{\xi_j}(-\lambda + 0)} - \overline{z_{\xi_j}(-\lambda - \Delta\lambda - 0)}. \tag{10.1.8}$$

Equations (10.1.2) and (10.1.3) may then be rewritten in the form

$$\rho_{\xi_j\xi_k}(t) = \int \cos t\lambda dG_{\xi_j\xi_k}(\lambda) + \int \sin t\lambda dS_{\xi_j\xi_k}(\lambda); \tag{10.1.9}$$

$$\xi_j(t) = \int \cos t\lambda du_{\xi_j}(\lambda) + \int \sin t\lambda dv_{\xi_j}(\lambda), \tag{10.1.10}$$

where the limits of integration are $0, \pi$ when ξ is a discrete-parameter process, and $0, \infty$ when ξ is a continuous-parameter process, and $G_{\xi_j\xi_k}(\lambda)$, $S_{\xi_j\xi_k}(\lambda)$ are real functions of bounded variation, for which

$$2(F_{\xi_j\xi_k}(\lambda + \Delta\lambda) - F_{\xi_j\xi_k}(\lambda)) = G_{\xi_j\xi_k}(\lambda + \Delta\lambda) - G_{\xi_j\xi_k}(\lambda) - i(S_{\xi_j\xi_k}(\lambda + \Delta\lambda) - S_{\xi_j\xi_k}(\lambda)); \tag{10.1.11}$$

$$2f_{\xi_j\xi_k}(\lambda) = g_{\xi_j\xi_k}(\lambda) - is_{\xi_j\xi_k}(\lambda);$$
$$g_{\xi_j\xi_k}(\lambda) = G'_{\xi_j\xi_k}(\lambda)\ s_{\xi_j\xi_k}(\lambda) = S'_{\xi_j\xi_k}(\lambda), \tag{10.1.12}$$

i.e.,

$$g_{\xi_j\xi_k}(\lambda) = 2\mathrm{Re}f_{\xi_j\xi_k}(\lambda),\ s_{\xi_j\xi_k}(\lambda) = -2\mathrm{Im}f_{\xi_j\xi_k}(\lambda), \tag{10.1.13}$$

and finally, $u_{\xi j} = \{u_{\xi j}(\lambda)\}$, $v_{\xi j} = \{v_{\xi j}(\lambda)\}$ are real valued one-dimensional processes with independent increments, for which

$$2(z_{\xi_j}(\lambda + \Delta\lambda) - z_{\xi_j}(\lambda)) = (u_{\xi_j}(\lambda + \Delta\lambda) - u_{\xi_j}(\lambda)) - i(v_{\xi_j}(\lambda + \Delta\lambda) - v_{\xi_j}(\lambda)) \tag{10.1.14}$$

and $u_{\xi j}(\lambda), v_{\xi j}(\lambda) \epsilon B_{\xi j}$, i.e., the processes $u_{\xi j}$ and $v_{\xi j}$ are linearly subordinate to ξ_j.

Gelfand [7, 7a] and Ito [14] have extended formulas (10.1.2) and (10.1.3) to generalized wide-sense stationary processes $\xi = \{\xi_1(\varphi_1), \ldots, \xi_n(\varphi_n))\}$, namely:

$$\rho_{\xi_j\xi_k}(\varphi_j, \varphi_k) = \mathbf{E}\xi_j(\varphi_j)\overline{\xi_k(\varphi_k)} = \int_{-\infty}^{\infty} \psi_j(\lambda)\overline{\psi_k(\lambda)}dF_{\xi_j\xi_k}(\lambda); \tag{10.1.15}$$

$$\xi_j(\varphi_j) = \int_{-\infty}^{\infty} \psi_j(\lambda)dz_{\xi_j}(\lambda), \tag{10.1.16}$$

where $\psi_j(\lambda) = \int_{-\infty}^{\infty} e^{it\lambda}\varphi_j(t)dt$ is the Fourier transform of the function $\varphi_j(\lambda)$, and $F_{\xi_j\xi_k}(\lambda)$ is a function such that for some positive integer m

$$\int_{-\infty}^{\infty} \frac{|dF_{\xi_j\xi_k}(\lambda)|}{(1 + \lambda^2)^m} < \infty. \tag{10.1.17}$$

The function $F_{\xi_j\xi_j}(\lambda)$ is called the spectral function of the process ξ_j; the function $F_{\xi_j\xi_k}(\lambda)$ is called the joint spectral function of the processes ξ_j and ξ_k. Finally, z_{ξ_j} is a one-dimensional complex-valued random process which satisfies the relations (10.1.4) and (10.1.5). When the generalized random process ξ is real valued, formulas (10.1.15) and (10.1.16) go over into

$$\rho_{\xi_j\xi_k}(\varphi_j, \varphi_k) = \int_0^{\infty} [c_j(\lambda)c_k(\lambda) + d_j(\lambda)d_k(\lambda)]dG_{\xi_j\xi_k}(\lambda)$$
$$+ \int_0^{\infty} [c_j(\lambda)d_k(\lambda) - c_k(\lambda)d_j(\lambda)]dS_{\xi_j\xi_k}(\lambda); \tag{10.1.18}$$

$$\xi_j(\varphi) = \int_0^{\infty} c_j(\lambda)du_{\xi_j}(\lambda) + \int_0^{\infty} d_j(\lambda)dv_{\xi_j}(\lambda), \tag{10.1.19}$$

where

$$c_j(\lambda) = \int_{-\infty}^{\infty} \cos t\lambda\varphi_j(t)dt, \; d_j(\lambda) = \int_{-\infty}^{\infty} \sin t\lambda\varphi_j(t)dt,$$

the functions $F_{\xi_j\xi_k}(\lambda)$, $G_{\xi_j\xi_k}(\lambda)$, $S_{\xi_j\xi_k}(\lambda)$ and processes $u_{\xi_j}(\lambda)$, $v_{\xi_j}(\lambda)$ satisfy the conditions (10.1.11), (10.1.14) respectively.

If ξ is a gaussian process (generalized or not), the processes $u_{\xi_j} = \{u_{\xi_j}(\lambda)\}$ and $v_{\xi_j} = \{v_{\xi_j}(\lambda)\}$, $j = 1, \ldots, n$ will also be gaussian.

Let us consider, along with the generalized wide sense stationary process $\xi = \{\xi(\varphi)\} = \{\xi_1(\varphi_1), \ldots, \xi_n(\varphi_n)\}$, the ordinary wide sense stationary process $\eta = \{\eta_1(t), \ldots, \eta_n(t)\}$:

$$\eta_j(t) = \int_{-\infty}^{\infty} e^{it\lambda}\frac{1}{(1 + i\lambda)^m}dz_{\xi_j}(\lambda). \tag{10.1.20}$$

Obviously the random variable $\xi_j(\varphi_j)$ is a linear combination of the random processes $\eta_j^{\varphi_j}(t) = \int_{-\infty}^{\infty} \varphi_j(\tau)\eta_j(t + \tau)d\tau$ and their derivatives at the point $t = 0$. From this it follows that the process ξ is finitely subordinate to the process η. Moreover, as was shown in [30], the process η is regularly subordinate to the process ξ. If the process ξ is stationary or gaussian, then the process η will be correspondingly stationary or gaussian.

LEMMA 10.1.1. If $\xi = \{\xi(\cdot)\}$ and $\eta = \{\eta(\cdot)\}$ are one-dimensional complex-valued random processes, stationary and stationarily correlated in the wide sense, and η is linearly subordinate to ξ, then the random processes $z_\xi(\lambda)$ and $z_\eta(\lambda)$, and the spectral functions $F_{\xi\xi}(\lambda)$, $F_{\eta\eta}(\lambda)$, $F_{\xi\eta}(\lambda)$ are connected by the relations

$$z_\eta(\lambda) = \int^\lambda \pi(\lambda')dz_\xi(\lambda'); \tag{10.1.21}$$

$$F_{\eta\eta}(\lambda) = \int^\lambda |\pi(\lambda')|^2 dF_{\xi\xi}(\lambda'),\ F_{\eta\xi}(\lambda) = \int^\lambda \pi(\lambda')dF_{\xi\xi}(\lambda'), \tag{10.1.22}$$

where the lower limits of the integrals are $-\Pi, -\infty$ or 0 according as ξ and η are discrete-parameter, continuous-parameter or generalized random processes, and $\Pi(\lambda)$ is a complex measurable function (Borel measurable) whose absolute square is summable with respect to the measure $dF_{\xi\xi}(\lambda)$.

The proof of this lemma is carried out in [17] (actually, only for discrete-parameter processes). From formula (10.1.22) it follows that

$$f_{\eta\eta}(\lambda) = |\pi(\lambda)|^2 f_{\xi\xi}(\lambda),\ f_{\eta\xi}(\lambda) = \pi(\lambda)f_{\xi\xi}(\lambda) \tag{10.1.23}$$

where

$$f_{\eta\eta}(\lambda) = F'_{\eta\eta}(\lambda),\ f_{\xi\xi}(\lambda) = F'_{\xi\xi}(\lambda),\ f_{\eta\xi}(\lambda) = F'_{\eta\xi}(\lambda).$$

Moreover, as a corollary of the lemma we can easily obtain the following result. Let $\xi = \{\xi(\cdot)\}$, $\eta_j = \{\eta_j(\cdot)\}$, $j = 1, \ldots, n$ be one-dimensional complex-valued processes, stationary and stationarily correlated in the wide sense, and suppose that the η_j are linearly subordinate to ξ. Then

$$f_{\eta_j\eta_k}(\lambda) = \frac{f_{\eta_j\xi}(\lambda)}{f_{\xi\xi}(\lambda)}\,\frac{f_{\eta_k\xi}(\lambda)}{f_{\xi\xi}(\lambda)}\, f_{\xi\xi}(\lambda). \tag{10.1.24}$$

We proceed now to the formulation of a result which extends to stationary random processes a property of multi-dimensional random variables which was considered in Section 9.5.

LEMMA 10.1.2. Let $\xi = \{\xi(\cdot)\} = \{(\xi_1(\cdot), \ldots, \xi_n(\cdot))\}$ and $\eta = \eta(\cdot) = \{(\eta_1(\cdot), \ldots, \eta_m(\cdot))\} = \{(\xi_{n+1}(\cdot), \ldots, \xi_{n+m}(\cdot))\}$ be respectively n and m-dimensional complex-valued processes, stationary and stationarily correlated in the weak sense. Then there exist n and m-dimensional complex-valued processes.

$$\xi' = \{(\xi'_1(\cdot), \ldots, \xi'_n(\cdot))\} \text{ and } \eta' = \{(\eta'_1(\cdot), \ldots, \eta'_m(\cdot))\},$$

such that:

(1) The processes ξ *and* ξ', η *and* η' *are mutually linearly subordinate.*

(2) The spaces $B_{\xi'_1}, \ldots, B_{\xi'_n}, B_{\eta'_1}, \ldots, B_{\eta'_m}$, *are pairwise orthogonal with the exception of pairs* $(B_{\xi'_j}, B_{\eta'_j}), j = 1, \ldots, k \leqslant \min(n, m)$, *i.e.,*

$$\rho_{\xi'_j\eta'_l}(\cdot) = \mathbf{E}\xi'_j(\cdot)\overline{\eta'_l(\cdot)} = 0,$$

$$\rho_{\xi'_j\xi'_l}(\cdot) = \rho_{\eta'_j\eta'_l}(\cdot) = 0, \; j \neq l \text{ or } j > k; \tag{10.1.25}$$

(3)

$$|r_{\xi'_j\eta'_j}(\lambda)|^2 \geqslant |r_{\xi'_j\eta'_l}(\lambda)|^2 \text{ for } j \leqslant l, \tag{10.1.26}$$

where

$$|r_{\xi'_j\eta'_j}(\lambda)|^2 = \frac{|f_{\xi'_j\eta'_j}(\lambda)|^2}{f_{\xi'_j\xi'_j}(\lambda)f_{\eta'_j\eta'_j}(\lambda)}.$$

The proof of this lemma, which is based upon the fact that the matrix $\|\Delta F_{\xi_j\xi_k}(\lambda)\|$ j, k = 1, . . . , m + n is positive definite and can therefore be considered as the correlation matrix of certain random variables, is almost obvious. However, in order to justify certain passages to the limit, one has to use Lemma 9.5.3 of Section 9.5.

We replace Lemmas 9.5.1 and 9.5.2 of Section 9.5 by the following:

LEMMA 10.1.3. Let $\xi = (\xi_1, \ldots, \xi_n)$, $\eta = (\eta_1, \ldots, \eta_m)$, $\zeta = (\zeta_1, \ldots, \zeta_l))$ *be processes stationary and stationarily correlated in the wide sense, and suppose that* ζ *is linearly subordinate to* η, *and let* $\xi' = (\xi'_1, \ldots, \xi'_n)$ *and* $\eta' = (\eta'_1, \ldots, \eta'_m)$, $\xi'' = (\xi''_1, \ldots, \xi''_n)$ *and* $\zeta' = (\zeta'_1, \ldots, \zeta'_l)$ *be the random processes corresponding to the pairs* (ξ, η), (ξ, ζ) *according to Lemma 10.1.2. Then*

$$|r_{\xi'_j\eta'_j}(\lambda)|^2 \geqslant |r_{\xi'_j\zeta'_j}(\lambda)|^2,$$

$$j = 1, \ldots, k \leqslant \min(l, m, n), \; r_{\xi''_j\zeta'_j}(\lambda) = 0, j > k. \tag{10.1.27}$$

LEMMA 10.1.4. Let $\xi = \{(\xi_1(\cdot), \ldots, \xi_n(\cdot))\}$, $\eta = \{(\eta_1(\cdot), \ldots, \eta_m(\cdot))\}$, $\zeta = \{(\zeta_1(\cdot), \ldots, \zeta_l(\cdot))\}$, $\nu = (\xi, \zeta)$ *be stationary and stationarily correlated (in the wide sense) random processes, and let* $\beta = \{(\beta_1(\cdot), \ldots, \beta_m(\cdot))\}$ *and* $\gamma = \{(\gamma_1(\cdot), \ldots, \gamma_l(\cdot))\}$ *be the stationary and stationarily correlated (in the wide sense) processes consisting of the perpendiculars* $\beta_j(\cdot)$ *and* $\gamma_k(\cdot)$, $j = 1, \ldots, m$; $k = 1, \ldots, l$ *from* $\eta_j(\cdot)$ *and* $\zeta_k(\cdot)$ *onto* B_ξ. *Then if* $\nu' = (\nu'_1, \ldots, \nu'_{n+l})$ *and* $\eta' = (\eta'_1, \ldots, \eta'_m)$, $\gamma' = (\gamma'_1, \ldots, \gamma'_l)$ *and* $\beta' = (\beta'_1, \ldots, \beta'_m)$ *are the random processes from Lemma 10.1.2 corresponding to the pairs* $(\nu, \eta) = ((\xi, \zeta), \eta)$ *and* (γ, β),

$$|r_{\gamma'_j\eta'_j}(\lambda)|^2 \geqslant |r_{\gamma'_j\beta'_j}(\lambda)|^2. \tag{10.1.28}$$

To Lemma 9.5.4 corresponds the following:

LEMMA 10.1.5. Let $\xi = \{\xi(\cdot)\} = \{(\xi_1(\cdot), \ldots, \xi_n(\cdot))\}$, $\eta = \{(\eta_1(\cdot), \ldots, \eta_m(\cdot))\} = \{(\xi_{n+1}(\cdot), \ldots, \xi_{n+m}(\cdot))\}$, *and* $\zeta = \{\zeta(\cdot)\} = \{(\zeta_1(\cdot), \ldots, \zeta_l(\cdot))\}$ *be stationary and stationarily correlated (in the wide sense) n, m and l-dimensional complex-valued random processes, and suppose that* η *and* ζ *are mutually linearly subordinate. Let* $\alpha = \{\alpha(.)\} = \{(\alpha_1(.), \ldots, \alpha_n(.))\}$ *be the n-dimensional wide-sense stationary complex-valued process consisting of the perpendiculars* $\alpha_j(\cdot), j = 1, \ldots, n$ *from* $\xi_j(\cdot)$ *onto* B_η, *and let the spectral and joint spectral functions of the process* (ξ, η, ζ) *be absolutely continuous. Then*

(1) The value of the determinant $\det A_\alpha(\lambda) = \det \|f_{\alpha_j\alpha_k}(\lambda)\|_{j,k=1,\ldots,n}$ *of the matrix* $A_\alpha(\lambda) = \|f_{\alpha_j\alpha_k}(\lambda)\|_{j,k=1,\ldots,m}$ *of the spectral and joint spectral densities of the process* α *is given by*

$$\det A_\alpha = \frac{\det A_{\xi\tilde{\eta}}(\lambda)}{\det A_{\tilde{\eta}}(\lambda)}, \tag{10.1.29}$$

where $\det A_{\tilde{\eta}}(\lambda) = \det \|f_{\eta_j\eta_k}(\lambda)\|_{j,k=s_1,\ldots,s_r}$ *is a non-vanishing principal minor of highest order r of the determinant* $\det A_{\xi\eta}(\lambda) = \det \|f_{\xi_j\xi_k}(\lambda)\|_{j,k=1,\ldots,n+m}$, *and* $\det A_{\xi\tilde{\eta}}(\lambda)$ *is the principal minor of order* $n + r$ *of the determinant* $\det A_{\xi\eta}(\lambda) = \det \|f_{\xi_j\xi_k}(\lambda)\|_{j,k=1,\ldots,n+m}$, *which contains* $\det A_{\tilde{\eta}}(\lambda)$ *and* $\det A_\xi(\lambda)$. *In the case where every principal minor of* $\det A_\eta(\lambda)$ *vanishes, we put*

$$\det A_{\tilde{\eta}}(\lambda) = 1, \ \det A_{\xi\tilde{\eta}}(\lambda) = \det A_\xi(\lambda). \tag{10.1.30}$$

In the particular case where $n = m = 1$, *formula (10.1.29) takes the form*

$$f_{\alpha\alpha}(\lambda) = \begin{cases} \dfrac{f_{\xi\xi}(\lambda)f_{\eta\eta}(\lambda) - |f_{\xi\eta}(\lambda)|^2}{f_{\eta\eta}(\lambda)} & \text{for } f_{\eta\eta}(\lambda) \neq 0; \\ f_{\xi\xi}(\lambda) & \text{for } f_{\eta\eta}(\lambda) = 0. \end{cases} \tag{10.1.31}$$

(2)

$$\frac{\det A_{\xi\tilde{\eta}}(\lambda)}{\det A_{\tilde{\xi}}(\lambda) A \det_{\tilde{\eta}}(\lambda)} = \frac{\det A_{\xi\tilde{\zeta}}(\lambda)}{\det A_{\tilde{\xi}}(\lambda) \det A_{\tilde{\zeta}}(\lambda)}. \tag{10.1.32}$$

Remark 1. Each wide-sense stationary one-dimensional complex-valued process ξ_j, $j = 1, \ldots, n$ can be decomposed into an orthogonal sum of random processes $\xi_j^I = \{\xi_j^I(\cdot)\}$ and $\xi_j^{II} = \{\xi_j^{II}(\cdot)\}$, $\xi_j(\cdot) = \xi_j^I(\cdot) + \xi_j^{II}(\cdot)$ such that $E\xi_j^I(\cdot)\xi_k^{II}(\cdot) = 0$, $j, k = 1, \ldots, n$, and the spectral and joint spectral functions $F_{\xi_j^I\xi_k^I}(\lambda)$, $F_{\xi_j^{II}\xi_k^{II}}(\lambda)$ are absolutely continuous and singular according to whether they concern the I-processes or the II-processes, i.e.,

$$f_{\xi_j\xi_k}(\lambda) = F'_{\xi_j\xi_k}(\lambda) = F'_{\xi_j^I\xi_k^I}(\lambda), \ F_{\xi_j^{II}\xi_k^{II}}(\lambda) = F_{\xi_j\xi_k}(\lambda) - F_{\xi_j^I\xi_k^I}(\lambda).$$

From this it is obvious that the proof of the lemma is still meaningful even when the spectral functions are not absolutely continuous. All that is required is to replace the words "spectral density and joint spectral density" by "the derivatives of the spectral and joint spectral functions," and to assume that the processes ξ^{I} and η^{I} are mutually linearly subordinate.

Remark 2. From part 1 of the lemma one can obtain a somewhat stronger result than was asserted in part 2, namely: if ξ, η, ζ are processes, stationary and stationarily correlated in the wide sense, and if the perpendiculars from $\xi_j(\cdot)$ onto B_η and B_ζ coincide, then (10.1.32) holds.

From Lemmas 10.1.2 and 10.1.5 follows:

COROLLARY 1. Let $\xi = (\xi_1, \ldots, \xi_n), \eta = (\eta_1, \ldots, \eta_m)$ be stationary and stationarily correlated (in the weak sense) complex-valued process, and let $\xi' = (\xi'_1, \ldots, \xi'_n), \eta' = (\eta'_1, \ldots, \eta'_m)$ be the processes from Lemma 10.1.2, corresponding to the pair (ξ, η). Then

$$\frac{\det A_{\bar\xi\bar\eta}(\lambda)}{\det A_{\bar\xi}(\lambda) \det A_{\bar\eta}(\lambda)} = \prod_{j=1}^{k} (1 - |r_{\xi'_j\eta'_j}(\lambda)|^2). \tag{10.1.33}$$

At the same time, from this corollary and also from Lemmas 10.1.3 and 10.1.4 can be obtained the following corollaries:

COROLLARY 2. Let $\xi = (\xi_1, \ldots, \xi_n), \eta = (\eta_1, \ldots, \eta_m)$, $\zeta = (\zeta_1, \ldots, \zeta_l)$ be stationary and stationarily correlated (in the wide sense) processes, and suppose that ζ is linearly subordinate to η. Then

$$\frac{\det A_{\bar\xi\bar\eta}(\lambda)}{\det A_{\bar\xi}(\lambda) \det A_{\bar\eta}(\lambda)} \leqslant \frac{\det A_{\bar\xi\bar\zeta}(\lambda)}{\det A_{\bar\xi}(\lambda) \det A_{\bar\zeta}(\lambda)}, \tag{10.1.34}$$

and equality holds if and only if equality holds in (10.1.27).

COROLLARY 3. Under the conditions of Lemma 10.1.4

$$\frac{\det A_{\bar\nu\bar\eta}(\lambda)}{\det A_{\bar\nu}(\lambda) \det A_{\bar\eta}(\lambda)} \leqslant \frac{\det A_{\bar\gamma\bar\beta}(\lambda)}{\det A_{\bar\gamma}(\lambda) \det A_{\bar\beta}(\lambda)}, \tag{10.1.35}$$

in which equality holds if and only if equality holds in (10.1.28).

In correlation theory the concepts of regularity and singularity go over in a natural way into the concepts of regularity and singularity in the wide sense. Let $\xi = \{(\xi_1(\cdot), \ldots, \xi_n(\cdot))\}$ be an n-dimensional complex-valued wide-sense stationary process. The process ξ is called regular in the wide sense if

$$\bigcap_{-\infty<T<\infty} B_{\xi T} = 0, \tag{10.1.36}$$

i.e., if there exists no one-dimensional random variable with finite variance which belongs simultaneously to all of the spaces $B_{\xi T}$, $-\infty < T < \infty$, and singular in the wide sense, if

$$\bigcap_{-\infty<T<\infty} B_{\xi_T} = B_\xi, \text{ i.e. } B_{\xi_T} = B_\xi, \ -\infty < T < \infty. \tag{10.1.37}$$

A complex-valued stationary process with finite variance which is regular is also regular in the wide sense, and one which is singular in the wide sense is also singular. For gaussian random processes the ordinary and wide-sense versions of regularity and singularity coincide respectively.

Every n-dimensional complex-valued wide-sense stationary process $\xi = \{(\xi_1(\cdot), \ldots, \xi_n(\cdot))\}$ can be represented in the form of an orthogonal sum

$$\xi_j(\cdot) = \alpha_j(\cdot) + \beta_j(\cdot), \tag{10.1.38}$$

where $\alpha = \{(\alpha_1(\cdot), \ldots, \alpha_n(\cdot))\}$ and $\beta = \{(\beta_1(\cdot), \ldots, \beta_n(\cdot))\}$ are stationary and stationarily correlated in the wide sense, and are respectively wide-sense regular and singular, for which

$$\mathbf{E}\alpha_j(\cdot)\overline{\beta_k(\cdot)} = 0, \ j, k = 1, \ldots, n, \tag{10.1.39}$$

and if $\xi_j(\cdot) \epsilon B_{\xi T}$, then $\alpha_j(\cdot), \beta_j(\cdot) \epsilon B_{\xi T}$

The random variables $\alpha_j(\cdot)$ and $\beta_j(\cdot)$ are defined uniquely by (10.1.38), up to sets of probability zero. At the same time, the stationary and regular (in the wide sense) process $\alpha = \{(\alpha_1(\cdot), \ldots, \alpha_n(\cdot))\}$ can be represented in the form

$$\alpha_j(t) = \sum_{l=1}^{p} \sum_{k=0}^{\infty} a_{jl}(k)\omega_l(t-k), \ p \leqslant n, \tag{10.1.40}$$

if α is a discrete-parameter process; $a_{jl}(k)$; $j = 1, \ldots, n$; $l = 1, \ldots, p$; $k = 1, 2, \ldots$ are complex numbers, and $\omega_l(t)$, $l = 1, \ldots, p$, $t = \ldots, -2, -1, 0, 1, 2, \ldots$ are uncorrelated and normalized random variables, i.e.,

$$\mathbf{E}\omega_l(t)\overline{\omega_r(\tau)} = \begin{cases} 1 \text{ for } l = r, t = \tau \\ 0 \text{ for } l \neq r, \text{ or } t \neq \tau, \end{cases} \quad \omega_l(t) \epsilon B_{\xi T}, \ t \leqslant T$$

while, if α is a continuous-parameter process,

$$\alpha_j(t) = \sum_{l=1}^{p} \int_0^{\infty} a_{jl}(\tau) d_\tau \omega_l(t - \tau), \tag{10.1.41}$$

where $a_{jl}(\tau), j = 1, \ldots, n;\ l = 1, \ldots, p$ are measurable complex-valued functions which have summable modulus square, and the $\omega_{l}(t)$ are random processes with uncorrelated increments, for which $E\omega_l(t)\overline{\omega_r(\tau)} = 0,\ l \neq r; E\omega_l(t)\overline{\omega_l(t)} = |t|\ ;\ \omega_l(t) - \omega_l(t-\tau) \epsilon B_\xi^T$ for $t, t-\tau \leqslant T$. Finally, if α is a generalized random process,

$$\alpha_j(\varphi_j) = \sum_{l=1}^{p} \int_0^{\infty} a_{jl}^{\varphi}(\tau) d_\tau \omega_l(t - \tau);\ \alpha_j(\varphi_j) \epsilon B_\xi^{t}, \tag{10.1.42}$$

where $a_{jl}^{\varphi}(\tau),\ j = 1, \ldots, n;\ l = 1, \ldots, p;\ 0 \leqslant \tau < \infty$ are measurable complex-valued functions with square, summable modulus and the $\omega_l(t)$ are random processes satisfying the same conditions as in the representation (10.1.41).

The number p appearing in all these representations is called the **rank of regularity** of the process ξ, and always $p \leqslant n$.

If ξ is real valued or gaussian, then in the representations (10.1.38), (10.1.40)–(10.1.42) the processes α, β, ω can also be taken as real valued or gaussian. If ξ is stationary, then α and β can also be taken as stationary.

Let us state a criterion for wide-sense regularity of rank n (so-called "full rank"); cf. [22].

In order that the wide-sense stationary random process $\xi = \{(\xi_1(\cdot), \ldots, \xi_n(\cdot))\}$ **be regular** in the wide sense, and **of rank** n, it is necessary and sufficient that the following set of conditions be fulfilled:

(1) *The spectral and joint spectral functions* $F_{\xi_j \xi_k}(\lambda)$, j,k = 1, ..., n *are absolutely continuous.*

(2) $$\int_{-\pi}^{\pi} |\log \det A_\xi(\lambda)| d\lambda < \infty \tag{10.1.43}$$

if ξ *is a discrete-parameter process, and*

$$\int_{-\infty}^{\infty} \frac{|\log \det A_\xi(\lambda)|}{1 + \lambda^2} d\lambda < \infty \tag{10.1.44}$$

if ξ *is a continuous-parameter or generalized process, where* $\det A_\xi(\lambda)$ *is the determinant of the matrix* $A_\xi(\lambda) = \| f_{\xi_j \xi_k}(\lambda) \|_{j,k=1,\ldots,n}$ *of densities* $f_{\xi_j \xi_k}(\lambda) = F'_{\xi_j \xi_k}(\lambda)$.

From this criterion for wide-sense regularity and the facts stated in Remark 1 above, it follows quickly that, in order that a wide-sense stationary process have rank of regularity n, it is necessary and sufficient that (10.1.43) hold in the discrete-parameter case, and that (10.1.44) hold in the continuous-parameter or generalized process case. By $A_\xi(\lambda)$ must be understood the matrix of derivatives $f_{\xi_j \xi_k}(\lambda)$, $j, k = 1, \ldots, n$ of the spectral and joint spectral functions of the process. We remark that in this case $A_\xi(\lambda)$ is the matrix of the spectral and joint spectral densities of the process $\alpha = \{(\alpha_1(\cdot), \ldots, \alpha_n(\cdot))\}$, while the spectral and joint spectral functions of the process $\beta = \{(\beta_1(\cdot), \ldots, \beta_n(\cdot))\}$ will be singular.

Let now $\xi = \{(\xi_1(t), \ldots, \xi_n(t))\}$ be a wide-sense stationary discrete-parameter process. We denote by $\hat{\xi}_j(t)$ the perpendicular from $\xi_j(t)$ onto the Hilbert space $B_{\xi^{t-1}}$, determined (as usual) by the random variables $\xi^{t-1} = \{(\xi_1(\tau), \ldots, \xi_n(\tau))\}$, $-\infty < \tau \leqslant t-1$. The random variables $\hat{\xi}_j(t)$ form a wide-sense stationary process $\hat{\xi} = (\hat{\xi}_1(t), \ldots, \hat{\xi}_n(t))$ and each $\hat{\xi}_j(t)$ is a linear combination of the random variables $\omega_l(t)$, $l = 1, \ldots, p$ occurring in the representation (10.1.40), and conversely, $\omega_l(t)$ is a linear combination of the $\hat{\xi}_j(t)$, $j = 1, \ldots, n$. From this it follows that the process ξ has rank of regularity p if and only if, among the $\hat{\xi}_j(t)$, $j = 1, \ldots, n$, there are exactly p which are linearly independent.

For the solution of various questions of the theory of information, it is important to establish not only the regularity, but also the complete regularity of a random process. It is interesting to note that a stationary regular process will be completely regular if

$$I(\xi^0, \xi_T) < \infty \tag{10.1.46}$$

for some $T > 0$. In a number of cases it turns out to be easy to establish the complete regularity of a given gaussian random process. For example, a multi-dimensional gaussian stationary Markov process is completely regular. From this it follows that any one-dimensional gaussian stationary process $\xi_1 = \{\xi_1(\cdot)\}$ with rational spectral density, i.e., with spectral density of the form

$$f_{\xi\xi}(\lambda) = -\frac{|b_0(b_1 - \lambda)\ldots(b_s - \lambda)|^2}{|a_0(a_1 - \lambda)\ldots(a_m - \lambda)|^2}, \tag{10.1.47}$$

is completely regular, since it is known that such a process can always be taken as a component of some multi-dimensional stationary gaussian Markov process $\xi = \{(\xi_1(\cdot), \ldots, \xi_n(\cdot))\}$. This assertion can also be extended to multi-dimensional stationary gaussian processes having rational spectral and joint spectral densities of the form

$$f_{\xi_j\xi_k}(\lambda) = \frac{N_{\xi_j\xi_k}(\lambda)}{E_{\xi_j\xi_k}(\lambda)}, \; j, k = 1, \ldots, n, \tag{10.1.48}$$

where $N_{\xi_j\xi_k}(\lambda)$ and $E_{\xi_j\xi_k}(\lambda)$ are polynomials such that $E_{\xi_j\xi_k}(\lambda)$, $N_{\xi_j\xi_k}(\lambda) \geqslant 0$ and $\overline{E_{\xi_j\xi_k}(-\lambda)} = E_{\xi_j\xi_k}(\lambda) \neq 0$, $-\infty < \lambda < \infty$.

THEOREM 10.1.1. Any n-dimensional stationary gaussian process $\xi = \{(\xi_1(\cdot), \ldots, \xi_n(\cdot))\}$ *which has rational spectral and joint spectral densities (as immediately preceding) is completely regular.*

The proof will be carried out by induction.

(1) For the case $n = 1$ we have already indicated how the result of the theorem is obtained.

(2) Let us assume the validity of the theorem for $p = n - 1$; we prove that it holds also for $p = n$. First of all we remark that without loss of generality we may assume that $N_{\xi_j\xi_j}(\lambda) = 1$, $-\infty < \lambda < \infty$. In fact, since $N_{\xi_j\xi_j}(\lambda) \geqslant 0$, there exists a polynomial $K_{\xi_j\xi_j}(\lambda)$ such that $N_{\xi_j\xi_j}(\lambda) = |K_{\xi_j\xi_j}(\lambda)|^2$, $K_{\xi_j\xi_j}(\lambda) = K_{\xi_j\xi_j}(-\lambda)$, and it is clear that the random process ξ_j is a linear combination of the gaussian process

$$\xi_j' = \{\xi_j'(t)\}, \quad \xi_j'(t) = \int_{-\infty}^{\infty} e^{it\lambda} \frac{1}{K_{\xi_j\xi_j}(\lambda)} dz_{\xi_j}(\lambda)$$

and its derivatives. Obviously $N_{\xi_j'\xi_j'}(\lambda) = 1$, and from the complete regularity of $\xi' = (\xi_1', \ldots, \xi_n')$ follows the complete regularity of ξ.

We denote by $\alpha_j = \{\alpha_j(\cdot)\}$, $j = 2, \ldots, n$ the gaussian stationary and stationarily correlated processes consisting of the projections $\alpha_j(\cdot)$ of the random variables $\xi_j(\cdot)$ onto B_{ξ_1}. Since

$$\mathbf{E}\alpha_j(\cdot)\overline{\xi_1(\cdot)} = \mathbf{E}\,\xi_j(\cdot)\overline{\xi_1(\cdot)},$$

then

$$f_{\alpha_j\xi_1}(\lambda) = f_{\xi_j\xi_1}(\lambda) = \frac{N_{\xi_j\xi_1}(\lambda)}{E_{\xi_j\xi_1}(\lambda)} = \frac{N_{\alpha_j\xi_1}(\lambda)}{E_{\alpha_j\xi_1}(\lambda)}. \tag{10.1.49}$$

Since the processes α_j, $j = 2, \ldots, n$ are linearly subordinate to the process ξ_1, according to formula (10.1.24)

$$f_{\alpha_j\alpha_k}(\lambda) = \frac{f_{\alpha_1\xi_1}(\lambda)\overline{f_{\alpha_k\xi_1}(\lambda)}}{f_{\xi_1\xi_1}(\lambda)f_{\xi_1\xi_1}(\lambda)} f_{\xi_1\xi_1}(\lambda) = \frac{N_{\alpha_j\alpha_k}(\lambda)}{E_{\alpha_j\alpha_k}(\lambda)}, \tag{10.1.50}$$

i.e., $f_{\alpha_j \alpha_k}(\lambda)$ is a rational function. We put

$$\nu_1(t) = \int_{-\infty}^{\infty} e^{it\lambda} \frac{1}{\prod_{k=2}^{n} E_{\xi_k \xi_1}(\lambda)} dz_{\xi_1}(\lambda) \quad \text{and } \nu_1 = \{\nu_1(t)\}. \tag{10.1.51}$$

Then we have

$$f_{\alpha_j \nu_1}(\lambda) = f_{\alpha_j \xi_1}(\lambda) \frac{1}{\prod_{k=2}^{n} \overline{E_{\xi_k \xi_1}(\lambda)}} = \frac{N_{\xi_j \xi_1}(\lambda)}{E_{\xi_j \xi_1}(\lambda) \prod_{k=2}^{n} \overline{E_{\xi_k \xi_1}(\lambda)}}; \tag{10.1.52}$$

$$f_{\nu_1 \nu_1}(\lambda) = f_{\xi_1 \xi_1}(\lambda) / \prod_{j=2}^{n} |E_{\xi_j \xi_1}(\lambda)|^2. \tag{10.1.53}$$

According to formulas (10. 1. 21) and (10. 1. 23)

$$\alpha_j(t) = \int_{-\infty}^{\infty} e^{it\lambda} \pi_j(\lambda) dz_{\nu_1}(\lambda), \tag{10.1.54}$$

where the function $\pi_j(\lambda)$ is defined by the equation

$$f_{\alpha_j \nu_1}(\lambda) = \pi_j(\lambda) f_{\nu_1 \nu_1}(\lambda). \tag{10.1.55}$$

Comparing (10. 1. 55) with (10. 1. 52) and (10. 1. 53), we find that

$$\pi_j(\lambda) = \frac{f_{\alpha_j \nu_1}(\lambda)}{f_{\nu_1 \nu_1}(\lambda)} = N_{\xi_j \xi_1}(\lambda) \prod_{\substack{k=1 \\ k \neq j}}^{n} E_{\xi_k \xi_1}(\lambda),$$

and consequently

$$\alpha_j(t) = \int_{-\infty}^{\infty} e^{it\lambda} N_{\xi_j \xi_1}(\lambda) \prod_{\substack{k=1 \\ k \neq j}}^{n} E_{\xi_k \xi_1}(\lambda)\, dz_{\nu_1}(\lambda). \tag{10.1.56}$$

From formula (10. 1. 51) and (10. 1. 56) we see that the random processes ξ_1, α_j, $j = 2, \dots, n$ can be obtained by taking linear combinations of the process $\nu_1 = \{\nu_1(t)\}$ and its derivatives. From this it follows that the random processes $\xi_k = \{\xi_k(t)\}$, $k = 1, \dots, n$ are linear combinations of the processes $\nu_1 = \{\nu_1(t)\}$, $\nu_j = \{\nu_j(t)\}$ where $\nu_j(t) = \xi_j(t) - \alpha_j(t)$, $j = 2, \dots, n$ and of derivatives of the process ν_1, and consequently if we look at the process $\nu = (\nu_1, \dots, \nu_n)$ we see that the random variables ξ^0, ξ_0^T, ξ_T are subordinate respectively to the random variables ν^0, ν_0^T, ν_T. Therefore, in order to establish the complete regularity of the process ξ it is sufficient to establish that of the process ν. From the definition of ν_1 it follows that ν_1 is real valued, and therefore gaussian. Now the process ν consists of the two mutually independent gaussian processes ν_1 and $(\nu_2, \ldots, \nu_n)$, each of which has rational spectral and (for the latter) joint spectral density functions. Thus, by the induction hypothesis both are completely regular, from which it easily follows that ν is completely regular, and hence that ξ is completely regular.

COROLLARY 1. A gaussian n-dimensional stationary process $\xi = \{(\xi_1(t), \ldots, \xi_n(t))\}$ *with rational spectral and joint spectral density functions can always be taken as a component of a multi-dimensional stationary gaussian Markov process.*

The proof will be carried out by induction.

(a) For $n = 1$ the assertion is well known.

(b) Assume the corollary to be valid for $p = n - 1$. We consider the process $\nu = (\nu_1, \ldots, \nu_n)$ constructed as in the proof of the preceding theorem. By the induction hypothesis we can construct mutually independent Markov processes $\eta' = \{(\eta_1'(t), \ldots, \eta_{l'}'(t))\}$ and $\eta'' = \{(\eta_1''(t), \ldots, \eta_{l''}''(t)\}$ of which ν_1 and $(\nu_2, \ldots, \nu_n)$ are components respectively. Clearly the process $(\eta', \eta'') = \eta$ satisfies the assertion of the corollary.

COROLLARY 2. Under the conditions of Theorem 10.1.1,

$$I(\xi^0, \xi_T) < \infty \tag{10.1.57}$$

for every $T > 0$. In fact, for the gaussian Markov process of the preceding corollary, the measure $P_{\eta^0 \eta_T}$ is not singular with respect to the measure $P_{\eta^0 \eta_T}$, and therefore by Corollary 2 to Lemma 9.6.1 (and if necessary, the remark following) $I(\eta^0, \eta_T) < \infty$. In order to obtain (10.1.57) from this, we have only to remark that ξ^0 and ξ_T are subordinate respectively to η^0 and η_T.

THEOREM 10.1.2. For any (n+m)-dimensional non-degenerate stationary gaussian process $\nu = (\xi, \eta) = ((\xi_1, \ldots, \xi_n), (\eta_1, \ldots, \eta_m))$ *with rational spectral and joint spectral densities*

$$EI(\nu^0, \nu_T/\xi_{-\delta}^{T+\delta}) < \infty \tag{10.1.58}$$

for every $T > 0$, $\delta > 0$. *If* ξ *is non-generalized, formula (10.1.57) goes over into*

$$\mathbf{E}I(\nu^0, \nu_T/\xi_0^T) < \infty. \tag{10.1.59}$$

In order to avoid overburdening the discussion, we will omit the proof.

10.2. INFORMATION RATE OF DISCRETE-PARAMETER GAUSSIAN PROCESSES

We introduce some notation. Let $\xi = \{\xi(t)\}$ and $\eta = \{\eta(t)\}$ be one-dimensional real-valued discrete-parameter wide-sense stationary and stationarily correlated processes. We put

$$|r_{\xi\eta}(\lambda)|^2 = \begin{cases} \dfrac{|f_{\xi\eta}(\lambda)|^2}{f_{\xi\xi}(\lambda)f_{\eta\eta}(\lambda)} & \text{for } f_{\xi\eta}(\lambda) \neq 0; \\ 0 & \text{for } f_{\xi\eta}(\lambda) = 0 \end{cases} \tag{10.2.1}$$

and

$$L_{\xi\eta} = -\frac{1}{4\pi}\int_{-\pi}^{\pi} \log(1 - |r_{\xi\eta}(\lambda)|^2)d\lambda = -\frac{1}{2\pi}\int_{0}^{\pi} \log(1 - |r_{\xi\eta}(\lambda)|^2)d\lambda \tag{10.2.2}$$

where

$$f_{\xi\xi}(\lambda) = F'_{\xi\xi}(\lambda),\ f_{\eta\eta}(\lambda) = F'_{\eta\eta}(\lambda),\ f_{\xi\eta}(\lambda) = F'_{\xi\eta}(\lambda)$$

are respectively the derivatives of the spectral and joint spectral functions of the processes ξ and η. In the case where the process $\eta = \{\eta(t)\}$ can be represented in the form

$$\eta(t) = \xi(t) + \nu(t), \tag{10.2.3}$$

where $\nu = \{\nu(t)\}$ is wide-sense stationary and uncorrelated with $\xi = \{\xi(t)\}$ (i.e., $\mathbf{E}\xi(t)\nu(\tau) = 0, -\infty < t, \tau < \infty$), formula (10.2.2) reduces to

$$L_{\xi\eta} = \frac{1}{4\pi}\int_{-\pi}^{\pi} \log\left(1 + \frac{f_{\xi\xi}(\lambda)}{f_{\nu\nu}(\lambda)}\right)d\lambda = \frac{1}{2\pi}\int_{0}^{\pi} \log\left(1 + \frac{f_{\xi\xi}(\lambda)}{f_{\nu\nu}(\lambda)}\right)d\lambda. \tag{10.2.4}$$

THEOREM 10.2.1. Suppose that the one-dimensional processes ξ and η together form a discrete-parameter stationary gaussian process $(\xi, \eta) = \{(\xi(t), \eta(t))\}$. Then

$$(1)\ \vec{I}(\xi, \eta) = L_{\xi\eta} \tag{10.2.5}$$

if ξ is not a singular process;

$$\vec{I}(\xi, \eta) = 0 \tag{10.2.6}$$

if ξ is a singular process.

$$(2)\ \bar{I}^{(g)}(\xi, \eta) = L_{\xi\eta} \tag{10.2.7}$$

for any ξ and η.

(3) For any ξ and η for which $\tilde{I}(\xi, \eta)$ and $\bar{I}(\xi, \eta)$ are defined,

$$\tilde{I}(\xi, \eta) \geqslant \bar{I}(\xi, \eta) \geqslant L_{\xi\eta}; \tag{10.2.8}$$

if ξ (or η) is non-singular, then $\tilde{I}(\xi, \eta)$ and $\bar{I}(\xi, \eta)$ are defined *and*

$$\bar{I}(\xi, \eta) = \bar{I}(\xi, \eta) = L_{\xi\eta}. \tag{10.2.9}$$

Proof. (1) By (7.1.1)

$$\vec{I}(\xi, \eta) = \mathbf{E}I(\xi_0^1, \eta/\xi^0) = \mathbf{E}I(\xi(1), \eta/\xi^0) \tag{10.2.10}$$

(we recall that ξ^0, ξ_s^t, $s < t$ are the random variables consisting respectively of the random variables $\xi(\tau)$ for $-\infty < \tau \leqslant 0$ and $s < \tau \leqslant t$). According to (3.6.3)

$$I(\xi(1), (\xi^0, \eta)) = I(\xi(1), \xi^0) + \mathbf{E}I(\xi(1), \eta/\xi^0);$$

$$I(\xi(1), (\xi^0, \eta)) = I(\xi(1), \eta) + \mathbf{E}I(\xi(1), \xi^0/\eta),$$

from which

$$\mathbf{E}I(\xi(1), \eta/\xi^0) = I(\xi(1), \eta) + \mathbf{E}I(\xi(1), \xi^0/\eta) - I(\xi(1), \xi^0). \tag{10.2.11}$$

Let us denote by $\nu(\tau)$ and $\hat{\xi}(\tau)$ the perpendiculars from $\xi(\tau)$ onto the spaces B_η and $B_{\xi^{\tau-1}}$ respectively. According to formula (9.2.15) we have

$$\begin{aligned} I(\xi(1), \eta) &= \frac{1}{2} \log \frac{\rho_{\xi\xi}(1)}{\rho_{\nu\nu}(1)}; \\ I(\xi(1), \xi^0) &= \frac{1}{2} \log \frac{\rho_{\xi\xi}(1)}{\rho_{\hat{\xi}\hat{\xi}}(1)}, \end{aligned} \tag{10.2.12}$$

where

$$\rho_{\xi\xi}(1) = \mathbf{E}|\xi(\tau)|^2, \ \rho_{\nu\nu}(1) = \mathbf{E}|\nu(\tau)|^2, \ \rho_{\hat{\xi}\hat{\xi}}(1) = \mathbf{E}|\hat{\xi}(\tau)|^2.$$

According to (9.3.12)

$$\mathbf{E}I(\xi(1), \xi^0/\eta) = I(\nu(1), \nu^0), \ \nu = \{\nu(t)\}$$

and, denoting by $\hat{\nu}(\tau)$ the perpendicular from $\nu(\tau)$ onto $B_{\nu^{\tau-1}}$, we obtain from (9.2.15) that

$$I(\nu(1), \nu^0) = \frac{1}{2} \log \frac{\rho_{\nu\nu}(1)}{\rho_{\hat{\nu}\hat{\nu}}(1)},$$

where

$$\rho_{\hat{\nu}\hat{\nu}}(1) = \mathbf{E}|\hat{\nu}(\tau)|^2,$$

i.e.,

$$\mathbf{E}I(\xi(1),\ \xi^0/\eta) = \frac{1}{2}\log\frac{\rho_{\nu\nu}(1)}{\rho_{\hat{\nu}\hat{\nu}}(1)}. \tag{10.2.13}$$

Comparing relations (10.2.10) and (10.2.11) with equations (10.2.12) and (10.2.13), and taking into account that the process ξ is non-singular, so that $\rho_{\hat{\hat{\xi}}\hat{\hat{\xi}}}(1) > 0$ and $\frac{1}{2}\log\frac{\rho_{\hat{\hat{\xi}}\hat{\hat{\xi}}}(1)}{\rho_{\hat{\xi}\hat{\xi}}(1)} < \infty$, we find that

$$\vec{I}(\xi,\eta) = \mathbf{E}I(\xi(1),\ \eta/\xi^0) = \frac{1}{2}\log\frac{\rho_{\xi\xi}(1)}{\rho_{\nu\nu}(1)} + \frac{1}{2}\log\frac{\rho_{\nu\nu}(1)}{\rho_{\hat{\nu}\hat{\nu}}(1)}$$

$$-\frac{1}{2}\log\frac{\rho_{\xi\xi}(1)}{\rho_{\hat{\xi}\hat{\xi}}(1)} = \frac{1}{2}\log\frac{\rho_{\hat{\hat{\xi}}\hat{\hat{\xi}}}(1)}{\rho_{\hat{\nu}\hat{\nu}}(1)}. \tag{10.2.14}$$

According to Kolmogorov's formula [17]

$$\rho_{\hat{\xi}\hat{\xi}}^{\frac{1}{2}}(1) = (2\pi)^{\frac{1}{2}}\exp\frac{1}{4\pi}\int_{-\pi}^{\pi}\log f_{\xi\xi}(\lambda)d\lambda,$$

$$\rho_{\hat{\nu}\hat{\nu}}^{\frac{1}{2}}(1) = (2\pi)^{\frac{1}{2}}\exp\frac{1}{4\pi}\int_{-\pi}^{\pi}\log f_{\nu\nu}(\lambda)d\lambda. \tag{10.2.15}$$

Substituting these expressions into (10.2.14), we obtain

$$\vec{I}(\xi,\eta) = \log\frac{2\pi\exp\frac{1}{4\pi}\int_{-\pi}^{\pi}\log f_{\xi\xi}(\lambda)d\lambda}{2\pi\exp\frac{1}{4\pi}\int_{-\pi}^{\pi}\log f_{\nu\nu}(\lambda)d\lambda} = \frac{1}{4\pi}\int_{-\pi}^{\pi}\log\frac{f_{\xi\xi}(\lambda)}{f_{\nu\nu}(\lambda)}d\lambda$$

$$= \frac{1}{2\pi}\int_{-0}^{\pi}\log\frac{f_{\xi\xi}(\lambda)}{f_{\nu\nu}(\lambda)}d\lambda = -\frac{1}{2\pi}\int_{0}^{\pi}\log\left(1 - \frac{f_{\xi\xi}(\lambda) - f_{\nu\nu}(\lambda)}{f_{\xi\xi}(\lambda)}\right)d\lambda. \tag{10.2.16}$$

The value of $f_{\nu\nu}(\lambda)$ can be obtained from formula (10.1.31):

$$f_{\nu\nu}(\lambda) = \begin{cases} \dfrac{f_{\xi\xi}(\lambda)f_{\eta\eta}(\lambda) - |f_{\xi\eta}(\lambda)|^2}{f_{\eta\eta}(\lambda)} & \text{for } f_{\eta\eta}(\lambda) \neq 0 \\ f_{\xi\xi}(\lambda) & \text{for } f_{\eta\eta}(\lambda) = 0. \end{cases}$$

Substituting this expression for $f_{\nu\nu}(\lambda)$ into (10.2.16) leads to (10.2.5). If ξ is a singular process, then (10.2.6) follows from the general result of Theorem 7.1.1.

(2) Let us assume first that one of the derivatives $f_{\xi\xi}(\lambda) = F'_{\xi\xi}(\lambda)$ or $f_{\eta\eta}(\lambda) = F'_{\eta\eta}(\lambda)$ (let us say, $f_{\xi\xi}(\lambda)$) is almost everywhere different from zero, and consider the decomposition of $\xi = \{\xi(t)\}$ into a sum of mutually independent processes $\xi^{I} = \{\xi^{I}(t)\}$, $\xi^{II} = \{\xi^{II}(t)\}$, $\xi(t) = \xi^{I}(t) + \xi^{II}(t)$ such that the spectral function $F_{\xi^I\xi^I}(\lambda)$ of the process ξ^I is absolutely continuous and the spectral function $F_{\xi^{II}\xi^{II}}(\lambda)$ of the process ξ^{II} is singular. We put

$$\xi'(t) = \int_{-\pi}^{\pi} e^{it\lambda} \frac{1}{\sqrt{f_{\xi\xi}(\lambda)}} dz_{\xi^I}(\lambda) + \xi^{II}(t), \; \xi' = \{\xi'(t)\}. \tag{10.2.17}$$

Obviously, the derivative $f_{\xi'\xi'}(\lambda)$ of the spectral function $F_{\xi'\xi'}(\lambda)$ of the process ξ' is equal to one almost everywhere; consequently the process $\xi' = \{\xi'(t)\}$ is non-singular, and

$$I(\xi'(1), (\xi')^0) = \frac{1}{2} \log \frac{\rho_{\xi'\xi'}(1)}{\rho_{\hat{\xi}'\hat{\xi}'}(1)} < \infty. \tag{10.2.18}$$

Therefore, from Theorem 7.4.2

$$\vec{I}(\xi', \eta) = \bar{I}^{(g)}(\xi', \eta) = \bar{I}(\xi', \eta) = \tilde{I}(\xi', \eta) \tag{10.2.19}$$

and by (10.2.5)

$$\vec{I}(\xi', \eta) = L_{\xi'\eta}.$$

From the representation (10.2.17) it is seen that the processes ξ and ξ' are mutually linearly subordinate, and therefore by Theorem 7.4.2 and Lemma 10.1.3

$$\bar{I}^{(g)}(\xi', \eta) = \bar{I}^{(g)}(\xi, \eta); \tag{10.2.20}$$

$$L_{\xi'\eta} = L_{\xi\eta}. \tag{10.2.21}$$

Comparing (10.2.19)–(10.2.21) we obtain

$$\bar{I}^{(g)}(\xi, \eta) = L_{\xi\eta}. \tag{10.2.22}$$

Suppose now that the measure defined by the spectral function $F_{\xi\xi}(\lambda)$ is concentrated on some set N, so that $f_{\xi\xi}(\lambda) \neq 0$ almost everywhere on N and $f_{\xi\xi}(\lambda) = 0$ for $\lambda \epsilon N$. Since the process ξ is real valued, we can assume that the set N is symmetrical with respect to the point $\lambda = 0$. We select some gaussian random process ζ which is independent of the processes ξ and η, and which has a spectral density of the form

$$f_{\zeta\zeta}(\lambda) = \begin{cases} 0 \text{ for } \lambda\in N \\ 1 \text{ for } \lambda\notin N \end{cases}$$

and consider the gaussian process $\xi' = \{\xi'(t)\}$, where

$$\xi'(t) = \xi(t) + \zeta(t) = \int_{\lambda\in N} e^{it\lambda}dz_{\xi}(\lambda) + \int_{\lambda\notin N} e^{it\lambda}dz_{\zeta}(\lambda) = \int_{-\pi}^{\pi} e^{it\lambda}dz_{\xi'}(\lambda). \tag{10.2.23}$$

Obviously the derivative of the spectral function $F_{\xi'\xi'}(\lambda)$ of the process ξ' is equal to

$$f_{\xi'\xi'}(\lambda) = f_{\xi\xi}(\lambda) + f_{\zeta\zeta}(\lambda) = \begin{cases} f_{\xi\xi}(\lambda) \text{ for } \lambda\in N \\ f_{\zeta\zeta}(\lambda) \text{ for } \lambda\notin N \end{cases} \tag{10.2.24}$$

and is therefore almost everywhere different from zero.

We have already proved that

$$\overline{I}^{(g)}(\xi', \eta) = L_{\xi'\eta}. \tag{10.2.25}$$

Since the process ζ is independent of the process $\eta, f_{\zeta\eta}(\lambda) = 0$, and therefore

$$f_{\xi'\eta}(\lambda) = f_{\xi\eta}(\lambda) + f_{\zeta\eta}(\lambda) = f_{\xi\eta}(\lambda). \tag{10.2.26}$$

Comparing (10.2.24) and (10.2.26), and recalling that $f_{\xi\eta}(\lambda) = 0$ for $\lambda\notin N$, we find that $|r_{\xi'\eta}(\lambda)|^2 = |r_{\xi\eta}(\lambda)|^2$, and consequently

$$L_{\xi'\eta} = L_{\xi\eta}. \tag{10.2.27}$$

From the representation (10.2.23) it is seen that the processes ξ' and (ξ, ζ) are mutally linearly subordinate, and therefore by Theorem 7.2.1

$$\overline{I}^{(g)}(\xi', \eta) = \overline{I}^{(g)}((\xi, \zeta), \eta). \tag{10.2.28}$$

On the other hand, it is obvious that the sequence of random variables $(\xi, \zeta), \xi, \eta$ forms a Markov chain, and by Theorem 7.2.1

$$\overline{I}^{(g)}((\xi, \zeta), \eta) = \overline{I}^{(g)}(\xi, \eta). \tag{10.2.29}$$

Comparing (10.2.27)–(10.2.29) proves the second part of the theorem.

(3) In the proof of the preceding part of the theorem it was shown that if the process ξ (or η) is non-singular, then

$$\vec{I}(\xi, \eta) = \bar{I}^{(g)}(\xi, \eta) = \bar{I}(\xi, \eta) = \tilde{I}(\xi, \eta).$$

Inequality (10.2.8) follows from the inequality

$$\bar{I}^{(g)}(\xi, \eta) \leqslant \bar{I}(\xi, \eta) \leqslant \tilde{I}(\xi, \eta),$$

and (10.2.9) follows from formula (10.2.7).

COROLLARY. If $\xi = \{\xi(t)\}$ is a stationary discrete-parameter gaussian process whose spectral function is singular, then

$$\bar{H}^{(g)}(\xi) = \bar{I}^{(g)}(\xi, \xi) = 0, \qquad (10.2.30)$$

i.e., the process ξ is completely singular.

Formula (10.2.30) follows from formula (10.2.7), taking into account that $L_{\xi\eta} = 0$.

On the other hand, a stationary gaussian process which has a spectral density can be obtained as a measurable function of a regular gaussian process, and consequently will be weakly regular.

To conclude this section, it is interesting to note that there exists a weakly regular stationary gaussian process for which formula (10.2.9) does not hold. For example, let (ξ, η) be a stationary gaussian process with spectral and joint spectral densities of the form

$$f_{\xi\xi}(\lambda) = f_{\eta\eta}(\lambda) = \begin{cases} c_{\xi_\eta} = \text{const} > 0 & \text{for } 0 \leqslant \lambda \leqslant \lambda_1 \\ 0 & \text{for } \lambda_1 < \lambda \leqslant \pi; \end{cases}$$

$$f_{\xi\eta}(\lambda) = \begin{cases} c_{\xi\eta} > 0; & \text{for } 0 \leqslant \lambda \leqslant \lambda_1 \\ 0 & \text{for } \lambda_1 < \lambda < \pi. \end{cases} \quad c_\xi \neq c_{\xi\eta}$$

Then it is obvious that

$$I(\xi_0^T, \eta_0^T) = \sum_{j=1}^{T} I(\hat{\xi}(j), \hat{\eta}(j)) = -\frac{T}{2} \log\left(1 - r^2_{\xi(1)\eta(1)}\right)$$

$$= -\frac{T}{2} \log\left(1 - \frac{c^2_{\xi\eta}}{c_\xi c_\eta}\right) \neq -\frac{T}{2\pi} \int_0^{\lambda_1} \log\left(1 - \frac{c^2_{\xi\eta}}{c_\xi c_\eta}\right) d\lambda$$

$$= -\frac{T}{2\pi} \int_0^{\pi} \log\left(1 - r^2_{\xi\eta}(\lambda)\right) d\lambda = TL_{\xi\eta}$$

where $\hat{\xi}(j)$ and $\hat{\eta}(j)$ are the perpendiculars from $\xi(j)$ and $\eta(j)$ onto $B_{\xi_0^{j-1}}$ and $B_{\eta_0^{j-1}}$ respectively.

10.3. INFORMATION RATE FOR CONTINUOUS-PARAMETER AND GENERALIZED GAUSSIAN RANDOM PROCESSES.

We introduce some notation. Let $\xi = \{\xi(\cdot)\}$ and $\eta = \{\eta(\cdot)\}$ be wide-sense stationary and stationarily correlated one-dimensional real-valued continuous parameter or generalized random processes. We put

$$L_{\xi\eta} = -\frac{1}{4\pi}\int_{-\infty}^{\infty}\log(1 - |r_{\xi\eta}(\lambda)|^2)d\lambda = -\frac{1}{2\pi}\int_0^{\infty}\log(1 - |r_{\xi\eta}(\lambda)|^2)d\lambda, \tag{10.3.1}$$

where $|r_{\xi\eta}(\lambda)|^2$ has the same meaning as in formula (10.2.1). If the process $\eta = \{\eta(\cdot)\}$ can be represented in the form

$$\eta(\cdot) = \xi(\cdot) + \nu(\cdot), \tag{10.3.2}$$

where $\nu = \{\nu(\cdot)\}$ is wide-sense stationary and uncorrelated with ξ, formula (10.3.1) takes the form

$$L_{\xi\eta} = \frac{1}{4\pi}\int_{-\infty}^{\infty}\log\left(1 + \frac{f_{\xi\xi}(\lambda)}{f_{\nu\nu}(\lambda)}\right)d\lambda = \frac{1}{2\pi}\int_0^{\infty}\log\left(1 + \frac{f_{\xi\xi}(\lambda)}{f_{\nu\nu}(\lambda)}\right)d\lambda. \tag{10.3.3}$$

THEOREM 10.3.1. Suppose that the one-dimensional continuous-parameter or generalized random processes $\xi = \{\xi(\cdot)\}$ *and* $\eta = \{\eta(\cdot)\}$ *form a stationary gaussian process* $(\xi, \eta) = \{(\xi(\cdot), \eta(\cdot))\}$. *Then:*

(1) $\vec{I}(\xi, \eta) = L_{\xi\eta}$ (10.3.4)

if ξ *is a non-singular process, and*

$$\vec{I}(\xi, \eta) = 0 \tag{10.3.5}$$

if ξ *is a singular process.*

(2) $\bar{I}^{(g)}(\xi, \eta) = L_{\xi\eta}$ (10.3.6)

for any ξ *and* η.

(3) For any ξ *and* η *for which* $\tilde{I}(\xi, \eta)$ *and* $\bar{I}(\xi, \eta)$ *are defined,*

$$\tilde{I}(\xi, \eta) \geqslant \bar{I}(\xi, \eta) \geqslant L_{\xi\eta}; \tag{10.3.7}$$

$$\tilde{I}(\xi, \eta) = \bar{I}(\xi, \eta) = L_{\xi\eta} \tag{10.3.8}$$

if the spectral density of the process ξ *has the form*

$$f_{\xi\xi}(\lambda) = f(\lambda) = R(\lambda)|\psi(\lambda)|^2, \tag{10.3.9}$$

where

$$R(\lambda) = R_{\xi\xi}(\lambda) = N_{\xi\xi}(\lambda)/E_{\xi\xi}(\lambda) \qquad (10.3.10)$$

is a rational function, and $\psi(\lambda)$ *is a measurable complex-valued function for which*

$$\int_{-\infty}^{\infty} | \log |\psi(\lambda)|^2 | d\lambda < \infty, \ |\psi(\lambda)| \leqslant 1. \qquad (10.3.11)$$

In particular, formula (10.3.8) holds whenever the spectral density of the process ξ *is rational. If the spectral and joint spectral densities of the processes* ξ *and* η *(i.e., of the process* (ξ, η)*) are rational, then from*

$$L_{\xi\eta} = \infty \qquad (10.3.12)$$

follows

$$I(\xi_0^T, \eta_0^T) = \infty \qquad (10.3.13)$$

for every positive T. Moreover, from (10.3.12) follows (10.3.13) whenever the process $\eta = \{\eta(\cdot)\}$ *can be represented in the form*

$$\eta(\cdot) = \xi(\cdot) + \nu(\cdot), \qquad (10.3.14)$$

where the random variables ξ *and* $\nu = \{\nu(\cdot)\}$ *are independent and the spectral density* $f_{\nu\nu}(\lambda)$ *of the process* ν *is of the form*

$$f_{\nu\nu}(\lambda) = R(\lambda)|\psi(\lambda)|^2, \qquad (10.3.15)$$

where $R(\lambda)$ *and* $\psi(\lambda)$ *satisfy the relations (10.3.10) and (10.3.11).*

For the proof of this theorem we have to establish the following lemma.

LEMMA 10.3.1. For any complex numbers $a_j, b_j, c_j, j = 1, \ldots, n$ *the following inequality holds:*

$$\frac{\left|\sum_{j=1}^{n} c_j\right|^2}{\sum_{j=1}^{n} |a_j|^2 \sum_{j=1}^{n} |b_j|^2} \leqslant \max_{j=1,\ldots,n} \frac{|c_j|^2}{|a_j|^2 |b_j|^2}. \qquad (10.3.16)$$

PROOF. Let a_j^{*2} and $b_j^{*2}, j = 1, \ldots, n$ be numbers defined by

$$a_j^{*2} = \min(|a_j|^2, |b_j|^2), \ b_j^{*2} = \max(|a_j|^2, |b_j|^2),$$

$$c_j^{*2} = |c_j|^2, \ c_j^* = \sqrt{c_j^{*2}}. \qquad (10.3.17)$$

The following relations are obvious:

$$\sum_{j=1}^{n} |a_j|^2 \sum_{j=1}^{n} |b_j|^2 \geqslant \sum_{j=1}^{n} a_j^{*2} \cdot \sum_{j=1}^{n} b_j^{*2}; \tag{10.3.18}$$

$$\frac{\left|\sum_{j=1}^{n} c_j\right|^2}{\sum_{j=1}^{n} |a_j|^2 \sum_{j=1}^{n} |b_j|^2} \leqslant \frac{\left(\sum_{j=1}^{n} c_j^*\right)^2}{\sum_{j=1}^{n} a_j^{*2} \sum_{j=1}^{n} b_j^{*2}} \tag{10.3.19}$$

Setting

$$l^2 = \min_{j=1,\dots n} \frac{a_j^{*2}}{b_j^{*2}},\ \tilde{a}_j^2 = \sqrt{l^2 a_j^{*2} b_j^{*2}},\ \tilde{b}_j^2 = \sqrt{a_j^{*2} b_j^{*2}/l^2},$$

we find that

$$a_j^{*2} b_j^{*2} = \tilde{a}_j^2\ \tilde{b}_j^2,\ \tilde{a}_j^2 = \tilde{b}_j^2\, l^2,\ \frac{c_j^{*2}}{\tilde{a}_j^2\ \tilde{b}_j^2} = \frac{|\,c_j\,|^2}{|\,a_j\,|^2\,|\,b_j\,|^2}$$

$$\sum_{j=1}^{n} \tilde{a}_j^2 \sum_{j=1}^{n} \tilde{b}_j^2 \leqslant \sum_{j=1}^{n} a_j^{*2} \sum_{j=1}^{n} b_j^{*2}. \tag{10.3.20}$$

Comparing inequalities (10.3.17), (10.3.19) and (10.3.20), we see that

$$\frac{\left|\sum_{j=1}^{n} c_j\right|^2}{\sum_{j=1}^{n} |a_j|^2 \sum_{j=1}^{n} |b_j|^2} \leqslant \frac{\left(\sum_{j=1}^{n} c_j^*\right)^2}{\sum_{j=1}^{n} a_j^{*2} \sum_{j=1}^{n} b_j^{*2}} \leqslant \frac{\left(\sum_{j=1}^{n} c_j^*\right)^2}{\sum_{j=1}^{n} \tilde{a}_j^2 \sum_{j=1}^{n} \tilde{b}_j^2} = \frac{\left(\sum_{j=1}^{n} c_j^*\right)^2}{l^2\left(\sum_{j=1}^{n} \tilde{b}_j^2\right)}$$

$$\leqslant \max_{j=1,\dots,n} \left(\frac{c_j^*}{l\tilde{b}_j^2}\right)^2 = \max_{j=1,\dots,n} \frac{c_j^{*2}}{\tilde{a}_j^2 \tilde{b}_j^2} = \max_{j=1,\dots,n} \frac{|c_j|^2}{|a_j|^2 |b_j|^2}. \tag{10.3.20.1}$$

which proves the lemma.

COROLLARY. If the series $\sum_{j=-\infty}^{\infty} |a_j|^2,\ \sum_{j=-\infty}^{\infty} |b_j|^2,\ \sum_{j=-\infty}^{\infty} |c_j|$ *converge, then*

$$\frac{\left|\sum_{j=-\infty}^{\infty} c_j\right|^2}{\sum_{j=-\infty}^{\infty} |a_j|^2 \sum_{j=-\infty}^{\infty} |b_j|^2} \leqslant \sup_{j=\dots-1,0,1,\dots} \frac{|c_j|^2}{|a_j|^2 |b_j|^2}. \tag{10.3.21}$$

In proving the theorem, it will be convenient to start with part 2.

(2) Let us consider first the case where ξ and η are non-generalized processes. According to (7.2.5),

$$\bar{I}^{(g)}(\xi, \eta) = \lim_{h\to+0} \frac{1}{h} I^{(g)}(\xi^{(h)}, \eta^{(h)}),$$

where $\xi^{(h)} = \{\xi^{(h)}(\eta)\} = \{\xi(nh)\}, \eta^{(h)} = \{\eta^{(h)}(n)\} = \{\eta(nh)\}$ are gaussian stationary and stationarily correlated discrete-parameter processes. By Theorem 10.2.1

$$\bar{I}^{(g)}(\xi^{(h)}, \eta^{(h)}) = L_{\xi^{(h)}\eta^{(h)}} = -\frac{1}{4\pi}\int_{-\pi}^{\pi} \log(1 - |r_{\xi^{(h)}\eta^{(h)}}(\lambda)|^2)\, d\lambda. \tag{10.3.22}$$

Thus, in order to compute $\bar{I}^{(g)}(\xi,\eta)$ we have to determine the value of $|r_{\xi^{(h)}\eta^{(h)}}(\lambda)|^2$, and to accomplish this we must determine the values of the derivatives of the spectral and joint spectral functions of the processes $\xi^{(h)}$ and $\eta^{(h)}$. We have

$$\rho_{\xi^{(h)}\eta^{(h)}}(n) = \mathbf{E}\xi^{(h)}(n)\xi^{(h)}(0) = \mathbf{E}\xi(nh)\xi(0) = \int_{-\infty}^{\infty} e^{inh\lambda} dF_{\xi\xi}(\lambda)$$

$$= \sum_{k=-\infty}^{\infty} \int_{-\frac{\pi}{h}}^{\frac{\pi}{h}} = e^{inh\lambda} dF_{\xi\xi}\left(\lambda + \frac{2k\pi}{h}\right) = \sum_{k=-\infty}^{\infty} \int_{-\pi}^{\pi} e^{in\lambda} dF_{\xi\xi}\left(\frac{\lambda + 2k\pi}{h}\right)$$

$$= \int_{-\pi}^{\pi} e^{in\lambda} d\left(\sum_{k=-\infty}^{\infty} F_{\xi\xi}\left(\frac{\lambda + 2k\pi}{h}\right)\right)$$

i.e., $F_{\xi^{(h)}\eta^{(h)}}(\lambda) = \sum_{k=-\infty}^{\infty} F_{\xi\xi}\left(\frac{\lambda + 2k\pi}{h}\right)$ is the spectral function of the process $\xi^{(h)} = \{\xi^{(h)}(n)\}$. Similarly, it can be shown that

$F_{\eta^{(h)}\eta^{(h)}}(\lambda) = \sum_{k=-\infty}^{\infty} F_{\eta\eta}\left(\frac{\lambda + 2k\pi}{h}\right)$ is the spectral function of the process $\eta^{(h)}$, and $F_{\xi^{(h)}\eta^{(h)}}(\lambda) = \sum_{k=-\infty}^{\infty} F_{\xi\eta}\left(\frac{\lambda + 2k\pi}{h}\right)$ is the joint spectral function of the processes $\xi^{(h)}$ and $\eta^{(h)}$. Hence

$$f_{\xi^{(h)}\eta^{(h)}}(\lambda) = F'_{\xi^{(h)}\xi^{(h)}}(\lambda) = \frac{1}{h}\sum_{k=-\infty}^{\infty} f_{\xi\xi}\left(\frac{\lambda + 2k\pi}{h}\right);$$

$$f_{\eta^{(h)}\eta^{(h)}}(\lambda) = F_{\eta^{(h)}\eta^{(h)}}(\lambda) = \frac{1}{h}\sum_{k=-\infty}^{\infty} f_{\eta\eta}\left(\frac{\lambda + 2k\pi}{h}\right);$$

$$f_{\xi^{(h)}\eta^{(h)}}(\lambda) = F'_{\xi^{(h)}\eta^{(h)}}(\lambda) = \frac{1}{h}\sum_{k=-\infty}^{\infty} f_{\xi\eta}\left(\frac{\lambda + 2k\pi}{h}\right).$$

According to (10.2.7),

$$\frac{1}{h}\bar{I}^{(g)}(\xi^{(h)}, \eta^{(h)}) = \frac{1}{h}L_{\xi^{(h)}\eta^{(h)}} =$$

$$-\frac{1}{4\pi h}\int_{-\pi}^{\pi} \log\left(1 - \frac{|f_{\xi^{(h)}\eta^{(h)}}(\lambda)|^2}{f_{\xi^{(h)}\xi^{(h)}}(\lambda) f_{\eta^{(h)}\eta^{(h)}}(\lambda)}\right) d\lambda$$

$$= -\frac{1}{4\pi h}\int_{-\pi}^{\pi} \log\left(1 - \left|\sum_{k=-\infty}^{\infty} f_{\xi\eta}\left(\frac{\lambda + 2k\pi}{h}\right)\right|^2 \Big/ \sum_{k=-\infty}^{\infty} f_{\xi\xi}\left(\frac{\lambda + 2k\pi}{h}\right) \sum_{k=-\infty}^{\infty} f_{\eta\eta}\left(\frac{\lambda + 2k\pi}{h}\right)\right) d\lambda$$

$$= -\frac{1}{4\pi h}\int_{-\frac{\pi}{h}}^{\frac{\pi}{h}} \log\left(1 - \left|\sum_{k=-\infty}^{\infty} f_{\xi\eta}\left(\lambda + \frac{2k\pi}{h}\right)\right|^2 \Big/ \sum_{k=-\infty}^{\infty} f_{\xi\xi}\left(\lambda + \frac{2k\pi}{h}\right) \sum_{k=-\infty}^{\infty} f_{\eta\eta}\left(\lambda + \frac{2k\pi}{h}\right)\right) d\lambda . \tag{10.3.23}$$

From the lemma it follows that the right side of the last expression does not exceed

$$-\frac{1}{4\pi}\int_{\frac{\pi}{h}}^{\frac{\pi}{h}} \log\left(1 - \sup_{k=\ldots,-1,0,1,2,\ldots} \frac{\left|f_{\xi\eta}\left(\lambda + \frac{2k\pi}{h}\right)\right|^2}{f_{\xi\xi}\left(\lambda + \frac{2k\pi}{h}\right) f_{\eta\eta}\left(\lambda + \frac{2k\pi}{h}\right)}\right) d\lambda$$

$$\leqslant -\frac{1}{4\pi}\int_{-\infty}^{\infty} \log\left(1 - \frac{|f_{\xi\eta}(\lambda)|^2}{f_{\xi\xi}(\lambda) f_{\eta\eta}(\lambda)}\right) d\lambda.$$

But as $h \to +0$ the sums

$$\sum_{k=-\infty}^{\infty} f_{\xi\xi}\left(\lambda + \frac{2k\pi}{h}\right),\ \sum_{k=-\infty}^{\infty} f_{\eta\eta}\left(\lambda + \frac{2k\pi}{h}\right),\ \sum_{k=-\infty}^{\infty} f_{\xi\eta}\left(\lambda + \frac{2k\pi}{h}\right)$$

converge in measure to $f_{\xi\xi}(\lambda), f_{\eta\eta}(\lambda)$ and $f_{\xi\eta}(\lambda)$ on any finite interval, and therefore as $h \to +0$, the left side of (10.3.23) converges to

$$-\frac{1}{4\pi}\int_{-\infty}^{\infty} \log\left(1 - \frac{|f_{\xi\eta}(\lambda)|^2}{f_{\xi\xi}(\lambda) f_{\eta\eta}(\lambda)}\right) d\lambda, \tag{10.3.24}$$

i.e.,

$$\bar{I}^{(g)}(\xi, \eta) = \lim_{h\to+0} \frac{1}{h}\bar{I}^{(g)}(\xi^{(h)}, \eta^{(h)}) = L_{\xi\eta}.$$

Now let ξ and η be generalized random processes. By formula (10.1.20) we can replace them by non-generalized random processes ν and ϑ such that ξ and ν, η and ϑ will be mutually linearly subordinate, and then

$$\bar{I}^{(g)}(\xi, \eta) = \bar{I}^{(g)}(\nu, \vartheta), \quad L_{\xi\eta} = L_{\nu\varphi}.$$

Since for the non-generalized processes ν and ϑ we have proved part 2 of the theorem, it follows that $\bar{I}^{(g)}(\xi,\eta) = L_{\xi\eta}$.

We proceed now to the proof of part 1 of the theorem.

(1) Once again we consider first the case where ξ and η are non-generalized random processes. In view of the inequality $\vec{I}(\xi,\eta) \leqslant \bar{I}^{(g)}(\xi,\eta)$ and formula (10.3.6),

$$\vec{I}(\xi,\eta) \leqslant L_{\xi\eta}. \tag{10.3.25}$$

If the process ξ is non-singular, then in the decomposition $\xi(t) = \xi^{I}(t) + \xi^{II}(t)$ of the process ξ into a sum of two mutually independent gaussian processes $\xi^{I} = \{\xi^{I}(t)\}$ and $\xi^{II} = \{\xi^{II}(t)\}$ having respectively absolutely continuous and singular spectral functions, the random process ξ^{I} will be regular, with spectral density $f_{\xi\xi}(\lambda)$, and the random process ξ^{II} will be singular. Let

$$\xi^{I}(t) = \int_0^\infty a(\tau) d_\tau \omega(t - \tau) \tag{10.3.26}$$

be the decomposition (10.1.41) of the regular process ξ^{I}. We consider the random process $\zeta = \{\zeta(t)\}$, defined by

$$\zeta(t) = \int_0^\infty e^{-c\tau}(\tau) d_\tau \omega(t - \tau), \tag{10.3.27}$$

where c is some positive number, and $\omega = \{\omega(t)\}$ is the gaussian random process defined by the decomposition (10.3.26).

The process $\zeta = \{\zeta(t)\}$ is a stationary gaussian Markov process, and ξ^{I} and ζ are regularly and linearly subordinate to one another. Hence, by Theorem 7.1.1 and Lemma 10.1.3

$$\vec{I}(\xi^{I}, \eta) = \vec{I}(\zeta, \eta); \tag{10.3.28}$$

$$L_{\xi\eta} = L_{\xi^{I}\eta} = L_{\zeta\eta}. \tag{10.3.29}$$

But ζ is a gaussian Markov process, and therefore

$$I(\zeta^0, \zeta_T) < \infty, \quad T > 0.$$

Thus the conditions of Theroem 7.4.2 are satisfied, and so

$$\vec{I}(\zeta, \eta) = \vec{I}^{(g)}(\zeta, \eta) = L_{\zeta\eta}. \tag{10.3.30}$$

Comparing (10.3.28)–(10.3.30) we find that

$$\vec{I}(\xi^{I}, \eta) = L_{\xi\eta}. \qquad (10.3.31)$$

Furthermore, let us consider the decomposition of the process η, $\eta(t) = \eta^{I}(t) + \eta^{II}(t)$, analogous to the earlier decomposition of the process ξ. The processes ξ and (ξ^{I}, ξ^{II}), η and (η^{I}, η^{II}) are mutually regularly subordinate, and the pair (ξ^{I}, η^{I}) is independent of the pair (ζ^{II}, η^{II}). Therefore

$$\vec{I}(\xi, \eta) = \vec{I}((\xi^{I}, \xi^{II}), (\eta^{I}, \eta^{II})) = \vec{I}(\xi^{I}, \eta^{I}) + \vec{I}(\xi^{II}, \eta^{II}); \qquad (10.3.32)$$

$$\vec{I}(\xi^{I}, \eta) = \vec{I}(\xi^{I}, (\eta^{I}, \eta^{II})) = \vec{I}(\xi^{I}, \eta^{I}). \qquad (10.3.33)$$

Comparing relations (10.3.31)–(10.3.33) shows that

$$\vec{I}(\xi, \eta) = \vec{I}((\xi^{I}, \xi^{II}), (\eta^{I}, \eta^{II})) \geqslant \vec{I}(\xi^{I}, \eta) = L_{\xi\eta}. \qquad (10.3.34)$$

Comparing (10.3.25) with (10.3.34) proves (10.3.4).

In the case where ξ and η are generalized random processes, we replace them by non-generalized random processes ν and ϑ given by formula (10.1.20). The processes ξ and ν, η and ϑ are mutually regularly subordinate and linearly subordinate, and therefore

$$\vec{I}(\xi, \eta) = \vec{I}(\nu, \vartheta), \; L_{\xi\eta} = L_{\nu\vartheta} \qquad (10.3.35)$$

and the validity of formula (10.3.4) follows from that of the same formula for the non-generalized processes ν and ϑ.

If ξ is a singular random process, then formula (10.3.5) follows from the general result of Theorem 7.1.1.

(3) Relation (10.3.7) follows from Theorem 7.4.1 and formula (10.3.6). The second assertion of this part of the theorem can be formulated in the following way: there exists a class $\mathscr{L}$ of stationary gaussian processes ξ such that for any gaussian process (ξ, η) which is stationarily correlated with $\xi \in \mathscr{L}$, formula (10.3.8) holds, and every process whose spectral density is of the form (10.3.9) belongs to the class $\mathscr{L}$. The proof of this assertion will be carried out in the following steps:

(a) We shall establish that the class $\mathscr{L}$ contains every process ξ whose spectral density is rational, i.e., $f_{\xi\xi}(\lambda) = R(\lambda)$.

(b) We shall establish that if every process with spectral density $f(\lambda)$ belongs to the class $\mathscr{L}$, then any process with spectral density of the form

$$f_{\xi\xi}(\lambda) = f(\lambda)|\psi(\lambda)|^2 \qquad (10.3.36)$$

belongs to $\mathscr{L}$, where $\psi(\lambda)$ is a complex-valued measurable function satisfying (10.3.11). We proceed to the proof.

(a) By Corollary 2 to Theorem 10.1.1, if ξ is a gaussian process with rational spectral density, then $I(\xi^0, \xi_T) < \infty$ for every $T > 0$, and so condition (7.4.28) holds. It follows from Theorem 7.4.2 that $\bar{I}^{(g)}(\xi,\eta) = \bar{I}(\xi,\eta) = \tilde{I}(\xi,\eta)$. In conjunction with (10.3.6), this shows that every process with rational spectral density belongs to the class $\mathscr{L}$.

(b) Let us consider the gaussian process $\check{\eta} = \{\check{\eta}(\cdot)\}$, consisting of the projections $\check{\eta}(\cdot)$ of the random variables $\xi(\cdot)$ onto the space B_η, and let $\alpha = \{\alpha(\cdot)\}$ be a stationary gaussian process which is independent of ξ and η, and which has spectral density $f_{\alpha\alpha}(\lambda) = f(\lambda) - f_{\xi\xi}(\lambda)$. Finally, let $\beta = \{\beta(\cdot)\}$ be the random process defined by $\beta(\cdot) = \alpha(\cdot) + \xi(\cdot)$, and $\gamma = \{\gamma(\cdot)\}$ the process defined by $\gamma(\cdot) = \alpha(\cdot) + \check{\eta}(\cdot)$. Obviously

$$f_{\beta\beta}(\lambda) = f_{\alpha\alpha}(\lambda) + f_{\xi\xi}(\lambda) = f(\lambda), \quad f_{\xi\check{\eta}}(\lambda) = f_{\check{\eta}\check{\eta}}(\lambda);$$
$$f_{\gamma\gamma}(\lambda) = f_{\beta\gamma}(\lambda) = f_{\alpha\alpha}(\lambda) + f_{\xi\check{\eta}}(\lambda) = f_{\alpha\alpha}(\lambda) + f_{\check{\eta}\check{\eta}}(\lambda),$$
$$f_{\beta\alpha}(\lambda) = f_{\alpha\alpha}(\lambda). \tag{10.3.37}$$

By formula (3.6.3)

$$I(\beta_0^T, (\gamma, \alpha)) = I(\beta_0^T, \alpha) + \mathbf{E}I(\beta_0^T, \gamma/\alpha). \tag{10.3.38}$$

Since the family of random variables $\nu(\cdot) = \beta(\cdot) - \gamma(\cdot) = \xi(\cdot) - \check{\eta}(\cdot)$ is independent of α, the sequence of random variables $\beta_0^T, \gamma, \alpha$ forms a Markov chain. Therefore

$$I(\beta_0^T, (\gamma, \alpha)) = I(\beta_0^T, \gamma). \tag{10.3.39}$$

Further,

$$\mathbf{E}I(\beta_0^T, \gamma/\alpha) = I(\xi_0^T, \check{\eta}). \tag{10.3.40}$$

Comparing the last three equations, we see that

$$I(\beta_0^T, \gamma) = I(\beta_0^T, \alpha) + I(\xi_0^T, \check{\eta})$$

and consequently,

$$I(\xi_0^T, \check{\eta}) = I(\beta_0^T, \gamma) - I(\beta_0^T, \alpha). \tag{10.3.41}$$

But by hypothesis, formula (10.3.8) holds for the process $\beta = \{\beta(\cdot)\}$ since its spectral density is $f_{bb}(\lambda) = f(\lambda)$, i.e.,

$$\tilde{I}(\beta, \gamma) = \bar{I}(\beta, \gamma) = -\frac{1}{2\pi}\int_0^\infty \log (1 - |r_{\beta\gamma}(\lambda)|^2 d\lambda$$

$$= -\frac{1}{2\pi}\int_0^\infty \log\left(1 - \frac{|f_{\beta\gamma}(\lambda)|^2}{f_{\beta\beta}(\lambda)f_{\gamma\gamma}(\lambda)}\right)d\lambda;$$

$$\tilde{I}(\beta, \alpha) = \bar{I}(\beta, \alpha) = -\frac{1}{2\pi}\int_0^\infty \log (1 - |r_{\beta\alpha}(\lambda)|^2)$$

$$= -\frac{1}{2\pi}\int_0^\infty \log\left(1 - \frac{|f_{\beta\alpha}(\lambda)|^2}{f_{\beta\beta}(\lambda)f_{\alpha\alpha}(\lambda)}\right)d\lambda$$

and according to (10.3.37)

$$\tilde{I}(\beta, \gamma) = \bar{I}(\beta, \gamma) = -\frac{1}{2\pi}\int_0^\infty \log\left(1 - \frac{(f_{\alpha\alpha}(\lambda) + f_{\xi\check{\eta}}(\lambda)}{f(\lambda)}\right)d\lambda$$

$$= -\frac{1}{2\pi}\int_0^\infty \log\frac{f_{\xi\xi}(\lambda) - f_{\xi\check{\eta}}(\lambda)}{f(\lambda)}d\lambda;$$

$$\tilde{I}(\beta, \alpha) = \bar{I}(\beta, \alpha) = -\frac{1}{2\pi}\int_0^\infty \log\left(1 - \frac{f_{\alpha\alpha}(\lambda)}{f_{\beta\beta}(\lambda)}\right)d\lambda$$

$$= -\frac{1}{2\pi}\int_0^\infty \log\left(1 - \frac{f_{\alpha\alpha}(\lambda)}{f(\lambda)}\right)d\lambda = -\frac{1}{2\pi}\int_0^\infty \log\frac{f_{\xi\xi}(\lambda)}{f(\lambda)}d\lambda.$$

From the last two relations and from (10.3.41) it follows that

$$\begin{aligned}\tilde{I}(\xi, \check{\eta}) &= \tilde{I}(\beta, \gamma) - \tilde{I}(\beta, \alpha) = -\frac{1}{2\pi}\int_0^\infty \log\frac{f_{\xi\xi}(\lambda) - f_{\xi\check{\eta}}(\lambda)}{f(\lambda)}d\lambda \\ &+ \frac{1}{2\pi}\int_0^\infty \log\frac{f_{\xi\xi}(\lambda)}{f(\lambda)}d\lambda = -\frac{1}{2\pi}\int_0^\infty \log\frac{f_{\xi\xi}(\lambda) - f_{\xi\check{\eta}}(\lambda)}{f_{\xi\xi}(\lambda)}d\lambda \\ &= -\frac{1}{2\pi}\int_0^\infty \log\left(1 - \frac{f_{\xi\check{\eta}}(\lambda)}{f_{\xi\xi}(\lambda)}\right)d\lambda = \\ &-\frac{1}{2\pi}\int_0^\infty \log\left(1 - \frac{f^2_{\xi\check{\eta}}(\lambda)}{f_{\xi\xi}(\lambda)f_{\check{\eta}\check{\eta}}(\lambda)}\right)d\lambda \\ &= -\frac{1}{2\pi}\int_0^\infty \log (1 - r^2_{\xi\check{\eta}}(\lambda))d\lambda = L_{\xi\check{\eta}}.\end{aligned} \tag{10.3.42}$$

Furthermore, the sequence of random variables $\xi_0^T, \check{\eta}, \eta$ forms a Markov chain, because the family of random variables $\hat{\eta}(\cdot) = \xi(\cdot) - \check{\eta}(\cdot)$, which are the perpendiculars from $\xi(\cdot)$ onto B_η, are independent of η. Therefore

$$I(\xi_0^T, (\check{\eta}, \eta)) = I(\xi_0^T, \check{\eta}).$$

On the other hand,

$$I(\xi_0^T, \eta) \geqslant I(\xi_0^T, \check{\eta})$$

since $\check{\eta}$ is subordinate to η. Comparing the last two relations, we see that

$$I(\xi_0^T, (\check{\eta}, \eta)) = I(\xi_0^T, \check{\eta}) = I(\xi_0^T, \eta)$$

and consequently

$$\tilde{I}(\xi, \check{\eta}) = \tilde{I}(\xi, \eta). \tag{10.3.43}$$

Finally, from Remark 2 and Corollary 1 to Lemma 10.1.5 it follows that

$$1 - r^2_{\xi\check{\eta}}(\lambda) = \frac{\det A_{\xi\check{\eta}}(\lambda)}{\det A_\xi(\lambda) \det A_{\check{\eta}}(\lambda)} = \frac{\det A_{\xi\eta}(\lambda)}{\det A_\xi(\lambda) \det A_\eta(\lambda)} = 1 - |r_{\xi\eta}(\lambda)|^2 \tag{10.3.43.1}$$

and consequently $L_{\xi\check{\eta}} = L_{\xi\eta}$. Comparing this equation with (10.3.43) and (10.3.42), we obtain (10.2.9).

Thus we have shown that if the class $\mathscr{L}$ contains every gaussian process with spectral density $f(\lambda)$, it also contains every process with spectral density $f(\lambda)|\psi(\lambda)|^2$. It remains to show that under the conditions stated in the theorem, $L_{\xi\eta} = \infty$ implies $I(\xi_0^T, \eta_0^T) = \infty$. We restrict ourselves to the case where (ξ, η) is a non-degenerate pair of non-generalized processes. By formula (3.6.6)

$$\mathbf{E}I((\xi^0, \eta), \xi_0^T/\xi_0^\delta) = \mathbf{E}I(\xi^0, \xi_0^T/\xi_0^\delta) + \mathbf{E}I(\eta, \xi_0^T/(\xi_0^\delta, \xi^0))$$
$$= \mathbf{E}I(\xi^0, \xi_0^T/\xi_0^\delta) + \mathbf{E}I(\xi_0^T, \eta/\xi^\delta) = \mathbf{E}I(\xi^0, \xi_0^T/\xi_0^\delta) + (T - \delta)\vec{I}(\xi, \eta)$$
$$\mathbf{E}I((\xi^0, \eta), \xi_0^T/\xi_0^\delta) = \mathbf{E}I(\eta, \xi_0^T/\xi_0^\delta) + \mathbf{E}I(\xi^0, \xi_0^T/(\xi_0^\delta, \eta))$$

for any $T > \delta > 0$. Since the left sides of these equations are the same, the right sides must be equal, i.e.

$$\mathbf{E}I(\xi^0, \xi_0^T/\xi_0^\delta) + (T - \delta)\vec{I}(\xi, \eta) = \mathbf{E}I(\eta, \xi_0^T/\xi_0^\delta) + \mathbf{E}I(\xi^0, \xi_0^T/(\xi_0^\delta, \eta))$$

from which

$$\mathbf{E}I(\eta, \xi_0^T/\xi_0^\delta) = (T - \delta)\vec{I}(\xi, \eta) + \mathbf{E}I(\xi^0, \xi_0^T/\xi_0^\delta) - \mathbf{E}I(\xi^0, \xi_0^T/(\xi_0^\delta, \eta)). \tag{10.3.44}$$

Obviously

$$\mathbf{E}I(\xi^0, \xi_0^T/(\xi_0^\delta, \eta))$$
$$= \mathbf{E}I(\xi^0, \xi_0^T/(\xi_0^\delta, \eta^0, \eta_0^\delta, \eta_\delta)) \leqslant \mathbf{E}I((\xi^0, \eta^0), (\xi_\delta, \eta_\delta))/(\xi_0^\delta, \eta_0^\delta)).$$

Comparing this equation with (10.3.44) we find that

$$\mathbf{E}\mathrm{I}(\eta,\ \xi_0^T/\xi_0^\delta) \geqslant (T-\delta)\vec{\mathrm{I}}(\xi,\ \eta) - \mathbf{E}\mathrm{I}((\xi^0,\ \eta^0),\ (\xi_\delta,\ \eta_\delta)/(\xi_0^\delta,\ \eta_0^\delta)). \tag{10.3.45}$$

Furthermore, from formula (3.6.6)

$$\mathbf{E}\mathrm{I}(\eta,\ \xi_0^T/\xi_0^\delta) = \mathbf{E}\mathrm{I}((\eta^0,\eta_0^{2T},\ \eta_{2T}),\ \xi_0^T/\xi_0^\delta)$$

$$= \mathbf{E}\mathrm{I}(\eta_0^{2T},\ \xi_0^T/\xi_0^\delta) + \mathbf{E}\mathrm{I}(\eta^0,\ \xi_0^T/\xi_0^\delta,\eta_0^{2T})) + \mathbf{E}\mathrm{I}(\eta_{2T},\xi_0^T/(\xi_0^\delta,\eta^{2T}))$$

from which

$$\mathbf{E}\mathrm{I}(\eta_0^{2T},\ \xi_0^T/\xi_0^\delta) = \mathbf{E}\mathrm{I}(\eta_1,\xi_0^T/\xi_0^\delta) - \mathbf{E}\mathrm{I}(\eta^0,\ \xi_0^T/(\xi_0^\delta,\ \eta_0^{2T}))$$

$$- \mathbf{E}\mathrm{I}(\eta_{2T},\xi_0^T/(\xi_0^\delta,\eta^{2T})). \tag{10.3.46}$$

Obviously

$$\mathbf{E}\mathrm{I}(\eta^0,\xi_0^T/(\xi_0^\delta,\ \eta_0^{2T})) \leqslant \mathbf{E}\mathrm{I}(\eta^0,(\xi_0^T,\ \eta_0^{2T})/(\xi_0^\delta,\ \eta_0^\delta))$$

$$\leqslant \mathbf{E}\mathrm{I}((\xi^0,\eta^0),(\xi_\delta,\eta_0)/(\xi_0^\delta,\eta_0^\delta)) = \mathbf{E}\mathrm{I}((\xi^0,\eta^0),(\xi_\delta,\eta_\delta)/(\xi_0^\delta,\eta_0^\delta));$$

$$\mathbf{E}\mathrm{I}(\eta_{2T},\ \xi_0^T/(\xi_0^\delta,\ \eta^{2T})) \leqslant \mathbf{E}\mathrm{I}(\eta_{2T},\ \xi_0^T/\eta^{2T}) \leqslant \mathbf{E}\mathrm{I}(\eta_{2T},\ (\xi_0^T,\ \eta^T)/\eta_T^{2T})$$

$$\leqslant \mathbf{E}\mathrm{I}((\eta_{2T},\ \xi_{2T}),\ (\xi^T,\ \eta^T)/\eta_T^{2T}) = \mathbf{E}\mathrm{I}((\eta_T,\ \xi_T),\ (\eta^0,\ \xi^0)/\eta_0^T).$$

Comparing this equation with (10.3.46), we find that

$$\mathbf{E}\mathrm{I}(\eta_0^{2T},\ \xi_0^T/\xi_0^\delta) \geqslant \mathbf{E}\mathrm{I}(\eta,\ \xi_0^T/\xi_0^\delta) - \mathbf{E}\mathrm{I}((\eta^0,\ \xi^0),\ (\xi_\delta,\ \eta_\delta)/(\xi_0^\delta,\ \eta_0^\delta))$$

$$- \mathbf{E}\mathrm{I}((\eta_T,\xi_T),\ (\eta^0,\ \xi^0)/\eta_0^T). \tag{10.3.47}$$

If the spectral and joint spectral densities of the process (ξ,η) are rational, then by Theorem 10.1.2, the terms on the right sides of equations (10.3.45) and (10.3.47) with minus signs are finite. At the same time, by part 1 of the theorem $\vec{\mathrm{I}}(\xi,\eta) = \mathbf{L}_{\xi\eta} = \infty$. Thus, comparing (10.3.45) and (10.3.47) it is evident that

$$\mathbf{E}\mathrm{I}(\eta_0^{2T},\xi_0^T/\xi_0^\delta) = \mathbf{E}\mathrm{I}(\eta,\ \xi_0^T/\xi_0^\delta) = \vec{\mathrm{I}}(\xi,\ \eta) = \infty.$$

It remains to note that

$$\mathrm{I}(\eta_0^{2T},\ \xi_0^T) \geqslant \mathbf{E}\mathrm{I}(\eta_0^{2T},\ \xi_0^T/\xi_0^\delta).$$

Now let the process $\eta = \{\eta(\cdot)\}$ be representable in the form (10.3.14). We can write down an equation similar to (10.3.44):

$$\mathbf{E}\mathrm{I}(\xi,\ \eta_0^T/\eta_0^\delta) = (T-\delta)\vec{\mathrm{I}}(\eta,\ \xi)$$

$$+ \mathbf{E}\mathrm{I}(\eta_0^T,\eta^0/\eta_0^\delta) - \mathbf{E}\mathrm{I}(\eta^0,\ \eta_0^T/(\xi,\ \eta_0^\delta)). \tag{10.3.48}$$

Since the process $\nu = \{\nu(\cdot)\}, \nu(\cdot) = \eta(\cdot) - \xi(\cdot)$ is independent of ξ,

$$\mathbf{E}\mathrm{I}(\eta^0, \eta_0^T/(\xi, \eta_0^\delta)) = \mathbf{E}\mathrm{I}(\nu^0, \nu_0^T/\nu_0^\delta).$$

If the spectral density of the process ν is rational, then the process η is non-singular, since its spectral function is the sum of the spectral functions of ξ and ν, and therefore by part 1 of the theorem $\vec{\mathrm{I}}(\xi, \eta) = \mathrm{L}_{\xi\eta} = \infty$. Moreover, according to Theorem 10.1.2

$$\mathbf{E}\mathrm{I}(\nu^0, \nu_0^T/\nu_0^\delta) < \infty.$$

Comparing this result with (10.3.48), we see that

$$\mathrm{I}(\xi, \eta_0^T) \geqslant \mathbf{E}\mathrm{I}(\xi, \eta_0^T/\eta_0^\delta) = \infty.$$

Since $\nu(\cdot) = \eta(\cdot) - \xi(\cdot)$ is independent of ξ, the random variables ξ, ξ_0^T, η_0^T form a Markov chain, and consequently

$$\mathrm{I}(\xi_0^T, \eta_0^T) = \mathrm{I}((\xi, \xi_0^T), \eta_0^T) = \mathrm{I}(\xi, \eta_0^T).$$

It remains only to consider the case where the spectral density $f_{\nu\nu}(\lambda)$ has the form (10.3.15). Since the considerations leading to the analysis of this case are entirely analogous to those which led to formula (10.3.8) when the spectral function of the process ξ was of the form (10.3.9), we will not detain ourselves over them.

In conclusion it is interesting to note that there exist stationary weakly regular gaussian processes for which formula (10.3.8) is not valid. For example, the process whose spectral and joint spectral densities are of the form

$$f_{\xi\xi}(\lambda) = f_{\eta\eta}(\lambda) = \begin{cases} c_\xi = \text{const} > 0 & \text{for } 0 \leqslant \lambda \leqslant \lambda_1 \\ 0 & \text{for } \lambda_1 < \lambda < \infty; \end{cases}$$

$$f_{\xi\eta}(\lambda) = \begin{cases} c_{\xi\eta} > 0 & \text{for } 0 \leqslant \lambda \leqslant \lambda_1 \\ 0 & \text{for } \lambda_1 < \lambda < \infty, \end{cases} \quad c_{\xi\eta} \neq c_\xi. \tag{10.3.49}$$

Indeed, as in the example of the preceding section we have, for sufficiently small $h > 0$,

$$\mathrm{I}(\xi_0^T, \eta_0^T) \geqslant \mathrm{I}((\xi(0), \xi(h), \ldots, \xi(nh)), (\eta(0), \eta(h), \ldots, \eta(nh))) = n\mathrm{I}(\xi(0), \eta(0)) \tag{10.3.50}$$

and since h can be taken arbitrarily small,

$$\mathrm{I}(\xi_0^T, \eta_0^T) = \infty \neq \mathrm{L}_{\xi\eta}. \tag{10.3.51}$$

10.4. INFORMATION RATE FOR MULTI-DIMENSIONAL GAUSSIAN PROCESSES.

We introduce some notation. Let $\xi = \{\xi(\cdot)\} = \{(\xi_1(\cdot), \ldots, \xi_n(\cdot))\}$ and $\eta = \{\eta(\cdot)\} = \{(\eta_1(\cdot), \ldots, \eta_m(\cdot))\}$ be real-valued stationary and stationarily correlated wide-sense processes, generalized or non-generalized. We put

$$L_{\xi\eta} = \frac{1}{2\pi} \int \log \frac{\det A_{\tilde{\xi}}(\lambda) \det A_{\tilde{\eta}}(\lambda)}{\det A_{\tilde{\xi}\tilde{\eta}}(\lambda)} d\lambda, \tag{10.4.1}$$

where $\det A_{\tilde{\xi}}(\lambda)$, $\det A_{\tilde{\eta}}(\lambda)$ and $\det A_{\tilde{\xi}\tilde{\eta}}(\lambda)$ have the same meaning as in Section 10.1. The limits of integration are $0, \pi$ if ξ and η are discrete-parameter processes, and $0, \infty$ if they are continuous-parameter or generalized processes. Let us consider a number of cases in which (10.4.1) takes a simpler form.

(a) Suppose $n = m$ and the pairs $(\xi_j, \eta_j), j = 1, \ldots, n$ are pairwise uncorrelated, i.e., the spaces $B_{\xi_j \eta_j}, j = 1, \ldots, n$ are mutually orthogonal. In this case

$$L_{\xi\eta} = -\frac{1}{2\pi} \sum_{j=1}^{n} \int \log (1 - |r_{\xi_j \eta_j}(\lambda)|^2) d\lambda. \tag{10.4.2}$$

(b) Let $n = m$, $\eta_j(\cdot) = \xi_j(\cdot) + \nu_j(\cdot)$, where $\det A_\nu(\lambda) \neq 0$, and $\nu = \{\nu(\cdot)\} = \{(\nu_1(\cdot), \ldots, \nu_n(\cdot))\}$ is wide-sense stationary and uncorrelated with ξ (in particular, if ξ and ν are independent); then

$$L_{\xi\eta} = \frac{1}{2\pi} \int \log \frac{\det A_\eta(\lambda)}{\det A_\nu(\lambda)} d\lambda. \tag{10.4.3}$$

In order to verify (10.4.3) it suffices to remark that by Lemma 10.1.5

$$\det A_\nu(\lambda) = \frac{\det A_{\tilde{\xi}\eta}(\lambda)}{\det A_{\tilde{\xi}}(\lambda)}.$$

(c) Let $n = m$, $\eta_j(\cdot) = \xi_j(\cdot) + \nu_j(\cdot)$, and the pairs (ξ_j, η_j), $j = 1, \ldots, n$ are pairwise uncorrelated. Then

$$L_{\xi\eta} = \frac{1}{2\pi} \sum_{j=1}^{n} \int \log \left(1 + \frac{f_{\xi_j \xi_j}(\lambda)}{f_{\nu_j \nu_j}(\lambda)}\right) d\lambda. \tag{10.4.4}$$

THEOREM 10.4.1. Suppose that the processes $\xi = \{\xi(\cdot)\} = \{(\xi_1(\cdot), \ldots, \xi_n(\cdot))\}$ *and* $\eta = \{\eta(\cdot)\} = \{(\eta_1(\cdot), \ldots, \eta_m(\cdot))\}$ *form an* $(n+m)$*-dimensional stationary gaussian process* (ξ, η). *Then*

(1) *Always*

$$\vec{I}(\xi, \eta) \leqslant L_{\xi\eta}. \tag{10.4.5}$$

If ξ *is a regular process, then*

$$\vec{I}(\xi, \eta) = L_{\xi\eta}. \tag{10.4.6}$$

If ξ *is a singular process, then*

$$\vec{I}(\xi, \eta) = 0. \tag{10.4.7}$$

(2) *For any* ξ *and* η

$$\vec{I}^{(g)}(\xi, \eta) = L_{\xi\eta}. \tag{10.4.8}$$

(3) *For any* ξ *and* η *for which* $\tilde{I}(\xi, \eta)$ *and* $\bar{I}(\xi, \eta)$ *are defined*

$$\tilde{I}(\xi, \eta) \geqslant \bar{I}(\xi, \eta) \geqslant L_{\xi\eta}; \tag{10.4.9}$$

and we will have

$$\tilde{I}(\xi, \eta) = \bar{I}(\xi, \eta) = L_{\xi\eta} \tag{10.4.10}$$

in the following cases:

(a) ξ *and* η *are discrete-parameter processes, and* ξ *has rank of regularity equal to n.*

(b) ξ *and* η *are continuous-parameter or generalized random processes, and* $\xi = \{(\xi_1(\cdot), \ldots, \xi_n(\cdot))\}$ *(or* η*) has rational spectral and joint spectral densities*

$$f_{\xi_j \xi_k}(\lambda) = \frac{N_{\xi_j \xi_k}(\lambda)}{E_{\xi_j \xi_k}(\lambda)}.$$

If (ξ, η) *has rational spectral and joint spectral densities and*

$$L_{\xi\eta} = \infty, \tag{10.4.11}$$

then

$$I(\xi_0^T, \eta_0^T) = \infty \tag{10.4.12}$$

for every $T > 0$.

PROOF. We begin by proving part 2.

(2) We construct the gaussian processes $\xi' = \{\xi'(\cdot)\} = \{(\xi_1'(\cdot), \ldots, \xi_n'(\cdot))\}$ and $\eta' = \{\eta'(\cdot)\} = \{(\eta_1'(\cdot), \ldots, \eta_m'(\cdot))\}$, which correspond, according to Lemma 10.1.2, to the pair (ξ, η). Since the processes ξ and ξ', η and η' are mutually linearly subordinate, by Lemma 10.1.5 and Theorem 7.2.1

$$\frac{\det A_{\tilde{\xi}\tilde{\eta}}(\lambda)}{\det A_{\tilde{\xi}}(\lambda) \det A_{\tilde{\eta}}(\lambda)} = \frac{\det A_{\tilde{\xi}'\tilde{\eta}'}(\lambda)}{\det A_{\tilde{\xi}'}(\lambda) \det A_{\tilde{\eta}'}(\lambda)} \tag{10.4.13}$$

and

$$\bar{I}^{(g)}(\xi, \eta) = \bar{I}^{(g)}(\xi', \eta'), \tag{10.4.14}$$

and consequently it suffices to verify (10.4.8) for the random processes ξ' and η'. But the processes $(\xi_1', \eta_1'), \ldots, (\xi_k', \eta_k')$, $\xi_{k+1}', \ldots, \xi_n', \eta_{k+1}', \ldots, \eta_n'$ are mutually independent, and therefore

$$\bar{I}^{(g)}(\xi', \eta') = \sum_{j=1}^{k} \bar{I}^{(g)}(\xi_j', \eta_j')$$

and according to Theorems 10.2.1 and 10.3.1

$$\bar{I}^{(g)}(\xi', \eta') = -\sum_{j=1}^{k} \frac{1}{2\pi} \int \log (1 - |r_{\xi_j'\eta_j'}(\lambda)|^2) d\lambda = L_{\xi'\eta'}.$$

This proves part 2 of the theorem. We turn to part 1.

(1) Formula (10.4.5) follows from (10.4.8) and the inequality $\vec{I}(\xi, \eta) \leqslant \bar{I}^{(g)}(\xi, \eta)$. If the process ξ is regular, then from the decompositions (10.1.38) and (10.1.40)–(10.4.42) it is evident that there exists a gaussian process $\xi'' = \{\xi''(\cdot)\} = \{(\xi_1''(\cdot), \ldots, \xi_p''(\cdot))\}$ (where p is the rank of regularity of ξ) such that ξ and ξ'' are mutually linearly and regularly subordinate, $\xi_1'', \ldots, \xi_p''$ are pairwise uncorrelated (i.e., $\mathbf{E}\xi_j''(\cdot)\xi_k''(\cdot) = 0, j \neq k$) and

(a)

$$\rho_{\xi_j''\xi_j''}(\tau) = \mathbf{E}\xi_j''(t+\tau)\xi_j''(t) = \begin{cases} 1 \text{ for } \tau = 0 \\ 0 \text{ for } \tau \neq 0 \end{cases}$$

when ξ is a discrete-parameter process;

(b) the spectral and joint spectral densities $f_{\xi_j''\xi_k''}(\lambda), j, k = 1, \ldots, p$ are rational when ξ is either a continuous-parameter or generalized process.

In both cases $I(\xi^0, \xi_T) < \infty$ for $T > 0$ and ξ is regular, and consequently, by Theorem 7.4.2

$$\vec{I}(\xi'', \eta) = \bar{I}^{(g)}(\xi'', \eta),$$

and so by part 2 of the theorem $\vec{I}(\xi'', \eta) = L_{\xi''\eta}$. It only remains to note that since ξ and ξ'' are mutually linearly and regularly subordinate, $\vec{I}(\xi, \eta) = \vec{I}(\xi'', \eta)$ and

$$\frac{\det A_{\tilde{\xi}\tilde{\eta}}(\lambda)}{\det A_{\tilde{\xi}}(\lambda) \det A_{\tilde{\eta}}(\lambda)} = \frac{\det A_{\tilde{\xi}''\tilde{\eta}}(\lambda)}{\det A_{\tilde{\xi}''}(\lambda) \det A_{\tilde{\eta}}(\lambda)}$$

If ξ is a singular process, then formula (10.4.7) follows from the general result of Theorem 7.1.1.

(3) Inequality (10.4.9) follows from Theorem 7.4.1 and from (10.4.8). If $\xi = \{\xi(\cdot)\} = \{(\xi_1(\cdot), \ldots, \xi_n(\cdot))\}$ is a discrete-parameter process with rank of regularity equal to n, it follows from the definition of rank that the perpendiculars $\hat{\xi}_j(1)$ from $\xi_j(1)$ onto B_{ξ^0} are linearly independent, and therefore

$$I(\xi^0, \xi_0^1) = I(\xi^0, \xi(1)) = \frac{1}{2} \log \frac{\det A_{\xi(1)}}{\det A_{\hat{\xi}(1)}},$$

in which $\det A_{\xi(1)}$ and $\det A_{\hat{\xi}(1)}$ are respectively the determinants of the correlation matrices of the random variables

$$\xi(1) = (\xi_1(1), \ldots, \xi_n(1)) \text{ and } \hat{\xi}(1) = (\hat{\xi}_1(1), \ldots, \hat{\xi}_n(1))$$

In this case, according to Theorem 7.4.2

$$\tilde{I}(\xi, \eta) = \bar{I}(\xi, \eta) = \bar{I}^{(g)}(\xi, \eta),$$

which, in view of (10.4.8), proves (10.4.10).

If $\xi = \{\xi(\cdot)\}$ is a continuous-parameter or generalized process with rational spectral densities, then by Corollary 2 to Theorem 10.1.1 $I(\xi^0, \xi_T) < \infty, T > 0$, and by Theorem 7.4.2 $\tilde{I}(\xi, \eta) = \bar{I}(\xi, \eta) = \bar{I}^{(g)}(\xi, \eta)$, which, in view of (10.4.8), proves (10.4.10).

The proof of the relation $I(\xi_0^T, \eta_0^T) = \infty$, under the conditions stated in the theorem, in no way differs from the proof of the corresponding result of Theorem 10.4.1. The proof is complete.

10.5. ENTROPY RATE OF ONE STATIONARY GAUSSIAN PROCESS WITH RESPECT TO ANOTHER.

Before presenting the results of this section, we remark that, as in every other section concerning entropy, every assertion will be formulated as briefly as possible, without the greatest possible generality and without proof.

In formulating our main results we need an auxiliary result concerning the theory of multi-dimensional wide-sense stationary processes, which is analogous to the well-known theorem on the simultaneous reduction of two quadratic forms to diagonal form.

LEMMA 10.5.1. Let $\xi = \{(\xi_1(\cdot), \ldots, \xi_n(\cdot))\}, \eta = \{(\eta_1, \ldots, \eta_n(\cdot))\}$ *be n-dimensional complex-valued wide-sense stationary processes. Then there exist n-dimensional complex-valued wide-sense stationary processes* $\xi' = \{(\xi_1'(\cdot), \ldots, \xi_n'(\cdot)\}$ *and* $\eta' = \{(\eta_1'(\cdot), \ldots, \eta_n'(\cdot))\}$ *such that*

(1) ξ' *and* ξ', η *and* η' *are stationarily correlated in the wide sense and are mutually linearly subordinate.*

$$(2)\ \mathbf{E}\xi_j'(\cdot)\overline{\xi_k'(\cdot)} = \mathbf{E}\eta_j'(\cdot)\overline{\eta_k'(\cdot)} = 0,\ j \neq k,\ i, k = 1, \ldots, n; \tag{10.5.1}$$

$$(3)\ f_{\xi_j'\xi_k}(\lambda) = \sum_{l=1}^{n} \psi_{lj}(\lambda) f_{\xi_l\xi_k}(\lambda),\quad f_{\eta_j'\eta_k}(\lambda) = \sum_{l=1}^{n} \psi_{lj}(\lambda) f_{\eta_l\eta_k}(\lambda), \tag{10.5.2}$$

where $f_{\xi_j'\xi_k}(\lambda), f_{\eta_j'\eta_k}(\lambda)$ *are the derivatives of the joint spectral functions of the processes* ξ_j' *and* ξ_k, η_j' *and* η_k*; and* $\psi_{lj}, j, l = 1, \ldots, n$ *are measurable functions.*

If ξ *and* η *are gaussian processes, then* ξ' *and* η' *can also be taken as gaussian, in which case (10.5.1) denotes independence.*

We now introduce some notation. Let $\xi = (\xi_1, \ldots, \xi_n)$ and $\eta = (\eta_1, \ldots, \eta_n)$ be n-dimensional stationary gaussian processes, and let $\xi' = (\xi_1', \ldots, \xi_n')$ and $\eta' = (\eta_1', \ldots, \eta_n)$ be the gaussian processes corresponding to (ξ, η) according to Lemma 10.5.1. We put

$$\ni_{\xi\eta} = \ni_{\xi'\eta'} = \sum_{j=1}^{\eta} \ni_{\xi_j'\eta_j'} = \frac{1}{2\pi} \sum_{j=1}^{n} \int \left(\frac{f_{\xi_j'\xi_j'}(\lambda)}{f_{\eta_j'\eta_j'}(\lambda)} - 1 - \log \frac{f_{\xi_j'\xi_j'}(\lambda)}{f_{\eta_j'\eta_j'}(\lambda)} \right) d\lambda, \tag{10.5.3}$$

where the limits of integration are $0, \pi$ if ξ and η are discrete-parameter processes, and $0, \infty$ if ξ and η are continuous-parameter or generalized processes. For the case where $\det A_\xi(\lambda)$ $\det A_\eta(\lambda) \neq 0$ it is easily shown that

$$\sum_{j=1}^{n} \log \frac{f_{\xi_j'\xi_j'}(\lambda)}{f_{\eta_j'\eta_j'}(\lambda)} = \log \frac{\det A_\xi(\lambda)}{\det A_\eta(\lambda)},\ \sum_{j=1}^{n} \frac{f_{\xi_j'\xi_j'}(\lambda)}{f_{\eta_j'\eta_j'}(\lambda)} = \sum_{j,k=1}^{n} f_{\xi_j\xi_k}(\lambda) f^{(-1)}_{\eta_k\eta_j}(\lambda), \tag{10.5.4}$$

where $A_\xi(\lambda) = \| f_{\xi_j\xi_k}(\lambda) \|$, $A_\eta(\lambda) = \| f_{\eta_j\eta_k}(\lambda)) \|_{j,k=1,\ldots,n}$ are the matrices of derivatives of the spectral and joint spectral functions of the processes $\xi = (\xi_1, \ldots, \xi_n)$, $\eta = (\eta_1, \ldots, \eta_n)$, and $f^{(-1)}_{\eta_j \eta_k}(\lambda)$ is a typical element of the inverse $A^{-1}_\eta(\lambda)$ of $A_\eta(\lambda)$. Substituting (10.5.4) into (10.5.3) we obtain

$$\ni_{\xi\eta} = \frac{1}{2\pi} \int \left(\sum_{j,k=1}^{n} f_{\xi_j \xi_k}(\lambda) f^{(-1)}_{\eta_k \eta_j}(\lambda) - n - \log \frac{\det A_\xi(\lambda)}{\det A_\eta(\lambda)} \right) d\lambda. \quad (10.5.5)$$

If the random processes $\eta_1, \ldots, \eta_n$ are mutually independent, (10.5.5) takes the form

$$\ni_{\xi\eta} = \frac{1}{2\pi} \sum_{j=1}^{n} \int \left(\frac{f_{\xi_j \xi_j}(\lambda)}{f_{\eta_j \eta_j}(\lambda)} - 1 - \frac{1}{n} \log \frac{\det A_\xi(\lambda)}{\det A_\eta(\lambda)} \right) d\lambda. \quad (10.5.6)$$

For $n = 1$, formulas (10.5.3), (10.5.5) and (10.5.6) reduce to a single formula:

$$\ni_{\xi\eta} = \frac{1}{2\pi} \int \left(\frac{f_{\xi\xi}(\lambda)}{f_{\eta\eta}(\lambda)} - 1 - \log \frac{f_{\xi\xi}(\lambda)}{f_{\eta\eta}(\lambda)} \right) d\lambda. \quad (10.5.7)$$

THEOREM 10.5.1. Let $\xi = \{\xi(\cdot)\}$ *and* $\eta = \{\eta(\cdot)\}$ *be one-dimensional stationary gaussian processes for which*

$$E\xi(\cdot) = E\eta(\cdot) = 0. \quad (10.5.8)$$

Then:

$$(1) \quad \overline{H}_\eta(\xi) = \lim_{T\to\infty} \frac{1}{T} H_{\eta_0^T}(\xi_0^T) = \ni_{\xi\eta} \quad (10.5.9)$$

in the following cases:

(a) η *is a regular discrete-parameter process, and the function* $f_{\xi\xi}(\lambda)/f_{\eta\eta}(\lambda)$ *is bounded above, i.e., there exists a constant* Γ, *independent of* λ, *such that*

$$f_{\xi\xi}(\lambda)/f_{\eta\eta}(\lambda) < \Gamma; \quad (10.5.10)$$

(b) η *is a regular continuous-parameter or generalized process with rational spectral density.*

(2) If ξ *and* η *are continuous-parameter or generalized random processes with rational spectral densities and* $f_{\eta\eta}(\lambda)$ *is different from zero almost everywhere, then from the equation* $\ni_{\xi\eta} = \infty$ *it follows that* $H_{\eta_0^T}(\xi_0^T) = \infty$ *for every* $T > 0$, *i.e., the measures* $P_{\xi_0^T}$ *and* $P_{\eta_0^T}$ *are mutually singular.*

COROLLARY. If the one-dimensional stationary gaussian processes ξ and η have rational spectral densities, then the following two alternatives are the only ones possible:

(1) $\lim_{\lambda\to\infty} \frac{f_{\xi\xi}(\lambda)}{f_{\eta\eta}(\lambda)} \neq 1$, *in which case the measures* $P_{\xi_0^T}$ *and* $P_{\eta_0^T}$ *are mutually singular for every* $T > 0$ *(see [37]).*

(2) $\lim_{\lambda\to\infty} \frac{f_{\xi\xi}(\lambda)}{f_{\eta\eta}(\lambda)} = 1$

in which case the measures $P_{\xi_0^T}$ *and* $P_{\eta_0^T}$ *are mutually absolutely continuous for every* $T > 0$ *(V.Pisarenko).*

Remark 1. It is interesting to note that the situation $\overline{H}_\eta(\xi) = \infty$ and $\overline{H}_\xi(\eta) < \infty$ is possible; for example, when ξ and η are one-dimensional gaussian processes with spectral densities $1/1 + \lambda^2$ and $\lambda^2/1 + \lambda^4$. At the same time, as has already been stated earlier, the entropies $H_\eta(\xi)$ and $H_\xi(\eta)$ of two gaussian random variables ξ and η are either both infinite or both finite. From this it becomes clear why the equation $\overline{H}_\eta(\xi) = \infty$ is insufficient to establish the singularity of the measures $P_{\xi_0^T}$ and $P_{\eta_0^T}$ with respect to each other.

Remark 2. As is known, the functions $F_{\xi\xi}(\lambda)$ and $F_{\eta\eta}(\lambda)$ of the processes ξ and η can be represented in the form

$$F_{\xi\xi}(\lambda) = F^{(H)}_{\xi\xi}(\lambda) + \sum_{\lambda'_j<\lambda} d^{(g)}_{\xi\xi}(\lambda'_j), F_{\eta\eta}(\lambda) = F^{(H)}_{\eta\eta}(\lambda) + \sum_{\lambda''_j<\lambda} d^{(g)}_{\eta\eta}(\lambda''_j),$$

where $F^{(H)}_{\xi\xi}(\lambda)$ and $F^{(H)}_{\eta\eta}(\lambda)$ are non-negative, non-decreasing and continuous functions, and $d^{(g)}_{\xi\xi}(\lambda)$ and $d^{(g)}_{\eta\eta}(\lambda)$ are non-negative functions which are different from zero only on the countable sets of points $\lambda'_1, \lambda'_2, \ldots, \lambda''_1, \lambda''_2, \ldots$.

In order that the measure P_ξ, defined by the entire process ξ, be absolutely continuous with respect to the measure P_η defined by the entire process η, it is necessary and sufficient that the following set of conditions be satisfied:

(a) $F^{(H)}_{\xi\xi}(\lambda) = F^{(H)}_{\eta\eta}(\lambda)$;

(b) $\sum_{j=1}^{\infty} \frac{(d^{(g)}_{\xi\xi}(\lambda_j) - d^{(g)}_{\eta\eta}(\lambda_j))^2}{d^{(g)}_{\xi\xi}(\lambda_j) d^{(g)}_{\eta\eta}(\lambda_i)} < \infty,$

where

$$\lambda_j = \begin{cases} \lambda'_k & \text{for } j = 2k, \\ \lambda''_k & \text{for } j = 2k - 1, \end{cases} \quad k = 1, 2, \ldots$$

For multi-dimensional gaussian random processes Theorem 10.5.1 goes over into:

THEOREM 10.5.2. Let $\xi = \{(\xi_1(\cdot), \ldots, \xi_n(\cdot))\}$ *and* $\eta = \{(\eta_1(\cdot), \ldots, \eta_n(\cdot))\}$ *be n-dimensional stationary gaussian processes for which*

$$E\xi_j(\cdot) = E\eta_j(\cdot) = 0. \tag{10.5.11}$$

Then:

(1) Formula (10.5.9) holds in the following cases:

(a) η *is a regular discrete-parameter process of rank n, and the function* $\sum_{j,k=1}^{n} f_{\xi_j\xi_k}(\lambda)\, f^{(-1)}_{\eta_k\eta_j}(\lambda)$ *is bounded above, i.e., there exists a constant* Γ *independent of* λ, *such that*

$$\sum_{j,k=1}^{n} f_{\xi_j\xi_k}(\lambda)\, f^{(-1)}_{\eta_k\eta_j}(\lambda) < \Gamma; \tag{10.5.12}$$

(b) η *is a regular continuous-parameter or generalized process with rational spectral and joint spectral densities.*

(2) If ξ *and* η *are continuous-parameter or generalized random processes with rational spectral and joint spectral densities, and each minor of the matrix* $A_\eta(\lambda) = \|f_{\eta_j\eta_k}(\lambda)\|_{j,k=1,\ldots,n}$ *of spectral densities is either identically zero or everywhere different from zero, then it follows from* $\ni_{\xi\eta} = \infty$ *that* $H_{\eta_0^T}(\xi_0^T) = \infty$ *for every* $T > 0$, *i.e., the measures* $P_{\xi_0^T}$ *and* $P_{\eta_0^T}$ *are mutually singular.*

Remark 1. Conditions (10.5.10) and (10.5.12) are fulfilled, for example, if $\eta_j(\cdot) = \xi_j(\cdot) + \nu_j(\cdot)$, where $\nu = \{(\nu_1(\cdot), \ldots, \nu_n(\cdot))\}$ is a stationary gaussian process independent of ξ.

Remark 2. It is easy to show that if ξ and η are n-dimensional stationary gaussian processes, then

$$\lim_{T\to\infty} \frac{1}{T} H_{\xi_0^T}(\eta_0^T) \geqslant \ni_{\xi\eta} \tag{10.5.13}$$

always holds.

The results of Theorems 10.5.1 and 10.5.2 can without particular difficulty be extended to a very much wider class of gaussian processes ξ and η, for example, when

$$\xi(t) = \nu(t) + m_1(t), \quad \eta(t) = \vartheta(t) + m_2(t),$$

where $\nu = \{\nu(t)\}$ and $\vartheta = \{\vartheta(t)\}$ are stationary gaussian processes with zero means and $m_1(t), m_2(t)$ are ordinary (i.e., non-random) functions. Here we restrict ourselves to the case where

$$\xi(t) = v(t) + m_1, \ \eta(t) = \vartheta(t) + m_2$$

and

$$f_{\eta\eta}(\lambda) = \frac{|b_0(b_1 - \lambda) \ldots (b_s - \lambda)|^2}{|a_0(a_1 - \lambda) \ldots (a_m - \lambda)|^2} \tag{10.5.14}$$

THEOREM 10.5.3. Let ξ *and* η *be one-dimensional non-generalized stationary gaussian processes. Then if the spectral density of the process* η *is rational,*

$$\bar{H}_\eta(\xi) = \lim_{T\to\infty} \frac{1}{T} H_{\eta_0^T}(\xi_0^T) = \ni_{\xi\eta} + \frac{(m_\eta - m_\xi)^2}{4\pi f_{\eta\eta}(0)}. \tag{10.5.15}$$

where $\boldsymbol{E}\xi(t) = m_\xi, \boldsymbol{E}\eta(t) = m_\eta$.

Example. Let $\xi = \{\xi(t)\}$ be a one-dimensional stationary gaussian process, and let $\eta(t) = \xi(t) + c$, where c is a constant; then

$$H_\eta(\xi) = \frac{c^2}{4\pi f_{\eta\eta}(0)} = \frac{c^2}{4\pi f_{\xi\xi}(0)}. \tag{10.5.16}$$

Chapter 11 Information stability of gaussian random processes

Here we formulate criteria for the information stability of stationary gaussian processes. The formulas given enable one to compute the rate of creation of reduced central moments, in particular the dispersion of the information density, and to judge the rate at which distribution of the information density converges to a normal distribution, and the asymptotic form of the parameters of this distribution. Generalizations given for these formulas characterize the behavior of the entropy density of one gaussian stationary process with respect to another. These results are entirely new.

11.1. INFORMATION STABILITY.

THEOREM 11.1.1. A pair $(\xi, \eta) = \{(\xi(\cdot), \eta(\cdot))\} = \{((\xi_1(\cdot), \ldots, \xi_n(\cdot)), (\eta_1(\cdot), \ldots, \eta_m(\cdot)))\}$ *which is an* $(n + m)$*-dimensional gaussian process is information stable.*

PROOF. There are only two possible cases: either $\lim_{T\to\infty} I(\xi_0^T, \eta_0^T) = I(\xi_0, \eta_0) = \infty$ or $\lim_{T\to\infty} I(\xi_0^T, \eta_0^T) = I(\xi_0, \eta_0) < \infty$. In the first case the information stability of the pair (ξ, η) follows from Theorem 9.6.1, and in the second case

$$\bar{I}(\xi, \eta) = \lim_{T\to\infty} \frac{1}{T} I(\xi_0^T, \eta_0^T) \leqslant \lim_{T\to\infty} \frac{1}{T} I(\xi_0, \eta_0) = 0,$$

which by definition implies the information stability of (ξ, η).

THEOREM 11.1.2. Under the conditions of the preceding theorem, the pair (ξ, η) *is relatively information stable.*

PROOF. The relative information stability of (ξ, η) is equivalent to the information stability of the pair $(\hat{\xi}, \hat{\eta}) = (\hat{\xi}_1(\cdot), \ldots, \hat{\xi}_n(\cdot)), (\hat{\eta}_1(\cdot), \ldots, \hat{\eta}_m(\cdot))$, where $\hat{\xi}_j(\cdot)$ and $\hat{\eta}_l(\cdot)$, $j = 1, \ldots, n$,

$l = 1, \ldots, m$ are the perpendiculars from $\xi_j(\cdot)$ and $\eta_l(\cdot)$ onto $B_{\xi 0}$. But by Theorem 11.1.1 the pair $(\hat{\xi}, \hat{\eta})$ is information stable.

Remark. If (ξ, η) is a multi-dimensional stationary gaussian process, it is easy to assert a necessary and sufficient condition for the relation $I(\xi, \eta) < \infty$.

In order to do this, we note first of all that the spectral and joint spectral functions of the process $(\xi, \eta) = ((\xi_1, \ldots, \xi_n), (\eta_1, \ldots, \eta_m)) = (\xi_1, \ldots, \xi_{n+m})$ can be represented in the form

$$F_{\xi_j \xi_k}(\lambda) = F^{(H)}_{\xi_j \xi_k}(\lambda) + \sum_{\lambda_l < \lambda} d^{(g)}_{\xi_j \xi_k}(\lambda_l), \tag{11.1.1}$$

where $j, k = 1, \ldots, n + m$, $F^{(H)}_{\xi_j \xi_k}(\lambda)$ is a continuous function of bounded variation, and $d^{(g)}_{\xi_j \xi_k}(\lambda)$ is a function which is different from zero at only countably many points $\lambda_1, \lambda_2, \ldots$

Let us denote by $\det A^{(d)}_{\bar{\xi}}(\lambda)$ and $\det A^{(d)}_{\bar{\eta}}(\lambda)$ highest order principal minors of the determinants $\det A^{(d)}_{\xi}(\lambda) = \det \| d^{(g)}_{\xi_j \xi_k}(\lambda) \|_{j,k=1,\ldots,n}$ and $\det A^{(d)}_{\eta}(\lambda) = \det \| d^{(g)}_{\eta_j \eta_k}(\lambda) \|_{j,k=1,\ldots,m}$ which do not vanish at the point λ, and let $\det A^{(d)}_{\bar{\xi}\bar{\eta}}(\lambda)$ be the principal minor of $\det A^{(d)}_{\xi\eta}(\lambda) = \det \| d^{(g)}_{\xi_j \xi_k}(\lambda) \|_{j,k=1,\ldots,n+m}$, of order $r + s$, which contains $\det A^{(d)}_{\bar{\xi}}(\lambda)$ and $\det A^{(d)}_{\bar{\eta}}(\lambda)$, whose orders are respectively r and s. Then $I(\xi, \eta) < \infty$ if and only if

$$F^{(H)}_{\xi_j \eta_k}(\lambda) \equiv 0, j = 1, \ldots, n; k = 1, \ldots, m,$$

$$I^{(d)}(\xi, \eta) = \frac{1}{2} \sum_j \log \frac{\det^{(d)}_{\bar{\xi}}(\lambda_j) \det A^{(d)}_{\bar{\eta}}(\lambda_j)}{\det A^{(d)}_{\bar{\xi}\bar{\eta}}(\lambda_j)} < \infty. \tag{11.1.2}$$

In this case

$$I(\xi, \eta) = I^{(d)}(\xi, \eta). \tag{11.1.3}$$

When $n = m = 1$, (11.1.3) takes the form

$$I(\xi, \eta) = -\frac{1}{2} \sum_j \log \left(1 - \frac{(d^{(g)}_{\xi\eta}(\lambda_j))^2}{d^{(g)}_{\xi\xi}(\lambda_j) d^{(g)}_{\eta\eta}(\lambda_j)}\right). \tag{11.1.4}$$

11.2. RATE OF CHANGE OF THE VARIANCE AND HIGHER MOMENTS OF THE INFORMATION DENSITY. CONVERGENCE OF THE DISTRIBUTION OF THE INFORMATION DENSITY TO A NORMAL DISTRIBUTION.

We introduce some notation. Let $\xi = \{\xi(\cdot)\} = \{(\xi_1(\cdot), \ldots, \xi_l(\cdot))\}$ and $\eta = \{\eta(\cdot)\} = \{(\eta_1(\cdot), \ldots, \eta_m(\cdot))\}$ be l- and m-dimensional wide-sense stationary and stationarily correlated processes, and let $\xi' = \{(\xi'_1(\cdot), \ldots, \xi'_l(\cdot))\}$ and $\eta' = \{(\eta'_1(\cdot), \ldots, \eta'_m(\cdot))\}$ be the stationary processes defined by Lemma 10.1.2, corresponding to the pair ξ, η.

We put

$$Q^{(n)}_{\xi\eta} = Q^{(n)}_{\xi'\eta'} = \sum_{j=1}^{k} Q^{(n)}_{\xi'_j\eta'_j} = \frac{1}{\pi}\sum_{j=1}^{k} \int |r_{\xi'_j\eta'_j}(\lambda)|^n d\lambda, \tag{11.2.1}$$

where $k \leqslant \min(l, m)$; $r_{\xi'_j\eta'_j}(\lambda) = \dfrac{f_{\xi'_j\eta'_j}(\lambda)}{\sqrt{f_{\xi'_j\xi'_j}(\lambda) f_{\eta'_j\eta'_j}(\lambda)}}$.

The limits of integration are $0, \pi$ if ξ and η are discrete-parameter processes, and $0, \infty$ if ξ and η are continuous-parameter or generalized processes. If $l = m = 1$, formula (11.2.1) becomes

$$Q^{(n)}_{\xi\eta} = \frac{1}{\pi}\int |r_{\xi_j\eta_j}(\lambda)|^n d\lambda.$$

THEOREM 11.2.1. Suppose that (ξ, η) is a stationary gaussian process consisting of the one-dimensional processes $\xi = \{\xi(\cdot)\}$ and $\eta = \{\eta(\cdot)\}$. Then if

$$\bar{I}(\xi, \eta) = L_{\xi\eta}, \tag{11.2.2}$$

where $L_{\xi\eta}$ has the same meaning as in the preceding chapter, then

$$\bar{I}^{(2)}_{\xi\eta} = \bar{D}(\xi, \eta) = \lim_{T\to\infty} \frac{1}{T} Di(\xi^T_0, \eta^T_0) = \lim \frac{1}{T}\mathbf{E}(i(\xi^T_0, \eta^T_0) - I(\xi^T_0, \eta^T_0))^2 = Q^{(2)}_{\xi\eta} \tag{11.2.3}$$

and $$\bar{I}^{(q)}_{\xi\eta} = \lim_{T\to\infty} I^{(q)}_{\xi^T_0\eta^T_0} = \lim_{T\to\infty} \frac{1}{T}\sum_j \mathbf{E}\{[(i((\xi^T_0)'_j, (\eta^T_0)'_j) - I((\xi^T_0)'_j, (\eta^T_0)'_j)]^q\}$$

$$= \begin{cases} g(q) Q^{(q)}_{\xi\eta} \text{ for } q = 2n \\ 0 \text{ for } q = 2n+1, \end{cases} \tag{11.2.4}$$

($g(q)$ is defined in the statement of Lemma 9.6.1) where $(\xi^T_0)'_1$, $(\xi^T_0)'_2, \ldots$; $(\eta^T_0)'_1$, $(\eta^T_0)'_2, \ldots$ are sequences of independent gaussian random variables which are the proper vectors of the operators $\Pi_{\xi^T_0\eta^T_0\xi^T_0}$ and $\Pi_{\eta^T_0\xi^T_0\eta^T_0}$ corresponding to non-zero proper values, and labeled so that their proper values $\lambda_1 \geqslant \lambda_2 \geqslant \ldots$ are in non-increasing order.

The quantity $\bar{I}^2_{\xi\eta}$ is called the rate of creation of variance of the information density of ξ and η, and $\bar{I}^{(n)}_{\xi\eta}$ is called the rate of creation of the reduced n-th central moment of the information density of ξ and η.

Before turning to the proof of this theorem, we establish the validity of several lemmas.

LEMMA 11.2.1. Let $\xi = \{\xi(\cdot)\}$ *and* $\eta = \{\eta(\cdot)\}$ *be one-dimensional complex-valued wide-sense stationary and stationarily correlated random processes, such that the spectral function of* ξ *is absolutely continuous, and let* α *be any random variable from* B_ξ, *and* $\hat{\alpha}$ *the perpendicular from* α *onto* B_η; *then*

$$\mathbf{E}|\alpha|^2 \inf_{f_{\xi\xi}(\lambda)\neq 0}(1 - |r_{\xi\eta}(\lambda)|^2) \leqslant \mathbf{E}|\hat{\alpha}|^2 \leqslant \sup_{f_{\xi\xi}(\lambda)\neq 0}(1 - |r_{\xi\eta}(\lambda)|^2)\mathbf{E}|\alpha|^2. \tag{11.2.5}$$

PROOF. Let U_t be the one-parameter group of unitary operators corresponding to the process (ξ, η), and $\alpha(t) = U_t\alpha$, $\hat{\alpha}(t) = U_t\hat{\alpha}$, $-\infty < t < \infty$.

Obviously $\alpha = \{\alpha(t)\}$ is linearly subordinate to ξ, and is wide-sense stationary and stationarily correlated with ξ, and $\hat{\alpha} = \{\hat{\alpha}(t)\}$ is in fact (as the notation suggests) wide-sense stationary, and $\hat{\alpha}(t)$ is the perpendicular from $\alpha(t)$ onto the space B_η. Therefore, according to Lemma 10.1.5 and the remarks following it

$$\frac{\begin{vmatrix} f_{\xi\xi}(\lambda) & \overline{f_{\xi\eta}(\lambda)} \\ f_{\xi\eta}(\lambda) & f_{\eta\eta}(\lambda)\end{vmatrix}}{f_{\xi\xi}(\lambda)f_{\eta\eta}(\lambda)} = \frac{\begin{vmatrix} f_{\alpha\alpha}(\lambda) & \overline{f_{\alpha\eta}(\lambda)} \\ f_{\alpha\eta}(\lambda) & f_{\eta\eta}(\lambda)\end{vmatrix}}{f_{\alpha\alpha}(\lambda)f_{\eta\eta}(\lambda)}; \quad f_{\hat{\alpha}\hat{\alpha}}(\lambda) = \frac{\begin{vmatrix} f_{\alpha\alpha}(\lambda) & \overline{f_{\alpha\eta}(\lambda)} \\ f_{\alpha\eta}(\lambda) & f_{\eta\eta}(\lambda)\end{vmatrix}}{f_{\eta\eta}(\lambda)}; \quad f_{\xi\xi}(\lambda),\ f_{\alpha\alpha}(\lambda) \neq 0,$$

from which

$$f_{\hat{\alpha}\hat{\alpha}}(\lambda) = \frac{\begin{vmatrix} f_{\xi\xi}(\lambda) & \overline{f_{\xi\eta}(\lambda)} \\ f_{\xi\eta}(\lambda) & f_{\eta\eta}(\lambda)\end{vmatrix} f_{\alpha\alpha}(\lambda)}{f_{\eta\eta}(\lambda)f_{\xi\xi}(\lambda)} = (1 - |r_{\xi\eta}(\lambda)|^2 f_{\alpha\alpha}(\lambda)$$

$$\text{and} \quad \mathbf{E}|\hat{\alpha}|^2 = \int f_{\hat{\alpha}\hat{\alpha}}(\lambda)d\lambda = \int (1 - |r_{\xi\eta}(\lambda)|^2)f_{\alpha\alpha}(\lambda)d\lambda,$$

and consequently

$$\mathbf{E}|\alpha|^2 \inf_{f_{\xi\xi}(\lambda)\neq 0}(1 - |r_{\xi\eta}(\lambda)|^2) \leqslant \int_{f_{\xi\xi}(\lambda')\neq 0} f_{\alpha\alpha}(\lambda')d\lambda' \inf_{f_{\xi\xi}(\lambda)\neq 0}(1 - |r_{\xi\eta}(\lambda)|^2)$$

$$\leqslant \int_{f_{\xi\xi}(\lambda)\neq 0}(1 - |r_{\xi\eta}(\lambda)|^2)f_{\alpha\alpha}(\lambda)d\lambda = \mathbf{E}|\hat{\alpha}|^2 = \int_{f_{\xi\xi}(\lambda')\neq 0} f_{\alpha\alpha}(\lambda')d\lambda'$$

$$\sup_{f_{\xi\xi}(\lambda)\neq 0}(1 - |r_{\xi\eta}(\lambda)|^2) = \mathbf{E}|\alpha|^2 \sup_{f_{\xi\xi}(\lambda)\neq 0}(1 - |r_{\xi\eta}(\lambda)|^2)$$

which proves the lemma.

COROLLARY 1. Let ξ and η be one-dimensional complex valued processes, stationary and stationarily correlated in the wide sense, where the spectral function of the process ξ is absolutely continuous, and let ν be a random variable which is linearly subordinate to the random variable ξ. Then

$$\inf_{f_{\xi\xi}(\lambda)\neq 0} |r_{\xi\eta}(\lambda)|^2 \leqslant \lambda_j \leqslant \sup_{f_{\xi\xi}(\lambda)\neq 0} |r_{\xi\eta}(\lambda)|^2, \tag{11.2.6}$$

where λ_j is any proper value of the operator $\Pi_{\nu\eta\nu}$.

In fact, let $\alpha^* \in B_\nu$ be any proper vector of the operator $\Pi_{\nu\eta\nu}$, with proper value λ_j, and let $\hat{\alpha}^*$ and β^* be respectively the perpendicular and the projection of α^* onto B_η; then

$$\lambda_j = r^2_{\alpha^*\beta^*} = \frac{(E\alpha^*\overline{\beta^*})}{E|\alpha^*|^2 E|\beta^*|^2} = \frac{(E|\beta^*|^2)^2}{E|\alpha^*|^2 E|\beta^*|^2} = \frac{E|\beta^*|^2}{E|\alpha^*|^2} = \frac{E|\alpha^* - \hat{\alpha}^*|^2}{E|\alpha^*|^2}$$

$$= \frac{E|\alpha^*|^2 - E|\hat{\alpha}^*|^2}{E|\alpha^*|^2} = 1 - \frac{E|\hat{\alpha}^*|^2}{E|\alpha^*|^2}$$

and in order to obtain (11.2.6) it suffices to apply (11.2.5).

COROLLARY 2. Let (ξ, η) be a two-dimensional discrete-parameter stationary gaussian process, where the spectral function of the process ξ is absolutely continuous. Then

$$g(2n)\, \inf |r_{\xi\eta}(\lambda)|^{2n} \leqslant \underline{\lim}_{T\to\infty} \frac{1}{T} I^{(2n)}_{\xi_0^T\eta} \leqslant \overline{\lim}_{T\to\infty} \frac{1}{T} I^{(2n)}_{\xi_0^T\eta} \leqslant g(2n) \sup |r_{\xi\eta}(\lambda)|^{2n}. \tag{11.2.7}$$

In fact, if λ_{jT}, $j = 1, \ldots, T$ are the proper values of the operator $\Pi_{\xi_0^T\eta\xi_0^T\eta}$, then by Corollary 1 $\inf|r_{\xi\eta}(\lambda)|^{2n} \leqslant \lambda_j^n \leqslant \sup|r_{\xi\eta}(\lambda)|^{2n}$.

From this relation and the equation $I^{(2n)}_{\xi_0^T\eta} = \sum_{j=1}^{n} g(2n)\, \lambda^n_{jT}$ follows (11.2.7).

LEMMA 11.2.2. Let (ξ, η, ν) be a gaussian random variable, let ν be linearly subordinate to ξ, and assume $I(\xi, \eta) < \infty$. Then the operators $\Pi_{\nu\eta\nu}$ and $\Pi_{\xi\eta\xi}$ are completely continuous, and the sequences of their non-zero proper values $\lambda_1' \geqslant \lambda_2' \geqslant \ldots, \lambda_1 \geqslant \lambda_2 \geqslant \ldots$ satisfy the relation

$$\frac{1}{2n} \sum_j (\lambda_j^n - \lambda'^n_j) \leqslant I(\xi, \eta) - I(\nu, \eta). \tag{11.2.8}$$

PROOF. The complete continuity of the operators $\Pi_{\nu\eta\nu}$ and $\Pi_{\xi\eta\xi}$ follows from the finiteness of the information $I(\xi, \eta)$. By Lemma 9.5.1 $\lambda_j' \leqslant \lambda_j$, so that the series on the left side of (11.2.3) consists of non-negative terms. According to (9.2.20)

$$I(\xi, \eta) = -\frac{1}{2}\sum_j \log(1 - \lambda_j), \; I(\nu, \eta) = -\frac{1}{2}\sum_j \log(1 - \lambda_j'),$$

and since $-\log(1 - x) \geqslant x$ and $\lambda_j', \lambda_j \leqslant 1$,

$$I(\xi, \eta) - I(\nu, \eta) = -\frac{1}{2}\sum_j \log(1 - \lambda_j) + \frac{1}{2}\sum_j \log(1 - \lambda_j')$$

$$= -\frac{1}{2}\sum_j \log\frac{1 - \lambda_j}{1 - \lambda_j'} = -\frac{1}{2}\sum_j \log\left(1 - \frac{\lambda_j - \lambda_j'}{1 - \lambda_j'}\right)$$

$$\geqslant \frac{1}{2}\sum_j \frac{\lambda_j - \lambda_j'}{1 - \lambda_j'} \geqslant \frac{1}{2}\sum_j (\lambda_j - \lambda_j')$$

Moreover

$$\lambda_j^n - \lambda_j'^n = (\lambda_j - \lambda_j')\sum_{k=0}^{n-1} \lambda_j^k \lambda_j'^{n-k-1} \leqslant (\lambda_j - \lambda_j')n.$$

Comparing the last two relations, we obtain (11.2.8).

COROLLARY. Under the conditions of the lemma

$$I_{\xi\eta}^{(2n)} - I_{\nu\eta}^{(2n)} \leqslant 2n\, g(2n)(I(\xi, \eta) - I(\nu, \eta)). \tag{11.2.9}$$

LEMMA 11.2.3. Let $(\xi, \eta) = \{(\xi(t), \eta(t))\}$ be as in Corollary 2 above, and let

$$0 < r_1^2 \leqslant |r_{\xi\eta}(\lambda)|^2 \leqslant r_2^2 < 1, \text{ for } \lambda \in N',$$

$$f_{\xi\xi}(\lambda) \begin{cases} \geqslant d \text{ for } \lambda \in N' \\ = d \text{ for } \lambda \in N'' \end{cases} \quad N' + N'' = (-\pi, \pi).$$

$$f_{\eta\eta}(\lambda) = 0 \text{ for } \lambda \in N''.$$

Then denoting by $\lambda_{jT}, j = 1, \ldots, T$ the proper values of the operator $\Pi_{\xi_0^T \eta \xi_0^T}$ and setting

$$r_1^2 = \inf_{\lambda \in N'} |r_{\xi\eta}(\lambda)|^2, \; r_2^2 = \sup_{\lambda \in N'} |r_{\xi\eta}(\lambda)|^2, \tag{11.2.10}$$

we have

$$\frac{\mu(N')}{2\pi} r_1^{2n} \leqslant \varliminf_{T\to\infty} \frac{1}{T}\sum_{j=1}^{T} \lambda_{jT}^n \leqslant \varlimsup_{T\to\infty} \frac{1}{T}\sum_{j=1}^{T} \lambda_{jT}^n \leqslant \frac{\mu(N')}{2\pi} r_2^{2n}, \tag{11.2.11}$$

where $\mu(N')$ is the Lebesgue measure of the set N'.

PROOF. We introduce discrete-parameter stationary and stationarily correlated gaussian processes ξ'' and η'' such that the pair (ξ'', η'') is independent of the pair (ξ, η), and the processes ξ'' and η'' have spectral and joint spectral densities of the form

$$f_{\xi''\xi''}(\lambda) = \begin{cases} b > d > 0 \\ \delta > 0, \delta < d \end{cases}; \; f_{\eta''\eta''}(\lambda) = \begin{cases} 1 \\ 0, \end{cases} \; f_{\xi''\eta''}(\lambda) = \begin{cases} \sqrt{r_1^2 b} & \text{for } \lambda \in N'' \\ 0 & \text{for } \lambda \in N', \end{cases}$$

so that

$$r^2_{\xi''\eta''}(\lambda) = \begin{cases} r_1^2 & \text{for } \lambda \in N'' \\ 0 & \text{for } \lambda \in N'. \end{cases} \tag{11.2.13}$$

Setting $\nu = (\xi, \xi'')$, $\zeta = (\eta, \eta'')$, $\xi'(t) = \xi(t) + \xi''(t)$, $\xi' = \{\xi'(t)\}$,
$\eta'(t) = \eta(t) + \eta''(t)$, $\eta' = \{\eta'(t)\}$,

we have

$$|r_{\xi'\eta'}(\lambda)|^2 = \frac{|f_{\xi'\eta'}(\lambda)|^2}{f_{\xi'\xi'}(\lambda) f_{\eta'\eta'}(\lambda)} = \begin{cases} \dfrac{|f_{\xi\eta}(\lambda)|^2}{(f_{\xi\xi}(\lambda) + \delta) f_{\eta\eta}(\lambda)} & \text{for } \lambda \in N''. \\ \dfrac{f^2_{\xi''\eta''}(\lambda)}{(f_{\xi''\xi''}(\lambda) + d) f_{\eta''\eta''}(\lambda)} = \dfrac{r_1^2 b}{b + d} & \text{for } \lambda \in N' \end{cases} \tag{11.2.14}$$

From (11.2.14) and (11.2.10) it is evident that for any $\epsilon > 0$ one can choose $\delta > 0$ sufficiently small and $b > 0$ sufficiently large so that

$$r_1^2 - \epsilon \leqslant |r_{\xi'\eta'}(\lambda)|^2 \leqslant r_2^2 + \epsilon. \tag{11.2.15}$$

But then by Corollary 1 of Lemma 11.2.1, the proper values λ'_{jT} of the operator $\Pi_{(\xi')_0^T \eta' (\xi')_0^T}$ satisfy the inequality

$$r_1^2 - \epsilon \leqslant \lambda'_{jT} \leqslant r_2^2 + \epsilon, \tag{11.2.16}$$

and so

$$(r_1^2 - \epsilon)^n \leqslant \frac{1}{T} \sum_{j=1}^{T} \lambda'^n_{jT} \leqslant (r_2^2 + \epsilon)^n. \tag{11.2.17}$$

Furthermore, since the random variables $(\xi')_0^T$ and η' are respectively linearly subordinate to the random variables $\nu_0^T = (\xi_0^T, (\xi'')_0^T)$ and $\zeta = (\eta, \eta'')$, according to Lemma 9.5.1 the j-th proper value $\tilde{\lambda}_{jT}$ of the operator $\Pi_{\nu_0^T \zeta \nu_0^T}$ is not less than the j-th proper value λ'_{jT} of the operator $\Pi_{(\xi')_0^T \eta' (\xi')_0^T}$, and by Lemma 11.2.2

$$\sum_{j=1}^{2T} \tilde{\lambda}^n_{jT} - \sum_{j=1}^{T} \lambda'^n_{jT} \leqslant 2n(I(\nu_0^T, \zeta) - I((\xi')_0^T, \eta')). \tag{11.2.18}$$

On the other hand, since the random variables (ξ, η) and (ξ'', η'') are mutually independent, the proper values $\tilde{\lambda}_{jT}$ of the operator $\Pi_{\nu_0^T \zeta \nu_0^T}$ consist of the proper values λ_{jT} and λ''_{jT} of the operators $\Pi_{\xi_0^T \eta \xi_0^T}$ and $\Pi_{(\xi'')_0^T \eta''(\xi'')_0^T}$ and

$$I(\nu_0^T, \zeta) = I(\xi_0^T, \eta) + I((\xi'')_0^T, \eta''). \tag{11.2.19}$$

Consequently, if we denote by l_T and l''_T the number of proper values of the operators $\Pi_{\xi_0^T \eta \xi_0^T}$ and $\Pi_{(\xi'')_0^T \eta''(\xi'')_0^T}$, satisfying the condition (11.2.16), then

$$l_T + l''_T \geqslant T. \tag{11.2.20}$$

Let us estimate the value of the quantity

$$\sum_{j=1}^{2T} \tilde{\lambda}_{jT}^n = \sum_{j=1}^{T} \lambda_{jT}^n + \sum_{j=1}^{T} \lambda''^n_{jT} \tag{11.2.21}$$

and the numbers l_T and l''_T.

According to (9.2.20) and the definition of l_T

$$I(\xi_0^T, \eta) = -\frac{1}{2}\sum_{j=1}^{T} \log(1 - \lambda_{jT}) \geqslant -\frac{1}{2} l_T \log(1 - r_1^2 + \epsilon),$$

which shows that

$$l_T \leqslant -\frac{2I(\xi_0^T, \eta)}{\log(1 - r_1^2 + \epsilon)} \quad \text{for } 1 - r_1^2 + \epsilon \leqslant 1 \tag{11.2.22}$$

Since $f_{\xi'\xi'}(\lambda) \geqslant d, f_{\xi\xi}(\lambda) \geqslant d, f_{\xi''\xi''}(\lambda) \geqslant \delta$, the processes ξ', ξ, ξ'' are non-singular. Therefore

$$\lim_{T\to\infty} \frac{1}{T} I((\xi')_0^T, \eta') = \bar{I}(\xi', \eta') = -\frac{1}{4\pi}\int_{-\pi}^{\pi} \log(1 - |r_{\xi'\eta'}(\lambda)|^2)d\lambda;$$

$$\lim_{T\to\infty} \frac{1}{T} I(\xi_0^T, \eta) = \bar{I}(\xi, \eta) = -\frac{1}{4\pi}\int_{-\pi}^{\pi} \log(1 - |r_{\xi\eta}(\lambda)|^2)d\lambda$$

$$= -\frac{1}{4\pi}\int_{N'} \log(1 - |r_{\xi\eta}(\lambda)|^2)d\lambda;$$

$$\lim_{T\to\infty} \frac{1}{T} I((\xi'')_0^T, \eta'') = \bar{I}(\xi'', \eta'') = -\frac{1}{4\pi}\int_{-\pi}^{\pi} \log(1 - |r_{\xi''\eta''}(\lambda)|^2)d\lambda$$

$$= -\frac{1}{4\pi}\int_{N''} \log(1 - |r_{\xi''\eta''}(\lambda)|^2)d\lambda = -\frac{\mu(N'')}{4\pi}\log(1 - r_1^2).$$

Comparing these relations with (11.2.18), (11.2.19) and (11.2.22), we find that for sufficiently small δ and sufficiently large b

$$\overline{\lim_{T\to\infty}} \frac{1}{T}\left(\sum_{j=1}^{2T} \tilde{\lambda}_{jT}^{n} - \sum_{j=1}^{T} \lambda_{jT}'^{n}\right) \leqslant -\frac{n}{2\pi}\int_{N'} \log\left(1 - |r_{\xi\eta}(\lambda)|^2 d\lambda\right.$$
$$-\frac{1}{2\pi}\int_{N''} \log\left(1 - r_{\xi''\eta''}^2(\lambda)\right)d\lambda + \frac{n}{2\pi}\int_{-\pi}^{\pi} \log\left(1 - |r_{\xi'\eta'}(\lambda)|^2\right)d\lambda < \epsilon^n \tag{11.2.23}$$

$$\overline{\lim_{T\to\infty}} \frac{1}{T} l_T \leqslant \frac{\frac{n}{2\pi}\int_{N'} \log\left(1 - |r_{\xi\eta}(\lambda)|^2\right)d\lambda}{\log\left(1 - r_1^2 + \epsilon\right)} \leqslant \frac{\frac{\mu(N')}{2\pi}\log\left(1 - r_2^2\right)}{\log\left(1 - r_1^2 + \epsilon\right)}. \tag{11.2.24}$$

Comparing inequality (11.2.23) with (11.2.17) and (11.2.21), we see that for sufficiently large T

$$(r_1^2 - \epsilon)^n - \epsilon^n \leqslant \frac{1}{T}\sum_{j=1}^{T} (\lambda_{jT}^n + \lambda_{jT}''^n) \leqslant (r_2^2 + \epsilon)^n + \epsilon^n. \tag{11.2.25}$$

Applying relation (11.2.24) to the pair (ξ'', η''), which satisfies the conditions of the lemma with $r_2^2 = r_1^2$ and N' replaced by N''; we have

$$\overline{\lim_{T\to\infty}} \frac{1}{T} l_T'' \leqslant \frac{\frac{\mu(N')}{2\pi}\log\left(1 - r_1^2\right)}{\log\left(1 - r_1^2 + \epsilon\right)}. \tag{11.2.26}$$

Now ϵ can be taken so small that from relations (11.2.25) (11.2.24) and (11.2.26) follows

$$r_1^{2n} - \sqrt{\epsilon} \leqslant \frac{1}{T}\sum_{j=1}^{T} (\lambda_{jT}^n + \lambda_{jT}''^n) \leqslant r_2^{2n} + \sqrt{\epsilon}\,; \tag{11.2.27}$$

$$\overline{\lim_{T\to\infty}} \frac{1}{T} l_T \leqslant \left(\frac{\mu(N')}{2\pi} + \sqrt{\epsilon}\right)\frac{\log\left(1 - r_2^2\right)}{\log\left(1 - r_1^2\right)};\quad \overline{\lim_{T\to\infty}} \frac{1}{T} l_T'' \leqslant \frac{\mu(N'')}{2\pi} + \sqrt{\epsilon}. \tag{11.2.28}$$

Before completing the proof of the lemma, we consider the particular case in which $r_1^2 = r_2^2$; then inequalities (11.2.27) and (11.2.28) become

$$r_1^{2n} - \sqrt{\epsilon} \leqslant \frac{1}{T}\sum_{j=1}^{T} (\lambda_{jT}^n + \lambda_{jT}''^n) \leqslant r_1^{2n} + \sqrt{\epsilon}\,; \tag{11.2.29}$$

$$\overline{\lim_{T\to\infty}}\frac{1}{T}l_T \leqslant \frac{\mu(N')}{2\pi} + \sqrt{\epsilon}, \quad \overline{\lim_{T\to\infty}}\frac{1}{T}l''_T \leqslant \frac{\mu(N'')}{2\pi} + \sqrt{\epsilon}. \tag{11.2.30}$$

In view of (11.2.20)

$$1 - \overline{\lim_{T\to\infty}}\frac{1}{T}l''_T \leqslant \underline{\lim}_{T\to\infty}\frac{1}{T}l_T. \tag{11.2.31}$$

Comparing (11.2.30) and (11.2.31), we see that

$$\frac{\mu(N')}{2\pi} - \sqrt{\epsilon} \leqslant \underline{\lim}_{T\to\infty}\frac{1}{T}l_T \leqslant \overline{\lim_{T\to\infty}}\frac{1}{T}l_T \leqslant \frac{\mu(N')}{2\pi} + \sqrt{\epsilon}. \tag{11.2.32}$$

In accordance with the definition of l_T, it follows from inequality (11.2.32) that for sufficiently small $\epsilon > 0$

$$\overline{\lim_{T\to\infty}}\frac{1}{T}\sum_{j=1}^{T}\lambda_{jT}^n \geqslant \underline{\lim}_{T\to\infty}\frac{1}{T}\sum_{j=1}^{T}\lambda_{jT}^n \geqslant \left(\frac{\mu(N')}{2\pi} - \sqrt{\epsilon}\right)(r_1^2 - \epsilon)^n$$
$$> \frac{\mu(N')}{2\pi} r_1^{2n} - \sqrt{\epsilon} \tag{11.2.33}$$

One can similarly show that for sufficiently small $\epsilon > 0$

$$\overline{\lim_{T\to\infty}}\frac{1}{T}\sum_{j=1}^{T}\lambda''^n_{jT} \geqslant \underline{\lim}_{T\to\infty}\frac{1}{T}\sum_{j=1}^{T}\lambda''^n_{jT}\,\frac{\mu(N'')}{2\pi} r_1^{2n} - \sqrt{\epsilon}. \tag{11.2.34}$$

Comparing (11.2.34) with (11.2.29), we find that

$$\underline{\lim}_{T\to\infty}\frac{1}{T}\sum_{j=1}^{T}\lambda_{jT}^n \leqslant \overline{\lim_{T\to\infty}}\frac{1}{T}\sum_{j=1}^{T}\lambda_{jT}^n \leqslant r_1^{2n} + \sqrt{\epsilon} - \left(\frac{\mu(N'')}{2\pi} r_1^{2n} - \sqrt{\epsilon}\right)$$
$$\leqslant \frac{\mu(N')}{2\pi} r_1^{2n} + 2\sqrt{\epsilon}. \tag{11.2.35}$$

Comparing (11.2.35) and (11.2.33), and taking into account the arbitrariness of ϵ, we see that

$$\lim_{T\to\infty}\frac{1}{T}\sum_{j=1}^{T}\lambda_{jT}^n \leqslant r_1^{2n}\frac{\mu(N')}{2\pi}. \tag{11.2.36}$$

i.e., we have obtained the conclusion of the lemma in the case $r_2^2 = r_1^2$. Applying (11.2.36) to the pair (ξ'', η'') leads to

$$\lim_{T\to\infty}\frac{1}{T}\sum_{j=1}^{T}\lambda''^n_{jT} \leqslant r_1^{2n}\frac{\mu(N'')}{2\pi}. \tag{11.2.37}$$

We return now to the general case, in which the equation $r_2^2 = r_1^2$ need not hold. Comparing (11.2.27) with (11.2.37) shows that

$$\underline{\lim}_{T\to\infty}\frac{1}{T}\sum_{j=1}^{T}\lambda_{jT}^{n} \geqslant (r_1^{2n}+\sqrt{\epsilon}) - r_1^{2n}\frac{\mu(N'')}{2\pi} = r_1^{2n}\frac{\mu(N')}{2\pi} - \sqrt{\epsilon}.$$

$$(11.2.38)$$

Since ϵ is arbitrary

$$\underline{\lim}_{T\to\infty}\frac{1}{T}\sum_{j=1}^{T}\lambda_{jT}^{n} \geqslant r_1^{2n}\frac{\mu(N')}{2\pi}. \qquad (11.2.39)$$

Similarly, one can establish the inequality

$$\overline{\lim}_{T\to\infty}\frac{1}{T}\sum_{j=1}^{T}\lambda_{jT}^{n} \leqslant r_2^{2n}\frac{\mu(N')}{2\pi}. \qquad (11.2.40)$$

if one uses the pair (ξ'', η''), as defined by (11.2.12) and (11.2.13), but with r_1 everywhere replaced by r_2, i.e., so that

$$r^2_{\xi''\eta''}(\lambda) = \begin{cases} r_2^2 \text{ for } \lambda\epsilon N'' \\ 0 \text{ for } \lambda\epsilon N'. \end{cases} \qquad (11.2.41)$$

Comparing inequalities (11.2.39) and (11.2.40) leads to formula (11.2.11).

COROLLARY. If (ξ, η) is a stationary gaussian process which satisfies the conditions of the lemma, then

$$g(2n)\frac{\mu(N')}{2\pi}r_1^{2n} \leqslant \underline{\lim}_{T\to\infty}\frac{1}{T}I^{(2n)}_{\xi_0^T\eta} = \overline{\lim}_{T\to\infty}\frac{1}{T}I^{(2n)}_{\xi_0^T\eta} \leqslant g(2n)\frac{\mu(N')}{2\pi}r_2^{2n}.$$

$$(11.2.42)$$

We proceed to the proof of the theorem. We distinguish three cases:

(1) ξ and η are discrete-parameter processes;
(2) ξ and η are continuous-parameter processes;
(3) ξ and η are generalized random processes.

(1) Let us first assume that

$$f_{\xi\xi}(\lambda) \geqslant d > 0, \quad |r_{\xi\eta}(\lambda)|^2 < c < 1. \qquad (11.2.43)$$

We subdivide the interval $(-\Pi, \Pi)$ into sets $N_1, \ldots, N_m$, on which

$$\frac{k-1}{m} \leqslant |r_{\xi\eta}(\lambda)|^2 < \frac{k}{m} \text{ for } \lambda\in N_k,\ k=1,\ldots,m, \qquad (11.2.44)$$

and introduce discrete-parameter stationary gaussian processes $\alpha_k = \{\alpha_k(t)\}$ which are independent of each other and of (ξ, η), and which have spectral densities of the form

$$f_{\alpha_k\alpha_k}(\lambda) = \begin{cases} 0 & \text{for } \lambda \in N_k \\ \dfrac{\epsilon}{m(m-1)} < d & \text{for } \lambda \notin N_k . \end{cases} \tag{11.2.45}$$

Setting

$$\beta = (\beta_1, \ldots, \beta_m),\ \beta_k(t) = \int_{N_k} e^{it\lambda} dz_\xi(\lambda)$$

$$+\ \alpha_k(t),\ \tilde{\beta} = \{\tilde{\beta}(t)\},\ \tilde{\beta}(t) = \sum_{k=1}^{m} \beta_k(t);$$

$$\gamma = (\gamma_1, \ldots, \gamma_m),\ \gamma_k(t) = \int_{N_k} e^{it\lambda} dz_\eta(\lambda),\ \ \eta = \{\eta(t)\},\ \eta(t) = \sum_{k=1}^{m} \gamma_k(t), \tag{11.2.46}$$

we have

$$f_{\beta_k\beta_k}(\lambda) = \begin{cases} f_{\xi\xi}(\lambda) \\ \dfrac{\epsilon}{m(m-1)} \end{cases};\ f_{\gamma_k\gamma_k}(\lambda) = \begin{cases} f_{\eta\eta}(\lambda) \\ 0 \end{cases};\ f_{\beta_k\gamma_k}(\lambda) = \begin{cases} f_{\xi\eta}(\lambda) & \text{for } \lambda \in N_k \\ 0 & \text{for } \lambda \notin N_k \end{cases} \tag{11.2.47}$$

and consequently

$$|r_{\beta_k\gamma_k}(\lambda)|^2 = -\frac{|f_{\beta_k\gamma_k}(\lambda)|^2}{f_{\beta_k\beta_k}(\lambda) f_{\gamma_k\gamma_k}} = \begin{cases} \dfrac{|f_{\xi\eta}(\lambda)|^2}{f_{\xi\xi}(\lambda) f_{\eta\eta}(\lambda)} = |r_{\xi\eta}(\lambda)|^2 & \text{for } \lambda \in N_k \\ 0 & \text{for } \lambda \notin N_k \end{cases} \tag{11.2.48}$$

and

$$|r_{\tilde{\beta}\eta}(\lambda)|^2 = \frac{|f_{\tilde{\beta}\eta}(\lambda)|^2}{f_{\tilde{\beta}\tilde{\beta}}(\lambda) f_{\eta\eta}(\lambda)} = \frac{|f_{\xi\eta}(\lambda)|^2}{\left(f_{\xi\xi}(\lambda) + \dfrac{\epsilon}{m}\right) f_{\eta\eta}(\lambda)} . \tag{11.2.49}$$

Obviously the pairs (β_k, γ_k), $k = 1, \ldots, m$ are independent of each other and, for $k > 1$, satisfy the conditions of Lemma 11.2.3, and so

$$I(\beta_0^T, \gamma) = \sum_{k=1}^{m} I((\beta_k)_0^T, \gamma_k);\ I^{(n)}_{\beta_0^T\gamma} = \sum_{k=1}^{m} I^{(n)}_{(\beta_k)_0^T\gamma_k} \tag{11.2.50}$$

Using the corollaries to Lemma 11.2.1 and 11.2.3, and setting $r_1^2 = \dfrac{k-1}{m}$, $r_2^2 = \dfrac{k}{m}$, $N' = N_k$, we have

$$g(2n)\left(\int_{N_1} |r_{\xi\eta}(\lambda)|^{2n} d\lambda - \left(\frac{1}{m}\right)^n\right) \leqslant 0 \leqslant \lim_{T\to\infty} \frac{1}{T} I^{(2n)}_{(\beta_1)_0^T\gamma_1}$$

$$\leqslant \overline{\lim_{T\to\infty}} \frac{1}{T} I^{(2n)}_{(\beta_1)_0^T\gamma_1} \leqslant g(2n)\left(\frac{1}{m}\right)^n \leqslant g(2n)\left(\int_{N_1} |r_{\xi\eta}(\lambda)|^{2n} d\lambda + \left(\frac{1}{m}\right)^n\right);$$

$$\frac{g(2n)}{2\pi}\int_{N_k}\left(|r_{\xi\eta}(\lambda)|^2 - \frac{1}{m}\right)^n d\lambda \leqslant \frac{g(2n)}{2\pi}\mu(N_k)\left(\frac{k-1}{m}\right)^n \leqslant \underline{\lim}_{T\to\infty} \frac{1}{T} I^{(2n)}_{(\beta_k)_0^T\gamma_k}$$

$$\leqslant \overline{\lim_{T\to\infty}} \frac{1}{T} I^{(2n)}_{(\beta_k)_0^T\gamma_k} \leqslant \frac{g(2n)}{2\pi}\mu(N_k)\left(\frac{k}{m}\right)^n \leqslant \frac{g(2n)}{2\pi}\int_{N_k}\left(|r_{\xi\eta}(\lambda)|^2 + \frac{1}{m}\right)^n d\lambda.$$

Summing each term of this series of inequalities with respect to k, and taking account of (11.2.50), we obtain

$$\frac{g(2n)}{2\pi}\left(\int_{-\pi}^{\pi}\left(|r_{\xi\eta}(\lambda)|^2 - \frac{1}{m}\right)^n d\lambda - 2\pi\left(\frac{1}{m}\right)^n\right) \leqslant \underline{\lim}_{T\to\infty} \frac{1}{T} I^{(2n)}_{\beta_0^T\gamma} \leqslant \overline{\lim_{T\to\infty}} \frac{1}{T} I^{(2n)}_{\beta_0^T\gamma}$$

$$\leqslant \frac{g(2n)}{2\pi}\left(\int_{-\pi}^{\pi}\left(|r_{\xi\eta}(\lambda)|^2 + \frac{1}{m}\right)^n d\lambda + 2\pi\left(\frac{1}{m}\right)^n\right). \qquad (11.2.51)$$

The random variables $\tilde{\beta}_0^T$ and η are respectively subordinate to the random variables β_0^T and γ, and of course ξ_0^T and $\tilde{\beta}_0^T$ are both subordinate to $(\xi_0^T, \tilde{\beta}_0^T)$. By the corollaries to Lemma 11.2.2

$$I^{(2n)}_{\beta_0^T\gamma} - I^{(2n)}_{\tilde{\beta}_0^T\eta} \leqslant 2ng(2n)(I(\beta_0^T, \gamma) - I(\tilde{\beta}_0^T, \eta))$$

$$= 2ng(2n)\left(\sum_{k=1}^{m} I((\beta_k)_0^T, \gamma_k) - I(\tilde{\beta}_0^T, \eta)\right) \qquad (11.2.52)$$

The sequence of random variables $\tilde{\beta}_0^T, \xi_0^T, \eta$ forms a Markov chain, therefore $I((\xi_0^T, \tilde{\beta}_0^T), \eta) = I(\xi_0^T, \eta)$, and the last two equations become

$$I^{(2n)}_{(\xi_0^T\tilde{\beta}_0^T)\eta} - I^{(2n)}_{\xi_0^T\eta} = 0; \qquad (11.2.53)$$

$$I^{(2n)}_{(\xi_0^T\tilde{\beta}_0^T)\eta} - I^{(2n)}_{\tilde{\beta}_0^T\eta} \leqslant 2n\, g(2n)(I(\xi_0^T, \eta) - I(\tilde{\beta}_0^T, \eta)). \qquad (11.2.54)$$

Since $f_{\tilde{\beta}\tilde{\beta}}(\lambda) \geqslant f_{\beta_k\beta_k}(\lambda) \geqslant \frac{\epsilon}{m^2}, f_{\xi\xi}(\lambda) \geqslant \frac{\epsilon}{m^2}$, the processes $\tilde{\beta}, \beta_k$ and ξ are non-singular, so that

$$\lim_{T\to\infty}\frac{1}{T} I((\beta_k)_0^T, \gamma_k) = \bar{I}(\beta_k, \gamma_k) = -\frac{1}{4\pi}\int_{-\pi}^{\pi} \log(1 - |r_{\beta_k\gamma_k}(\lambda)|^2) d\lambda$$

$$= -\frac{1}{4\pi}\int_{N_k} \log(1 - |r_{\xi\eta}(\lambda)|^2) d\lambda;$$

$$\lim_{T\to\infty} \frac{1}{T} I((\tilde{\beta}_0^T, \eta) = \tilde{I}(\tilde{\beta}, \eta) = -\frac{1}{4\pi}\int_{-\pi}^{\pi} \log (1 - |r_{\tilde{\beta}\eta}(\lambda)|^2) d\lambda;$$

$$\lim_{T\to\infty} \frac{1}{T} I(\xi_0^T, \eta) = \tilde{I}(\xi, \eta) = -\frac{1}{4\pi}\int_{-\pi}^{\pi} \log (1 - |r_{\xi\eta}(\lambda)|^2) d\lambda.$$

Comparing these relations with (11.2.52) and (11.2.54), we find that

$$\overline{\lim_{T\to\infty}} \frac{1}{T}\left(I^{(2n)}_{\beta_0^T\gamma} - I^{(2n)}_{\tilde{\beta}_0^T\eta}\right) \leqslant 2n\, g(2n)\Big(-\frac{1}{4\pi}\sum_{k=1}^{m}\int_{N_k} \log (1 - |r_{\xi\eta}(\lambda)|^2) d\lambda$$

$$+ \frac{1}{4\pi}\int_{-\pi}^{\pi} \log (1 - |r_{\tilde{\beta}\eta}(\lambda)|^2) d\lambda\Big) = 2n\, g(2n)(L_{\xi\eta} - L_{\tilde{\beta}\eta});$$

$$\overline{\lim_{T\to\infty}} \frac{1}{T}\left(I^{(2n)}_{(\xi_0^T\tilde{\beta}_0^T)} - I^{(2n)}_{\tilde{\beta}_0^T\eta}\right) \leqslant 2n\, g(2m) L_{\xi\eta} - L_{\tilde{\beta}\eta}).$$

From (11.2.49) it follows that the right side of the last relation will be less than ϵ for sufficiently large m, and so

$$\overline{\lim_{T\to\infty}} \frac{1}{T}\left(I^{(2n)}_{\beta_0^T\gamma} - I^{(2n)}_{\tilde{\beta}_0^T\eta}\right) < \epsilon; \quad \overline{\lim_{T\to\infty}} \frac{1}{T}\left(I^{(2n)}_{(\xi_0^T\tilde{\beta}_0^T)\eta} - I^{(2n)}_{\tilde{\beta}_0^T\eta}\right) < \epsilon.$$

Comparing this last result with (11.2.53) shows that

$$\overline{\lim_{T\to\infty}} \frac{1}{T}\left(I^{(2n)}_{\beta_0^T\gamma} - I^{(2n)}_{\xi_0^T\eta}\right) \leqslant 2\epsilon. \tag{11.2.55}$$

If we compare (11.2.51) with (11.2.55) and keep in mind that $\epsilon > 0$ and $m > 0$ are arbitrary, we arrive at

$$\lim_{T\to\infty} \frac{1}{T} I^{(2n)}_{\xi_0^T\eta} = \frac{g(2n)}{2\pi}\int_{-\pi}^{\pi} |r_{\xi\eta}(\lambda)|^{2n} d\lambda .$$

In order to obtain formula (11.2.4) it is sufficient to note that

$$I^{(2n+1)}_{\xi_0^T\eta_0^T} = 0 \text{ and } \overline{\lim_{T\to\infty}} \frac{1}{T}\left(I^{(2n)}_{\xi_0^T\eta} - I^{(2n)}_{\xi_0^T\eta_0^T}\right)$$

$$\leqslant \lim \frac{1}{T} 2n\, g(2n)(I(\xi_0^T, \eta) - I(\xi_0^T, \eta_0^T)) = 2n\, g(2n)(L_{\xi\eta} - L_{\xi\eta}) = 0.$$

If condition (11.2.43) is not fulfilled, then together with ξ we consider the process $\alpha = \{\alpha(t)\}$, $\alpha(t) = \xi(t) + \nu(t)$, where $\nu = \{\nu(t)\}$

is a stationary gaussian process which is independent of the pair (ξ, η), and which has spectral density of the form $f_{\nu\nu}(\lambda) = \delta(1 + f_{\xi\xi}(\lambda))$, where δ is a constant. The process α satisfies condition (11.2.43), and therefore

$$\lim_{T\to\infty} \frac{1}{T} I^{(2n)}_{\alpha_0^T \eta_0^T} = \frac{g(2n)}{2\pi} \int_{-\pi}^{\pi} |r_{\alpha\eta}(\lambda)|^{2n} d\lambda = g(2n) Q^{(2n)}_{\alpha\eta}. \qquad (11.2.56)$$

It is obvious that

$$\lim_{\delta\to+0} L_{\alpha\eta} = L_{\xi\eta}, \quad \lim_{\delta\to+0} Q^{(2n)}_{\alpha\eta} = Q^{(2n)}_{\xi\eta}. \qquad (11.2.57)$$

The sequence of random variables $\alpha_0^T, \xi_0^T, \eta^T$ forms a Markov chain, so that $I((\alpha_0^T, \xi_0^T), \eta_0^T) = I(\xi_0^T, \eta_0^T)$. Therefore

$$I^{(2n)}_{(\alpha_0^T \xi_0^T)\eta_0^T} - I^{(2n)}_{\xi_0^T \eta_0^T} \leqslant 2ng(2n)(I((\alpha_0^T, \xi_0^T), \eta_0^T) - I(\xi_0^T, \eta_0^T)) = 0;$$

$$\overline{\lim_{T\to\infty}} \frac{1}{T}\left(I^{(2n)}_{(\alpha_0^T \xi_0^T)\eta_0^T} - I^{(2n)}_{\alpha_0^T \eta_0^T}\right) \leqslant 2ng(2n) \lim_{T\to\infty} \frac{1}{T} (I((\alpha_0^T, \xi_0^T), \eta_0^T) - I(\alpha_0^T, \eta_0^T))$$

$$= 2ng(2n) \lim_{T\to\infty} \frac{1}{T} (I(\xi_0^T, \eta_0^T) - I(\alpha_0^T, \eta_0^T)) = 2ng(2n)(L_{\xi\eta} - L_{\alpha\eta})$$

from which follows

$$\overline{\lim_{T\to\infty}} \frac{1}{T} \left|I^{(2n)}_{\xi_0^T \eta_0^T} - I^{(2n)}_{\alpha_0^T \eta_0^T}\right| \leqslant 2ng(2n)(L_{\xi\eta} - L_{\alpha\eta}). \qquad (11.2.58)$$

Comparing (11.2.56)–(11.2.58) we see that

$$\bar{I}^{(2n)}_{\xi\eta} \lim_{T\to\infty} \frac{1}{T} I^{(2n)}_{\xi_0^T \eta_0^T} = g(2n) Q^{(2n)}_{\xi\eta}.$$

The case where the function $F_{\xi\xi}(\lambda)$ is not absolutely continuous leads in a similar manner to the case (11.2.43); one has only to make use of the fact that any gaussian process is decomposable into the sum of mutually independent processes with absolutely continuous and singular spectral functions.

This proves part 1 of the theorem.

(2) We consider the stationary and stationarily correlated discrete-parameter processes

$$\xi^{(h)} = \{\xi^{(h)}(n)\} = \{\xi(nh)\} \qquad \text{and} \qquad \eta^{(h)} = \{\eta^{(h)}(n)\} = \{\eta(nh)\},$$
$$h > 0, n = \ldots, -1, 0, 1, 2, \ldots,$$

which depend upon the "step" h. As was shown in the proof of Theorem 10.3.1

$$|r_{\xi^{(h)}\eta^{(h)}}(\lambda)|^{2n} = \frac{|f_{\xi^{(h)}\eta^{(h)}}(\lambda)|^{2n}}{(f_{\xi^{(h)}\xi^{(h)}}(\lambda)f_{\eta^{(h)}\eta^{(h)}}(\lambda))^n}$$
$$= \frac{\left|\sum_{k=-\infty}^{\infty} f_{\xi\eta}\left(\frac{\lambda + 2k\pi}{h}\right)\right|^{2n}}{\left(\sum_{k=-\infty}^{\infty} f_{\xi\xi}\left(\frac{\lambda + 2k\pi}{h}\right)^n \sum_{k=-\infty}^{\infty} f_{\eta\eta}\left(\frac{\lambda + 2k\pi}{h}\right)\right)^n}.$$

Let us assume first the process $\xi^{(h)}$ is not singular for any h (which will be the case, for example, if the process ξ is non-singular). Then the quantities $\bar{I}(\xi^{(h)}, \eta^{(h)}), \bar{\bar{I}}(\xi^{(h)}, \eta^{(h)})$ are defined, and according to part 1 of the present theorem and Lemma 10.3.1

$$\frac{1}{h}\bar{I}^{(2n)}_{\xi^{(h)}\eta^{(h)}} = \frac{1}{h}\lim_{T\to\infty}\frac{1}{T} \; I^{(2n)}_{(\xi^{(h)})_0^T(\eta^{(h)})_0^T} = \frac{1}{h}\,g(2n)Q^{(2n)}_{\xi^{(h)}\eta^{(h)}};$$

$$\lim_{h\to+0}\frac{1}{h}\,Q^{(2n)}_{\xi^{(h)}\eta^{(h)}} = \lim_{h\to+0}\frac{1}{2\pi h}\int_{-\pi}^{\pi}|r_{\xi^{(h)}\eta^{(h)}}(\lambda)|^{2n}d\lambda$$

$$= \lim_{h\to+0}\frac{1}{2\pi h}\int_{-\pi}^{\pi}\frac{\left|\sum_{k=-\infty}^{\infty} f_{\xi\eta}\left(\frac{\lambda + 2k\pi}{h}\right)\right|^{2n}}{\left(\sum_{k=-\infty}^{\infty} f_{\xi\xi}\left(\frac{\lambda + 2k\pi}{h}\right)\sum_{k=-\infty}^{\infty} f_{\eta\eta}\left(\frac{\lambda + 2k\pi}{h}\right)\right)^n}d\lambda$$

$$= \lim_{h\to+0}\frac{1}{2\pi}\int_{-\frac{\pi}{h}}^{\frac{\pi}{h}}\frac{\left|\sum_{k=-\infty}^{\infty} f_{\xi\eta}\left(\lambda + \frac{2k\pi}{h}\right)\right|^{2n}}{\left(\sum_{k=-\infty}^{\infty} f_{\xi\xi}\left(\lambda + \frac{2k\pi}{h}\right)\sum_{k=-\infty}^{\infty} f_{\eta\eta}\left(\lambda + \frac{2k\pi}{h}\right)^n\right)}d\lambda$$

$$= \frac{1}{2\pi}\int_{-\infty}^{\infty}\frac{|f_{\xi\eta}(\lambda)|^{2n}}{(f_{\xi\xi}(\lambda)f_{\eta\eta}(\lambda))^n}\,d\lambda = Q^{(2n)}_{\xi\eta}.$$

i.e.,

$$\lim_{h\to+0}\lim_{T\to\infty}\frac{1}{Th}I^{(2n)}_{(\xi^{(h)})_0^T(\eta^{(h)})_0^T} = g(2n)Q^{(2n)}_{\xi\eta}. \tag{11.2.59}$$

Obviously the random variable $(\xi^{(h)})_0^T = (\xi(h), \ldots, \xi(Th))$ is subordinate to the random variable ξ_0^{Th}, and similarly $(\eta^{(h)})_0^T$ is subordinate to η_0^{Th}. Therefore, according to the corollaries to Lemma 11.2.2

$$0 \leqslant \frac{1}{Th}\left(I^{(2n)}_{\xi_0^{Th}\eta_0^{Th}} - I^{(2n)}_{(\xi^{(h)})_0^T(\eta^{(h)})_0^T}\right)$$
$$\leqslant \frac{2ng(2n)}{Th}(I(\xi_0^{Th}, \eta_0^{Th}) - I((\xi^{h})_0^T, (\eta^{(h)})_0^T). \tag{11.2.60}$$

For the discrete-parameter non-singular processes $\xi^{(h)}$ $\bar{I}(\xi^{(h)}, \eta^{(h)}) = \bar{I}^{(g)}(\xi^{(h)}, \eta^{(h)})$, and therefore

$$\lim_{h\to+0}\lim_{T\to\infty}\frac{1}{Th}\bar{I}((\xi^{(h)})_0^T, (\eta^{(h)})_0^T) = \lim_{h\to+0}\frac{1}{h}\bar{I}(\xi^{(h)}, \eta^{(h)})$$

$$= \lim_{h\to+\infty}\frac{1}{h}\bar{I}^{(g)}(\xi^{(h)}, \eta^{(h)}) = \bar{I}^{(g)}(\xi, \eta) = L_{\xi\eta}. \tag{11.2.61}$$

By hypothesis

$$\lim_{T\to\infty}\frac{1}{Th}I(\xi_0^{Th}, \eta_0^{Th}) = L_{\xi\eta}. \tag{11.2.62}$$

Comparing (11.2.59) with (11.2.60)–(11.2.62), we find that

$$\bar{I}^{(2n)}_{\xi\eta} = \lim_{T\to\infty}\frac{1}{Th}I^{(2n)}_{\xi_0^{Th}\eta_0^{Th}} = g(2n)\,Q^{(2n)}_{\xi\eta}.$$

Moreover,

$$\bar{I}^{(2n+1)}_{\xi\eta} = \lim_{T\to\infty}\frac{1}{T}I^{(2n+1)}_{\xi_0^T\eta_0^T} = 0.$$

Thus part 2 of the theorem is proved in the case where the processes $\xi^{(h)}$ are non-singular. In the general case we introduce the stationary gaussian process $\alpha = \{\alpha(t)\}$, $\alpha(t) = \xi(t) + \nu(t)$, where $\nu = \{\nu(t)\}$ is a stationary gaussian process, independent of (ξ, η), and which has spectral density of the form

$$f_{\nu\nu}(\lambda) = \frac{\delta}{1+\lambda^2}, \quad \delta > 0. \tag{11.2.63}$$

Obviously

$$\lim_{\delta\to+0} = L_{\alpha\eta} = L_{\xi\eta} \text{ and } \lim_{\delta\to+0} Q^{(n)}_{\alpha\eta} = Q^{(n)}_{\xi\eta}. \tag{11.2.64}$$

The process $\alpha^{(h)}$ is non-singular for every $h > 0$, and therefore formulas (11.2.59), (11.2.61), which for the case in hand take the form

$$\lim_{h\to+0}\lim_{T\to\infty}\frac{1}{Th}\, I^{(2n)}_{(\alpha^{(h)})_0^T(\eta^{(h)})_0^T} = g(2n)Q^{(2n)}_{\alpha\eta};\ \lim_{h\to+0}\lim_{T\to\infty} I((\alpha^{(h)})_0^T,\ (\eta^{(h)})_0^T) = L_{\alpha\eta} \tag{11.2.65}$$

are valid. By the corollaries to Lemma 11.2.2

$$I^{(2n)}_{(\alpha_0^{Th}\xi_0^{Th})\eta_0^{Th}} - I^{(2n)}_{\xi_0^{Th}\eta_0^{Th}} \leqslant 2ng(2n)(I((\alpha_0^{Th},\ \xi_0^{Th}),\ \eta_0^{Th}) - I(\xi_0^{Th}, \eta_0^{Th})); \tag{11.2.66}$$

$$I^{(2n)}_{(\alpha_0^{Th}\xi_0^{Th})\eta_0^{Th}} - I^{(2n)}_{(\alpha^{(h)})_0^T(\eta^{(h)})_0^T} \leqslant 2ng(2n)(I((\alpha_0^{Th},\ \xi_0^{Th}),\ \eta_0^{Th}) - I((\alpha^{(h)})_0^T,\ (\eta^{(h)})_0^T)). \tag{11.2.67}$$

Since the sequence of random variables $\alpha_0^T, \xi_0^T, \eta_0^T$ forms a Markov chain, as a consequence of which $I((\alpha_0^T, \xi_0^T), \eta_0^T) = I(\xi_0^T, \eta_0^T)$, formulas (11.2.66) and (11.2.67) may be rewritten in the following form:

$$I^{(2n)}_{(\alpha_0^{Th}\xi_0^{Th})\eta_0^{Th}} - I^{(2n)}_{\xi_0^{Th}\eta_0^{Th}} = 0; \tag{11.2.68}$$

$$I^{(2n)}_{(\alpha_0^{Th}\xi_0^{Th})\eta_0^{Th}} - I^{(2n)}_{(\alpha^{(h)})_0^T(\eta^{(h)})_0^T} \leqslant 2ng(2n)(I(\xi_0^{Th},\ \eta_0^{Th}) - I((\alpha^{h})_0^T,\ (\eta^{(h)})_0^T. \tag{11.2.69}$$

From a comparison of these last two formulas we find that

$$I^{(2n)}_{\xi_0^{Th}\eta_0^{Th}} - I^{(2n)}_{(\alpha^{(h)})_0^T(\eta^{(h)})_0^T} \leqslant 2ng(2n)(I(\xi_0^{Th},\ \eta_0^{Th}) - I((\alpha^{(h)})_0^T,\ (\eta_0^{(h)})_0^T)). \tag{11.2.70}$$

In view of (11.2.65) and (11.2.2) it follows from this that

$$0 \leqslant \overline{\lim_{h\to+0}}\ \overline{\lim_{T\to\infty}}\ \frac{1}{Th}\left(I^{(2n)}_{\xi_0^{Th}\eta_0^{Th}} - I^{(2n)}_{(\alpha^{(h)})_0^T(\eta^{(h)})_0^T}\right) \leqslant 2ng(2n)(L_{\xi\eta} - L_{\alpha\eta}).$$

Comparing this result with (11.2.64) and (11.2.65), we see that

$$\lim_{T\to\infty}\frac{1}{T} I^{(2n)}_{\xi_0^T\eta_0^T} = \lim_{T\to\infty}\frac{1}{Th} I^{(2n)}_{\xi_0^{Th}\eta_0^{Th}} = g(2n)Q^{(2n)}_{\xi\eta}.$$

Thus the second part of the theorem is proved.

(3) Let $\varphi(t)$ be any function from the basic space Φ which is non-zero on the interval $(0, 1)$ and which vanishes outside this interval. The family of random variables

$$\xi_\varphi(\tau) = \xi(\varphi(t+\tau)) = \int_{-\infty}^{\infty} e^{i\tau\lambda}\psi(\lambda)dz_\xi(\lambda); \tag{11.2.71}$$

$$\eta_\varphi(\tau) = \eta(\varphi(t+\tau)) = \int_{-\infty}^{\infty} e^{i\tau\lambda}\psi(\lambda)dz_\eta(\lambda), \tag{11.2.72}$$

where

$$\psi(\lambda) = \int_0^1 e^{i\tau\lambda}\varphi(t)dt, \tag{11.2.73}$$

forms a stationary gaussian random process $(\xi_\varphi, \eta_\varphi) = \{(\xi_\varphi(t), \eta_\varphi(t))\}$.

It is evident from (11.2.73) that $\psi(\lambda)$ is an analytic function, and therefore is almost everywhere different from zero. Therefore, in the decomposition

$$\xi(\cdot) = \xi^{I}(\cdot) + \xi^{II}(\cdot), \qquad \eta(\cdot) = \eta^{I}(\cdot) + \eta^{II}(\cdot),$$

$$\xi_\varphi(t) = \xi_\varphi^{I}(t) + \xi_\varphi^{II}(t), \qquad \eta_\varphi(t) = \eta_\varphi^{I}(t) + \eta_\varphi^{II}(t)$$

of the processes $\xi, \eta, \eta_\varphi, \xi_\varphi$ into orthogonal sums of processes with absolutely continuous and singular spectral functions, the processes $\xi^{I} = \{\xi^{I}(\cdot)\}$ and $\xi_\varphi^{I} = \{\xi_\varphi^{I}(\cdot)\}, \eta^{I} = \{\eta^{I}(\cdot)\}$ and $\eta_\varphi^{I} = \}\eta_\varphi^{I}(\cdot)\}$ are mutually linearly subordinate, and according to the remark following Lemma 10.1.5

$$1 - |r_{\xi\eta}(\lambda)|^2 = \frac{\det A_{\xi\eta}(\lambda)}{\det A_\xi(\lambda)\det A_\eta(\lambda)} = \frac{\det A_{\xi_\varphi\eta_\varphi}(\lambda)}{\det A_{\xi_\varphi}(\lambda)\det A_{\eta_\varphi}(\lambda)}$$
$$= 1 - |r_{\xi_\varphi\eta_\varphi}(\lambda)|^2,$$

so that

$$L_{\xi\eta} = L_{\xi_\varphi\eta_\varphi} \text{ and } Q_{\xi\eta}^{(n)} = Q_{\xi_\varphi\eta_\varphi}^{(n)} \tag{11.2.74}$$

for any $n > 0$.

From the definition of the processes ξ_φ and η_φ it follows that the random variables $(\xi_\varphi)_0^T$ and $(\eta_\varphi)_0^T$ are subordinate respectively to the random variables ξ_0^{T+1} η_0^{T+1}, and therefore

$$\overline{\lim_{T\to\infty}} \frac{1}{T} I((\xi_\varphi)_0^T, (\eta_\varphi)_0^T) \leqslant \lim_{T\to\infty} \frac{T+1}{T}\frac{1}{T+1} I(\xi_0^{T+1}, \eta_0^{T+1}) = \bar{I}(\xi, \eta)$$
$$= L_{\xi\eta} = L_{\xi_\varphi\eta_\varphi}. \tag{11.2.75}$$

But by Theorem 10.3.1 and the remarks following Theorem 7.4.1

$$\lim_{T\to\infty} \frac{1}{T} I((\xi_\varphi)_0^T, (\eta_\varphi)_0^T) \geqslant \bar{I}^{(g)}(\xi_\varphi, \eta_\varphi) = L_{\xi_\varphi\eta_\varphi}. \tag{11.2.76}$$

Comparing (11.2.75) and (11.2.76), we find that

$$\lim_{T\to\infty} \frac{1}{T} I((\xi_\varphi)_0^T, (\eta_\varphi)_0^T) = \bar{I}(\xi_\varphi, \eta_\varphi) = L_{\xi_\varphi\eta_\varphi}. \tag{11.2.77}$$

Therefore, according to part 2 of the present theorem, as applied to the continuous-parameter processes ξ_φ and η_φ,

$$\bar{I}^{(2n)}_{\xi_\varphi\eta_\varphi} = g(2n)Q^{(2n)}_{\xi_\varphi\eta_\varphi}. \tag{11.2.78}$$

Making use of the corollary to Lemma 11.2.2 and of equations (11.2.77), (11.2.74), we obtain the formula

$$\lim_{T\to\infty} \frac{1}{T} (I^{(2n)}_{\xi_0^{T+1}\eta_0^{T+1}} - I^{(2n)}_{(\xi_\varphi)_0^T(\eta_\varphi)_0^T}) \leqslant 2ng(2n) \lim_{T\to\infty} \frac{1}{T} (I(\xi_0^{T+1}, \eta_0^{T+1})$$
$$- I((\xi_\varphi)_0^T, (\eta_\varphi)_0^T) = 2ng(2n)(L_{\xi\eta} - L_{\xi_\varphi\eta_\varphi}) = 0. \tag{11.2.79}$$

Comparing (11.2.78) with (11.2.79) and (11.2.74) shows that

$$\bar{I}^{(2n)}_{\xi\eta} = g(2n)Q^{(2n)}_{\xi_\varphi\eta_\varphi} = g(2n)Q^{(2n)}_{\xi\eta}.$$

which completes the proof of the theorem.

Remark. Let us denote by $\pi_T(\lambda)$ the number of proper values of the operator $\Pi_{\xi_0^T\eta_0^T\xi_0^T}$, which exceed λ. Repeating almost verbatim the considerations used in the proof of the theorem, it can be shown that under the conditions of the theorem

$$\lim_{T\to\infty} \frac{1}{T} \pi_T(\lambda) = \frac{1}{2\pi} M(|r_{\xi\eta}(\lambda')|^2 > \lambda) \tag{11.2.80}$$

at the points of continuity of the function $\psi(\lambda) = \mu(|r_{\xi\eta}(\lambda')|^2 > \lambda)$, where μ is Lebesgue measure.

From this result follows (11.2.4).

COROLLARY 1. If (ξ, η) is a two-dimensional stationary gaussian process and $\bar{I}(\xi, \eta) = L_{\xi\eta}$, then

$$\lim_{T\to\infty} P\{a < \frac{i(\xi_0^T, \eta_0^T) - I(\xi_0^T, \eta_0^T)}{\sqrt{Di(\xi_0^T, \eta_0^T)}} \leqslant b\} = \lim_{T\to\infty} P\{a < \frac{i(\xi_0^T, \eta_0^T) - I(\xi_0^T, \eta_0^T)}{\sqrt{TQ_{\xi\eta}^{(2)}}} \leqslant b\}$$

$$= \frac{1}{\sqrt{2\pi}} \int_a^b e^{-\frac{x^2}{2}} dx. \qquad (11.2.81)$$

COROLLARY 2. Formula (11.2.4) holds in the following cases: (a) (ξ, η) is a two-dimensional discrete-parameter stationary gaussian process, and either ξ or η is non-singular. (b) (ξ, η) is a continuous-parameter or generalized stationary gaussian process, and either ξ or η has absolutely continuous spectral function with rational spectral density.

In fact, as was proved in Chapter 10, in these cases $\bar{I}(\xi, \eta) = L_{\xi\eta}$.

COROLLARY 3. If (ξ, η) is a two-dimensional stationary gaussian process, then

$$\varliminf_{T\to\infty} \frac{1}{T} I^{(2n)}_{\xi_0^T \eta_0^T} \geqslant g(2n) Q_{\xi\eta}^{(2n)}. \qquad (11.2.82)$$

PROOF. We introduce a stationary gaussian process $\nu = \{\nu(t)\}$ which is independent of (ξ, η) and which has spectral density of the form $\frac{\delta}{1 + \lambda^2}$, and set

$$\alpha = \{\alpha(\cdot)\}, \quad \alpha(\cdot) = \xi(\cdot) + \nu(\cdot).$$

If ξ and η are non-generalized processes, formulas (11.2.64), (11.2.65) and (11.2.70) apply, from which (11.2.82) follows. If ξ and η are generalized random processes, the proof is analogous to that of part 3 of the theorem; one has only to replace equation (11.2.78) by inequality (11.2.82) for the non-generalized processes ξ_φ and η_φ.

COROLLARY 4. Let (ξ, η) be a two-dimensional stationary gaussian process. Then if the function $|r_{\xi\eta}(\lambda)|^2$ is different from zero on a set of positive measure, there are only two possible alternatives:

(1) For all T sufficiently large the measure $P_{\xi_0^T \eta_0^T}$ is singular with respect to the measure $P_{\xi_0^T \times \eta_0^T}$.

(2) As $T \to \infty$ the distribution of the information density $i(\xi_0^T, \eta_0^T)$ converges to a normal distribution.

In fact, for a gaussian random variable (ξ_0^T, η_0^T) there are only two possible cases: either for some $S > 0$ the measure $P_{\xi_0^S \eta_0^S}$ is singular with respect to the measure $P_{\xi_0^S \times \eta_0^S}$, or else the measure $P_{\xi_0^T \eta_0^T}$ is absolutely continuous with respect to $P_{\xi_0^T \times \eta_0^T}$ for every $T > 0$. In the first case, the measure $P_{\xi_0^T \eta_0^T}$ will be singular with respect to $P_{\xi_0^T \times \eta_0^T}$ for every $T \geqslant S$; in the second case

$$\lim_{T\to\infty} \mathrm{Di}(\xi_0^T, \eta_0^T) \geqslant \lim_{T\to\infty} T \int |r_{\xi\eta}(\lambda)|^2 d\lambda = \infty$$

by Corollary 3. From this it follows according to Theorem 9.6.1 that the distribution of the information density $i(\xi_0^T, \eta_0^T)$ converges to a normal distribution.

The theorem which has already been proved generalizes to the case of multi-dimensional processes in the following way.

THEOREM 11.2.2. Suppose that the l *and* m*-dimensional processes* $\xi = \{(\xi_1(\cdot), \ldots, \xi_l(\cdot))\}$ *and* $\eta = \{(\eta_1(\cdot), \ldots, \eta_m(\cdot))\}$ $= \{(\xi_{l+1}(\cdot), \ldots, \xi_{l+m}(\cdot))\}$ *form a stationary gaussian process* (ξ, η). *If* $\bar{I}(\xi, \eta) = L_{\xi\eta}$, *then, using the same notation as in the beginning of the present section, formulas (11.2.3) and (11.2.4) hold.*

PROOF. In accordance with the notation which we have been using in this section, $\xi' = (\xi_1', \ldots, \xi_l')$ and $\eta_1', \ldots, \eta_m')$ are the random processes corresponding to the pair (ξ, η), as defined in Lemma 10.1.2, according to which $\xi_1', \ldots, \xi_l', \eta_1', \ldots, \eta_m'$ are pairwise independent with the exception of pairs (ξ_j', η_j'), $j = 1, \ldots, k \leqslant \min(l, m)$. We put $\xi'' = (\xi_1', \ldots, \xi_k'), \eta'' = (\eta_1', \ldots, \eta_k'), \nu = (\eta, \eta'')$. Obviously $\xi_1', \ldots, \xi_k'$ and $\eta_1', \ldots, \eta_k'$ are the first k components of the random processes defined by Lemma 10.1.2 and corresponding to the pairs $(\xi, \eta), (\xi, \nu), (\xi, \eta''), (\xi'', \eta'')$. Therefore

$$Q_{\xi\eta}^{(2n)} = Q_{\xi\nu}^{(2n)} = Q_{\xi\eta''}^{(2n)} = Q_{\xi''\eta''}^{(2n)} = \frac{1}{\pi} \sum_{j=1}^{k} \int |r_{\xi_j'\eta_j'}(\lambda)|^{2n} d\lambda \qquad (11.2.83)$$

and according to Corollary 2 of Lemma 10.1.5

$$\frac{\det A_{\tilde{\xi}\tilde{\eta}}(\lambda)}{\det A_{\tilde{\xi}}(\lambda) \det A_{\tilde{\eta}}(\lambda)} = \frac{\det A_{\tilde{\xi}\tilde{\nu}}(\lambda)}{\det A_{\tilde{\xi}}(\lambda) \det A_{\tilde{\nu}}(\lambda)}$$

$$\frac{\det A_{\tilde{\xi}\eta''}(\lambda)}{\det A_{\tilde{\xi}}(\lambda) \det A_{\eta''}(\lambda)} = \frac{\det A_{\xi''\eta''}(\lambda)}{\det A_{\xi''}(\lambda) \det A_{\eta''}(\lambda)} = \sum_{j=1}^{k} (1 - |r_{\xi_j'\eta_j'}(\lambda)|^2).$$

Using the definition of $L_{\xi\eta}$, we obtain from this series of equalities

$$L_{\xi\eta} = L_{\xi\nu} = L_{\xi\eta''} = L_{\xi''\eta''}. \qquad (11.2.84)$$

We show now that the proof of the theorem can easily be reduced to the case where the functions $f_{\xi_j' \xi_j'}(\lambda)$ and $f_{\eta_j' \eta_j'}(\lambda)$ are almost everywhere different from zero. In fact, if this is not already the case, we replace ξ_j' and η_j' respectively by $\alpha_j' = \{\alpha_j'(\cdot)\}$ and $\beta_j' = \beta_j'(\cdot)$, where $\alpha_j'(\cdot) = \xi_j(\cdot) + \gamma_j(\cdot), \beta_j'(\cdot) = \eta_j'(\cdot) + \zeta_j(\cdot)$ and $\{\gamma_j(\cdot)\}, \zeta_j = \{\zeta_j(\cdot)\}$, $j = 1, \ldots, k, \alpha_j'(\cdot) = \xi_j'(\cdot) + \gamma_j(\cdot)$, are mutually independent stationary gaussian processes which are independent of (ξ, η), and which have spectral densities $f_{\gamma_j \gamma_j}(\lambda), f_{\zeta_j \zeta_j}(\lambda)$ which are different from zero at those points respectively at which $f_{\xi_j' \xi_j'}(\lambda), f_{\eta_j' \eta_j'}(\lambda)$ vanish. We put

$$\xi^* = (\xi_1, \ldots, \xi_l; \gamma_1, \ldots, \gamma_k), \quad \eta^* = (\eta_1, \ldots, \eta_m, \zeta_1 \ldots, \zeta_k).$$

It is clear that

$$I(\xi_0^T, \eta_0^T) = I((\xi^*)_0^T, (\eta^*)_0^T); \quad \frac{\det A_{\tilde{\xi}\tilde{\eta}}(\lambda)}{\det A_{\tilde{\xi}}(\lambda) \det A_{\eta}(\lambda)} = \frac{\det A_{\tilde{\xi}^*\tilde{\eta}^*}(\lambda)}{\det A_{\tilde{\xi}^*}(\lambda) \det A_{\tilde{\eta}^*}(\lambda)};$$

$$\sum_{j=1}^{k} |r_{\xi_j' \eta_j'}(\lambda)|^{2n} = \sum_{j=1}^{k} |r_{\xi_j^{*\prime} \eta_j^{*\prime}}(\lambda)|^{2n}, \quad I^{(2n)}_{\xi_0^T \eta_0^T} = I^{(2n)}_{(\xi^*)_0^T (\eta^*)_0^T}.$$

Consequently

$$\bar{I}(\xi, \eta) = \bar{I}(\xi^*, \eta^*) = L_{\xi\eta}, \quad \bar{I}^{(2n)}_{\xi\eta} = \bar{I}^{(2n)}_{\xi^*\eta^*}, \quad Q^{(2n)}_{\xi\eta} = Q^{(2n)}_{\xi^*\eta^*}.$$

From the equations which have been written down it is evident that it suffices to carry out the proof of the theorem for the processes ξ^* and η^*. Now for the processes $\xi_1^{*\prime}, \ldots, \xi_k^{*\prime} \eta_1^{*\prime}, \ldots, \eta_k^{*\prime}$ defined by Lemma 10.1.2, corresponding to the pair (ξ^*, η^*), we can take the processes $\alpha_1', \ldots, \alpha_k', \beta_1', \ldots, \beta_k'$, and the processes ξ^* and η^* satisfy the condition stated earlier: the functions $f_{\xi_j^{*\prime} \xi_j^{*\prime}}(\lambda) = f_{\alpha_j' \alpha_j'}(\lambda), f_{\eta_j^{*\prime} \eta_j^{*\prime}}(\lambda) = f_{b_j' b_j'}(\lambda)$ are almost everywhere different from zero. Thus we may assume that $f_{\xi_j' \xi_j'}(\lambda), f_{\eta_j' \eta_j'}(\lambda)$, $j = 1, \ldots, k$ are almost everywhere different from zero. As in the preceding theorem, we will break up the proof of the present theorem into three parts.

(1) Assume that ξ and η are discrete-parameter processes. Here we may assume that

$$f_{\xi_j' \xi_j'}(\lambda) = f_{\eta_j' \eta_j'}(\lambda) = 1, j = 1, \ldots, l, \tag{11.2.85}$$

for in the contrary case we can always replace the processes ξ_j' and η_j' by processes α_j and β_j whose spectral are identically equal to 1, and such that ξ_j' and α_j, η_j' and β_j are mutually linearly subordinate. If condition (11.2.85) is fulfilled, it is obvious that the processes $\xi'' = (\xi_1', \ldots, \xi_k')$ and $\eta'' = (\eta_1', \ldots, \eta_k')$ have rank of regularity equal to k, and therefore by Theorem 10.4.1

$$\bar{I}(\eta'', \xi) = \bar{I}(\xi, \eta'') = L_{\xi\eta''}, \bar{I}(\xi'', \eta'') = \bar{I}(\eta'', \xi'') = L_{\xi''\eta''} . \quad (11.2.86)$$

Let us assume now that the rank of regularity of the process ξ is equal to l; then by Theorem 10.4.1

$$\bar{I}(\xi, \eta) = L_{\xi\eta}, \bar{I}(\xi, \nu) = \bar{I}(\xi, (\eta, \eta'')) = L_{\xi\nu}. \quad (11.2.87)$$

Comparing formulas (11.2.84), (11.2.86) and (11.2.87) shows that

$$\bar{I}(\xi, \eta) = \bar{I}(\xi, \nu) = \bar{I}(\xi, \eta'') = \bar{I}(\eta'', \xi) = \bar{I}(\xi'', \eta'') = L_{\xi''\eta''}$$

$$= -\frac{1}{4\pi}\int_{-\pi}^{\pi}\sum_{j=1}^{k}\log\,(1 - |r_{\xi_j'\eta_j'}(\lambda)|^2)d\lambda. \quad (11.2.88)$$

Since the pairs (ξ_j', η_j'), $j = 1, \ldots, k$ are independent of each other,

$$I^{(2n)}_{(\xi'')_0^T(\eta'')_0^T} = \sum_{j=1}^{k} I^{(2n)}_{(\xi_j')_0^T(\eta_j')_0^T}.$$

Since the processes ξ_j' are non-singular, $\bar{I}(\xi_j', \eta_j') = L_{\xi_j'\eta_j'}$, and therefore by Theorem 11.2.1

$$\bar{I}^{(2n)}_{\xi_j'\eta_j'} = \lim_{T\to\infty}\frac{1}{T} I^{(2n)}_{(\xi_j')_0^T(\eta_j')_0^T} = g(2n)Q^{(2n)}_{\xi_j'\eta_j'} = \frac{g(2n)}{\pi}\int_0^{\pi}|r_{\xi_j'\eta_j'}(\lambda)|^{2n}d\lambda$$

and consequently

$$\bar{I}^{(2n)}_{\xi''\eta''} = \lim_{T\to\infty}\frac{1}{T} I^{(2n)}_{(\xi'')_0^T(\eta'')_0^T} = \sum_{j=1}^{k}\lim_{T\to\infty} I^{(2n)}_{(\xi_j')_0(\eta_j')_0^T}$$

$$= \sum_{j-1}^{k}\frac{g(2n)}{\pi}\int_0^{\pi}|r_{\xi_j'\eta_j'}(\lambda)|^{2n}\,d\lambda = g(2n)Q^{(2n)}_{\xi\eta}. \quad (11.2.89)$$

On the other hand, according to the corollary to Lemma 11.2.2 and equation (11.2.88)

$$0 \leqslant \varliminf_{T\to\infty}\frac{1}{T}(I^{(2n)}_{\xi_0^T\nu_0^T} - I^{(2n)}_{\xi_0^T\eta_0^T}) \leqslant \varlimsup_{T\to\infty}\frac{1}{T}(I^{(2n)}_{\xi_0^T\nu_0^T} - I^{(2n)}_{\xi_0^T\eta_0^T})$$

$$\leqslant 2n\,g(2n)\lim_{T\to\infty}\frac{1}{T}\,(I(\xi_0^T, \nu_0^T) - I(\xi_0^T, \eta_0^T)) = 2n\,g(2n)(L_{\xi''\eta''} - L_{\xi''\eta''}) = 0.$$

One can show similarly that

$$\lim_{T\to\infty}\frac{1}{T}(I^{(2n)}_{\xi_0^T\eta_0^T} - I^{(2n)}_{\xi_0^T(\eta'')_0^T}) = \lim_{T\to\infty}\frac{1}{T}(I^{(2n)}_{(\eta'')_0^T\xi} - I^{(2n)}_{\xi_0^T(\eta'')_0^T})$$

$$= \lim_{T\to\infty}\frac{1}{T}(I^{(2n)}_{(\eta'')_0^T\xi} - I^{(2n)}_{(\xi'')_0^T(\eta'')_0^T}) = 0.$$

Comparing these relations, we see that

$$\lim_{T\to\infty}\frac{1}{T}|I^{(2n)}_{\xi_0^T\eta_0^T} - I^{(2n)}_{(\xi'')_0^T(\eta'')_0^T}| = 0,$$

$$\bar{I}^{(2n)}_{\xi\eta} = \lim_{T\to\infty}\frac{1}{T}I^{(2n)}_{\xi_0^T\eta_0^T} = \lim_{T\to\infty}\frac{1}{T}I^{(2n)}_{(\xi'')_0^T(\eta'')_0^T} = \bar{I}^{(2n)}_{\xi''\eta''}.$$

Comparing this last relation with (11.2.89), we obtain (11.2.4). If the rank of regularity of the process ξ is not equal to l, we introduce stationary gaussian processes $\beta_1 = \{\beta_1(t)\}, \ldots, \beta_l = \{\beta(t)\}$ such that $\beta_1, \ldots, \beta_l, (\xi, \eta)$ are mutually independent and

$$f_{\beta_1\beta_1}(\lambda) = \ldots = f_{\beta_l\beta_l}(\lambda) = \delta, \quad \delta > 0.$$

We set

$$\beta = (\beta_1, \ldots, \beta_l) \text{ and } \alpha_j(t) = \xi_j(t) + \beta_j(t), j = 1, \ldots, l,$$
$$\alpha = (\alpha_1, \ldots, \alpha_l) = \{(\alpha_1(t), \ldots, \alpha_l(t))\}.$$

Obviously

$$\int_{-\pi}^{\pi} |\log\det\|f_{\alpha_j\alpha_r}(\lambda)\|_{j,r=1,\ldots,l}|d\lambda > \infty$$

and so, by the theorem of Zasukhin, α has rank of regularity equal to l. Hence it follows from Theorem 10.4.1 and what we have already proved that

$$\tilde{I}(\alpha, \eta) = \bar{I}(\alpha, \eta) = L_{\alpha\eta}, \tilde{I}(\alpha, \eta'') = \bar{I}(\alpha, \eta'') = L_{\alpha\eta''}; \qquad (11.2.90)$$

$$\bar{I}^{(2n)}_{\alpha\eta} := g(2n)Q^{(2n)}_{\alpha\eta}, \bar{I}^{(2n)}_{\alpha\eta''} = g(2n)^{(2n)}_{\alpha\eta}. \qquad (11.2.91)$$

But the processes η and η' are mutually linearly subordinate, and the random variable $(\eta'_{k+1}, \ldots, \eta'_m)$ is independent of ξ, and a fortiori of α. Consequently

$$I(\alpha_0^T, \eta) = I(\alpha_0^T, \eta') = I(\alpha_0^T, \eta''), \tilde{I}(\alpha, \eta) = \tilde{I}(\alpha, \eta')$$

$$= \tilde{I}(\alpha, \eta''), \quad I^{(2n)}_{\alpha_0^T\eta} = I^{(2n)}_{\alpha_0^T\eta'} = I^{(2n)}_{\alpha_0^T\eta''}.$$

Comparing this last equation with equations (11.2.90), we find that

$$\tilde{I}(\alpha, \eta) = \bar{I}(\alpha, \eta) = \tilde{I}(\alpha, \eta'') = \bar{I}(\alpha, \eta'') = L_{\alpha\eta} = L_{\alpha\eta''}. \quad (11.2.92)$$

Furthermore, the sequence of random variables $\alpha_0^T, \xi_0^T, \eta_0^T$ forms a Markov chain, and therefore

$$\frac{1}{2\pi}\int_0^\pi \log\frac{\det A_{\tilde{\alpha}}(\lambda)\det A_{\tilde{\eta}}(\lambda)}{\det A_{\tilde{\alpha}\tilde{\eta}}(\lambda)}\,d\lambda = L_{\alpha\eta} = \lim_{T\to\infty}\frac{1}{T}I(\alpha_0^T, \eta_0^T)$$
$$\leqslant \lim_{T\to\infty}\frac{1}{T}I((\alpha_0^T, \xi_0^T), \eta_0^T) = \lim_{T\to\infty}\frac{1}{T}I(\xi_0^T, \eta_0^T) = L_{\xi\eta}$$
$$= \frac{1}{2\pi}\int_0^\pi \log\frac{\det A_{\tilde{\xi}}(\lambda)\det A_{\tilde{\eta}}(\lambda)}{\det A_{\tilde{\xi}\tilde{\eta}}(\lambda)}$$

On the other hand, it is obvious that

$$\lim_{\delta\to+0}\frac{\det A_{\tilde{\alpha}}(\lambda)\det A_{\tilde{\eta}}(\lambda)}{\det A_{\tilde{\alpha}\tilde{\eta}}(\lambda)} \geqslant \frac{\det A_{\tilde{\xi}}(\lambda)\det A_{\tilde{\eta}}(\lambda)}{\det A_{\tilde{\xi}\tilde{\eta}}(\lambda)}.$$

Comparing the last two relations, it is clear that

$$\lim_{\delta\to+0}\bar{I}(\alpha, \eta) = \bar{I}((\alpha, \xi), \eta) = \bar{I}(\xi, \eta). \quad (11.2.93)$$

Using the ordinary inequality for the absolute value of a sum, and the corollary to Lemma 11.2.2, we obtain the relation

$$\overline{\lim_{T\to\infty}}\frac{1}{T}\left|I^{(2n)}_{\xi_0^T\eta_0^T} - I^{(2n)}_{\alpha_0^T\eta_0^T}\right| \leqslant \overline{\lim_{T\to\infty}}\frac{1}{T}\left[\left(I^{(2n)}_{(\alpha_0^T\eta_0^T)\eta_0^T} - I^{(2n)}_{\xi_0^T\eta_0^T}\right)\right.$$
$$\left.+\left(I^{(2n)}_{(\alpha_0^T\xi_0^T)\eta_0^T} - I^{(2n)}_{\alpha_0^T\eta_0^T}\right)\right] \leqslant 2ng(2n)\lim_{T\to\infty}\frac{1}{T}[I((\alpha_0^T, \xi_0^T), \eta_0^T) - I(\xi_0^T, \eta_0^T)$$
$$+ I((\alpha_0^T, \xi_0^T), \eta_0^T) - I(\alpha_0^T, \eta_0^T)] = 2ng(2n)[\bar{I}((\alpha, \xi), \eta)$$
$$- \bar{I}(\xi, \eta) + \bar{I}((\alpha, \xi), \eta) - \bar{I}(\alpha, \eta)],$$

and, in view of (11.2.93)

$$\lim_{\delta\to+0}\overline{\lim_{T\to\infty}}\frac{1}{T}\left|I^{(2n)}_{\xi_0^T\eta_0^T} - I^{(2n)}_{\alpha_0^T\eta_0^T}\right| = 0,$$

i.e.,

$$\lim_{\delta\to+0}\bar{I}^{(2n)}_{\alpha\eta} = \lim_{T\to\infty}\frac{1}{T}I^{(2n)}_{\xi_0^T\eta_0^T} = I^{(2n)}_{\xi\eta}. \quad (11.2.94)$$

Similarly, one can show that

$$\lim_{\delta\to+0} \bar{I}^{(2n)}_{\alpha\eta''} = \lim_{T\to\infty} \frac{1}{T} I^{(2n)}_{\xi_0^T (\eta'')_0^T} = \bar{I}^{(2n)}_{\xi\eta''}. \tag{11.2.95}$$

Finally,

$$\overline{\lim_{T\to\infty}} \frac{1}{T} |I^{(2n)}_{\alpha_0^T \eta_0^T} - I^{(2n)}_{\alpha_0^T (\eta'')_0^T}| \leqslant \lim_{T\to\infty} \frac{1}{T} [(I^{(2n)}_{\alpha_0^T \eta} - I^{(2n)}_{\alpha_0^T \eta_0^T}) + (I^{(2n)}_{\alpha_0^T \eta} - I^{(2n)}_{\alpha_0^T (\eta'')_0^T})]$$

$$\leqslant 2ng(2n) \lim_{T\to\infty} \frac{1}{T} [I(\alpha_0^T, \eta) - I(\alpha_0^T, \eta_0^T) + I(\alpha_0^T, \eta) - I(\alpha_0^T, (\eta'')_0^T)]$$

$$= 2ng(2n)(\tilde{I}(\alpha, \eta) - \bar{I}(\alpha, \eta) + \tilde{I}(\alpha, \eta) - \bar{I}(\alpha, \eta''))$$

and in view of (11.2.92)

$$\lim_{T\to\infty} \frac{1}{T} |I^{(2n)}_{\alpha_0^T \eta_0^T} - I^{(2n)}_{\alpha_0^T (\eta'')_0^T}| = 0,$$

i.e.

$$\bar{I}^{(2n)}_{\alpha\eta} = \bar{I}^{(2n)}_{\alpha\eta''}. \tag{11.2.96}$$

Comparing (11.2.94)–(11.2.96) we see that $\bar{I}^{(2n)}_{\xi\eta} = \bar{I}^{(2n)}_{\xi\eta''}$. To complete the proof of part 1 of the theorem it suffices to note, that since the process η'' has rank of regularity k, $\bar{I}^{(2n)}_{\xi\eta''} = \bar{I}^{(2n)}_{\eta''\xi} = Q^{(2n)}_{\xi\eta''}$, and by (11.2.83), $Q^{(2n)}_{\xi\eta''} = Q^{(2n)}_{\xi\eta}$.

(2) We assume now that ξ and η are continuous-parameter processes. Here we can assume that

$$f_{\xi_j'\xi_j'}(\lambda) = f_{\eta_j'\eta_j'}(\lambda) = \frac{1}{1+\lambda^2}, \tag{11.2.97}$$

for in the contrary case we can replace ξ_j', η_j' by processes α_j, β_j which satisfy (11.2.97) and such that α_j and ξ_j', β_j and η_j' are mutually linearly subordinate.

Obviously, if condition (11.2.97) is fulfilled, the processes $\xi'' = (\xi_1', \ldots, \xi_k'), \eta'' = \eta_1', \ldots, \eta_k')$ are Markovian, and therefore from Theorem 10.4.1 together with formula (11.2.84) it follows that

$$\bar{I}(\xi, \eta'') = \bar{I}(\xi', \eta'') = \bar{I}(\xi'', \eta'') = L_{\xi\eta}. \tag{11.2.98}$$

We consider the discrete-parameter processes

$$\xi^{(h)} = (\xi_1^{(h)}, \ldots, \xi_l^{(h)}) = \{(\xi_1(nh), \ldots, \xi_l(nh)\},$$

$$\eta^{(h)} = (\eta_1^{(h)}, \ldots, \eta_m^{(h)}) = \{(\eta_1(nh), \ldots, \eta_m(nh))\},$$

$$\xi''^{(h)} = (\xi_1'^{(h)}, \ldots, \xi_k'^{(h)}) = \{(\xi_1'(nh), \ldots, \xi_k'(nh))\};$$

$$\eta''^{(h)} = (\eta_1'^{(h)}, \ldots, \eta_k'^{(h)}) = \{(\eta_1'(nh), \ldots, \eta_k'(nh))\}.$$

The rank of regularity of the processes $\xi''^{(h)}$ and $\eta''^{(h)}$ is equal to k, and so by Theorem 10.4.1

$$\bar{I}(\xi''^{(h)}, \eta''^{(h)}) = \bar{I}^{(g)}(\xi''^{(h)}, \eta''^{(h)}) = L_{\xi''^{(h)}\eta''^{(h)}}. \tag{11.2.99}$$

Let us assume now that the rank of regularity of the process ξ is equal to l; then $\xi^{(h)}$ also has rank of regularity l, and by Theorem 10.4.1

$$\bar{I}^{(g)}(\xi^{(h)}, \eta^{(h)}) = \bar{I}(\xi^{(h)}, \eta^{(h)} = L_{\xi^{(h)}\eta^{(h)}};$$

$$\bar{I}^{(g)}(\xi^{(h)}, (\eta^{(h)}, \eta''^{(h)})) = \bar{I}(\xi^{(h)}, (\eta^{(h)}, \eta''^{(h)})) = L_{\xi^{(h)}(\eta^{(h)}\eta''^{(h)})};$$

$$\bar{I}^{(g)}(\xi^{(h)}, \eta''^{(h)}) = \bar{I}(\xi^{(h)}, \eta''^{(h)}) = L_{\xi^{(h)}\eta''^{(h)}};$$

$$\bar{I}^{(g)}(\eta''^{(h)}, (\xi^{(h)}, \xi''^{(h)})) = \bar{I}(\eta''^{(h)}, (\xi^{(h)}, \xi''^{(h)})) = L_{\eta''^{(h)}(\xi^{(h)}\xi''^{(h)})}. \tag{11.2.100}$$

According to formula (7.2.5) and Theorem 10.4.1

$$\lim_{h\to+0} \frac{1}{h}\bar{I}^{(g)}(\xi^{(h)}, \eta^{(h)}) = \bar{I}^{(g)}(\xi, \eta) = L_{\xi\eta}$$

for any gaussian process (ξ, η). Therefore, from relations (11.2.84), (11.2.99) and (11.2.100) we obtain

$$\lim_{h\to+0} \frac{1}{h}\bar{I}(\xi^{(h)}, \eta^{(h)}) = \lim_{h\to+0} \frac{1}{h}\bar{I}(\xi^{(h)}, (\eta^{(h)}, \eta''^{(h)})) = \lim_{h\to+0} \frac{1}{h}\bar{I}(\xi^{(h)}, \eta''^{(h)})$$

$$= \lim_{h\to+0} \frac{1}{h}\bar{I}(\eta''^{(h)}, (\xi^{(h)}, \xi''^{(h)})) = \lim_{h\to+0} \frac{1}{h}\bar{I}(\xi''^{(h)}, \eta''^{(h)}) = L_{\xi\eta}. \tag{11.2.101}$$

Using these relations and the corollaries to Lemma 11.2.2, we obtain, after not difficult calculations similar to others which we have gone through more than once, that

$$\lim_{h\to+0} \frac{1}{h}\bar{I}^{(2n)}_{\xi^{(h)}\eta^{(h)}} = \lim_{h\to+0} \frac{1}{h}\bar{I}^{(2n)}_{\xi''^{(h)}\eta''^{(h)}}. \tag{11.2.102}$$

Furthermore, it is obvious that

$$\bar{I}^{(2n)}_{\xi''^{(h)}\eta''^{(h)}} = \sum_{j=1}^{k} \bar{I}^{(2n)}_{\xi_j'^{(h)}\eta_j'^{(h)}}.$$

From this equation and formula (11.2.59), applied to every pair of processes (ξ'_j, η'_j), j = 1, . . . , k, we obtain

$$\lim_{h \to +0} \frac{1}{h} \bar{I}^{(2n)}_{\xi''(h)\eta''(h)} = \sum_{j=1}^{k} \lim_{h \to +0} \frac{1}{h} \bar{I}^{(2n)}_{\xi'_j(h)\eta'_j(h)}$$

$$= \frac{g(2n)}{\pi} \sum_{j=1}^{k} \int_0^{\infty} |r_{\xi'_j \eta'_j}(\lambda)|^{2n} d\lambda = g(2n) Q^{(2n)}_{\xi''\eta''}.$$

This relation and (11.2.102), (11.2.83) enable us to write down the equation

$$\lim_{h \to +0} \frac{1}{h} \bar{I}^{(2n)}_{\xi(h)\eta(h)} = g(2n) Q^{(2n)}_{\xi\eta}. \tag{11.2.103}$$

On the other hand, in view of the condition $\bar{I}(\xi, \eta) = L_{\xi\eta}$ and (11.2.101) there is an h' sufficiently small and a T' sufficiently large so that for $h < h'$ and $T > T'$

$$\frac{1}{Th}[I(\xi_0^{Th}, \eta_0^{Th}) - I((\xi^{(h)})_0^T, (\eta^{(h)})_0^T)] \leqslant \epsilon.$$

From this inequality and from (11.2.103), applying Corollary 2 of Lemma 11.2.2, we obtain formula (11.2.4). Thus part 2 is proved for processes $\xi = (\xi_1, \ldots, \xi_l)$ which have rank of regularity equal to l.

If the rank of regularity of ξ is not equal to l, then, just as in the one-dimensional case, we introduce a stationary gaussian process $\nu = (\nu_1, \ldots, \nu_l) = \{(\nu_1(t), \ldots, \nu_l(t))\}$, independent of (ξ, η), such that the processes $\nu_1, \ldots, \nu_l$ are mutually independent, with spectral densities of the form

$$f_{\nu_j \nu_j}(\lambda) = \frac{\delta}{1 + \lambda^2}, \; \delta > 0$$

and we set

$$\alpha_j(t) = \xi_j(t) + \nu_j(t).$$

The further considerations which lead to formula (11.2.4) in the present continuous-parameter case are completely analogous to those employed in the discrete-parameter case, and we will not detain ourselves over them.

(3) We assume now that $\xi = (\xi_1, \ldots, \xi_l)$ and $\eta = (\eta_1, \ldots, \eta_m) = (\xi_{l+1}, \ldots, \xi_{l+m})$ are generalized random processes.

Let $\varphi(t)$ be any function from the basic space which is non-zero on the interval (0, 1) and vanishes outside this interval. The family of random variables

$$\xi_j^\varphi(\tau) = \xi_j(\varphi(t+\tau))$$
$$= \int_{-\infty}^{\infty} e^{i\tau\lambda}\psi(\lambda)dz_{\xi_j}(\lambda),\ j = 1, \ldots, l+m,$$

where

$$\psi(\lambda) = \int_{-\infty}^{\infty} e^{it\lambda}\varphi(t)dt = \int_0^1 e^{it\lambda}\varphi(t)dt$$

forms a stationary gaussian process

$$(\xi_1^\varphi, \ldots, \xi_{l+m}^\varphi) = (\xi_1^\varphi, \ldots, \xi_l^\varphi, \eta_1^\varphi, \ldots, \eta_m^\varphi) = (\xi^\varphi, \eta^\varphi).$$

By means of considerations completely analogous to, and repeating almost verbatim, those used in Theorem 11.2.1, one can show that

$$\bar{I}(\xi^\varphi, \eta^\varphi) = L_{\xi\eta}, \bar{I}^{(2n)}_{\xi^\varphi\eta^\varphi} = g(2n)Q^{(2n)}_{\xi\eta}$$

$$\lim_{T\to\infty} \frac{1}{T}\, I^{(2n)}_{(\xi_0^{T+1}, \eta_0^{T+1})} - I^{(2n)}_{(\xi^\varphi)_0^T(\eta^\varphi)_0^T} = 0. \qquad (11.2.104)$$

From this we obtain (11.2.4). The theorem is proved.

Remark. It is easily seen that for every λ (more precisely, for almost every λ) $|r_{\xi'_j\eta'_j}(\lambda)|^2$, $j = 1, \ldots, k$ are the proper values of the operator $\Pi_{\beta(\lambda)\alpha(\lambda)\beta(\lambda)}$ corresponding to the random variables $(\alpha(\lambda), \beta(\lambda)) = ((\alpha_1(\lambda), \ldots, \alpha_l(\lambda)), \beta_1(\lambda), \ldots, \beta_m(\lambda)))$, whose correlation matrix is given by

$$\| f_{\xi_s\xi_r}(\lambda) \|_{s,r=1,\ldots,l+m}.$$

Therefore $\sum_{j=1}^{k} |r_{\xi'_j\eta'_j}(\lambda)|^{2n}$ is the sum of the n-th power of the proper values of the operator $\Pi_{\beta(\lambda)\alpha(\lambda)\beta(\lambda)}$, and in order to obtain $Q^{(2n)}_{\xi\eta}$ it is not necessary to construct the random process (ξ', η').

COROLLARY 1. *If (ξ, η) is a multi-dimensional stationary gaussian process, and $0 < \bar{I}(\xi, \eta) = L_{\xi\eta} < \infty$, then*

$$\lim_{T\to\infty} P\left\{a \leqslant \frac{i(\xi_0^T, \eta_0^T) - I(\xi_0^T, \eta_0^T)}{\sqrt{Di(\xi_0^T, \eta_0^T)}} \leqslant b\right\}$$

$$= \lim_{T\to\infty} P\left\{a \leqslant \frac{i(\xi_0^T, \eta_0^T) - I(\xi_0^T, \eta_0^T)}{\sqrt{TQ^{(2)}_{\xi\eta}}} \leqslant b\right\}$$

$$= \frac{1}{\sqrt{2\pi}} \int_a^b e^{-\frac{x^2}{2}} dx. \qquad (11.2.105)$$

COROLLARY 2. *Formula (11.2.4) holds in the following cases: (a)* $(\xi, \eta) = (\xi_1, \ldots, \xi_l, \eta_1, \ldots, \eta_m)$ *is an* $(l+m)$*-dimensional discrete-parameter stationary gaussian process, one of the processes* ξ *and* η *has full rank of regularity, and* $L_{\xi\eta} < \infty$.

(b) (ξ, η) *is a continuous-parameter or generalized stationary gaussian process,* ξ *or* η *has rational spectral densities, and* $L_{\xi\eta} < \infty$.

In fact, in these cases, according to Theorem 10.4.1,

$$0 \leqslant \bar{I}(\xi, \eta) = L_{\xi\eta} < \infty.$$

COROLLARY 3. *If* (ξ, η) *is a multi-dimensional stationary gaussian process, then*

$$\lim_{T\to\infty} \frac{1}{T} I^{(2n)}_{\xi_0^T \eta_0^T} \geqslant g(2n) Q^{(2n)}_{\xi\eta}.$$

The proof of this corollary repeats almost verbatim the proof of Corollary 3 to Theorem 11.2.1.

COROLLARY 4. *Let* (ξ, η) *be a multi-dimensional stationary gaussian process. If the expression* $\dfrac{\det A_{\bar{\xi}\bar{\eta}}(\lambda)}{\det A_{\bar{\xi}}(\lambda) \det A_{\bar{\eta}}(\lambda)}$ *is different from zero on a set of positive measure, then there are only two possible alternatives:*

(1) For all sufficiently large T *the measure* $P_{\xi_0^T \eta_0^T}$ *is singular with respect to the measure* $P_{\xi_0^T \times \eta_0^T}$.

(2) As $T \to \infty$ *the distribution of the information density* $i(\xi_0^T, \eta_0^T)$ *converges to a normal distribution.*

The proof of this corollary is similar to that of Corollary 4, Theorem 11.2.1.

Remark. The result of this corollary remain valid in the following cases: (1) For any values of j, k, λ

$$F^{(H)}_{\xi_j \eta_k}(\lambda) \neq 0;$$

(2) For any j, k

$$\sum_i \frac{|d^{(g)}_{\xi_j \eta_k}(\lambda_i)|^2}{d^{(g)}_{\xi_j \xi_j}(\lambda_i) d^{(g)}_{\eta_k \eta_k}(\lambda_i)} = \infty. \qquad (11.2.106)$$

In this we are using the notation of Section 11.1.

We will now state a theorem which permits us to characterize the behavior of the distribution of the conditional information $\bar{i}(\xi_0^T, \eta_0^T | \xi^\delta)$, $\delta > 0$, as $T \to \infty$. We will use the following notation: if $(\xi, \eta) = \{(\xi_1(\cdot), \ldots, \xi_l(\cdot), \eta_1(\cdot), \ldots, \eta_m(\cdot))\}$ is a gaussian random process, then $\hat{\xi} = \{\hat{\xi}(\cdot)\} = \{(\hat{\xi}(\cdot), \ldots, \hat{\xi}_l(\cdot))\}$ and $\{(\hat{\eta} = \{(\hat{\eta}_1(\cdot), \ldots, \hat{\eta}_m(\cdot))\} = \{(\hat{\xi}_{l+1}(\cdot), \ldots, \hat{\xi}_{l+m}(\cdot))\}$ are the gaussian random processes consisting of the perpendiculars from $\xi_j(\cdot)$ and $\eta_j(\cdot)$ onto B_{ξ^δ}

THEOREM 11.2.3. Suppose that the l *and* m*-dimensional processes* $\xi = \{(\xi_1(\cdot), \ldots, \xi_l(\cdot))\}$ *and* $\eta = \{(\eta_1(\cdot), \ldots, \eta_m(\cdot))\}$ *form a stationary gaussian process* (ξ, η). *If*

$$\vec{I}(\xi, \eta) = L_{\xi\eta}, \tag{11.2.107}$$

then

$$\vec{I}_{\xi\eta}^{(2)} = \vec{D}(\xi, \eta) = \lim_{T\to\infty} \frac{1}{T} D\bar{i}(\xi_{-\delta}^T, \eta/\xi^0) = \lim_{T\to\infty} \frac{1}{T} \mathbf{E}(\bar{i}(\xi_{-\delta}^T, \eta/\xi^0)$$

$$- \mathbf{E}I(\xi_{-\delta}^T, \eta/\xi^0))^2 = \lim_{T\to\infty} \frac{1}{T} \mathbf{E}(\bar{i}(\xi_{-\delta}^T, \eta/\xi^0) - T\vec{I}(\xi, \eta))^2 = Q_{\xi\eta}^{(2)}, \delta > 0;$$

(11.2.108)

$$\vec{I}_{\xi\eta}^{(q)} = \lim_{T\to\infty} \frac{1}{T} I^{(q)}_{\xi_{-\delta}^T \hat{\eta}} = \begin{cases} g(q) Q_{\xi\eta}^{(q)} \text{ for } q = 2n \\ 0 \text{ for } q = 2n + 1 \end{cases} \tag{11.2.109}$$

Remark. If (ξ, η) is a non-generalized process, the theorem holds also for $\delta = 0$.

Before commencing with the proof of the theorem, we state an auxiliary lemma.

LEMMA 11.2.4. Let $\xi = \{\xi_t\}, \eta = \{\eta_\tau\}, \zeta = \{\zeta_s\}, \nu = (\xi, \zeta)$, (ξ, η, ζ) *(*$t \in N, \tau \in E, s \in F$*; N, E, F are arbitrary sets) be gaussian random variables, and* $\beta = \{\beta_\tau\}, \gamma = \{\gamma_s\}$ *be the random variables consisting of the perpendiculars* β_τ, γ_s *from* η_τ *and* ζ_s *onto* B_ξ, *and let* $I((\xi, \zeta), \eta) < \infty$. *Then the operators* $\Pi_{\eta\nu\eta}$ *and* $\Pi_{\beta\gamma\beta}$ *are completely continuous, and the sequences, in non-increasing order, of their proper values* $\lambda_1 \geq \lambda_2 \geq \ldots, \lambda_1' \geq \lambda_2' \geq \ldots$ *satisfy the relation*

$$\sum_j (\lambda_j^n - \lambda_j'^n) \leq 2n(I((\xi, \zeta,)\eta)$$

$$- \mathbf{E}I(\zeta, \eta/\xi)) = 2n(I((\xi, \zeta), \eta) - I(\gamma, \beta)). \tag{11.2.110}$$

The proof of this lemma, which makes use of the result of Lemma 9.5.2, in no way differs from that of Lemma 11.2.2.

COROLLARY. Under the conditions of the lemma

$$I^{(2n)}_{(\xi\zeta)\eta} - I^{(2n)}_{\gamma\beta} = I^{(2n)}_{\nu\eta} - I^{(2n)}_{\gamma\beta} \leqslant 2n\, g(2n)(I((\xi, \zeta), \eta) - \mathbf{E}I(\zeta, \eta/\xi)). \tag{11.2.111}$$

We will carry out the proof of the theorem for the case where ξ and η are non-generalized processes. The extension of the theorem to generalized processes, using formula (10.1.20), is obvious.

Let $\xi_j(t) = \alpha_j(t) + \beta_j(t)$, $j = 1, \ldots, l$ be the decomposition of the process ξ into its regular and singular components $\alpha = \{\alpha(t)\} = \{(\alpha_1(t), \ldots, \alpha_{(l)}(t))\}$ and $\beta = \{\beta(t)\} = \{(\beta_1(t), \ldots, \beta_{(l)}(t))\}$ respectively, and let $\gamma = \{\gamma_1(t), \ldots, \gamma_m(t))\}$ be the gaussian process consisting of the perpendiculars $\gamma_j(t)$, $j = 1, \ldots, m$, $-\infty < t < \infty$, from $\eta_j(t)$ onto B_β. Since the spaces B_β and $B_{\alpha T}$ are orthogonal and $B_\beta, B_{\alpha T} \subseteq B_{\xi T}$, the perpendiculars $\hat{\alpha}_j(t)$ and $\hat{\gamma}_k(t)$ from $\alpha_j(t)$ and $\gamma_k(t)$ onto B_{α^0} coincide with the perpendiculars $\hat{\xi}_j(t)$ and $\hat{\eta}_k(t)$ from $\xi_j(t)$ and $\eta_k(t)$ onto $B_{\xi^0} = B_{(\beta, \alpha^0)}$. Therefore

$$I^{(2n)}_{\hat{\xi}^T_0 \hat{\eta}^T_0} = I^{(2n)}_{\hat{\alpha}^T_0 \hat{\gamma}^T_0} \tag{11.2.112}$$

and

$$T\vec{I}(\xi, \eta) = \mathbf{E}I(\xi^T_0, \eta/\xi^0) = I(\hat{\xi}^T_0, \hat{\eta}) = I(\hat{\alpha}^T_0, \hat{\gamma}) = \mathbf{E}I(\alpha^T_0, \gamma/\alpha^0)$$

$$= T\vec{I}(\alpha, \gamma),$$

i.e.

$$\vec{I}(\xi, \eta) = \vec{I}(\alpha, \gamma). \tag{11.2.113}$$

Since the process α is regular, by Theorem 10.4.1 $\vec{I}(\alpha, \gamma) = L_{\alpha\gamma}$. Comparing this equality with equations (11.2.107) and (11.2.113), we find that

$$\frac{1}{2\pi} \int \log \frac{\det A_{\tilde{\xi}}(\lambda) \det A_{\tilde{\eta}}(\lambda)}{\det A_{\tilde{\xi}\tilde{\eta}}(\lambda)} d\lambda$$

$$= L_{\xi\eta} = L_{\alpha\gamma} = \frac{1}{2\pi} \int \log \frac{\det A_{\tilde{\alpha}}(\lambda) \det A_{\tilde{\gamma}}(\lambda)}{\det A_{\tilde{\alpha}\tilde{\gamma}}(\lambda)} d\lambda. \tag{11.2.114}$$

But by Corollary 3 of Lemma 10.1.5

$$\frac{\det A_{\tilde{\xi}\tilde{\eta}}(\lambda)}{\det A_{\tilde{\xi}}(\lambda) \det A_{\tilde{\eta}}(\lambda)} \leqslant \frac{\det A_{\tilde{\alpha}\tilde{\gamma}}(\lambda)}{\det A_{\tilde{\alpha}}(\lambda) \det A_{\tilde{\gamma}}(\lambda)} \leqslant 1.$$

This relation together with equation (11.2.114) shows that

$$\frac{\det A_{\tilde{\xi}\tilde{\eta}}(\lambda)}{\det A_{\tilde{\xi}}(\lambda) \det A_{\tilde{\eta}}(\lambda)} = \frac{\det A_{\tilde{\alpha}\tilde{\gamma}}(\lambda)}{\det A_{\tilde{\alpha}}(\lambda) \det A_{\tilde{\gamma}}(\lambda)}. \tag{11.2.115}$$

At the same time, from (11.2.115) and Corollary 3 of Lemma 10.1.5 it follows that

$$\sum_j |r_{\xi'_j\eta'_j}(\lambda)|^{2n} = \sum_j |r_{\alpha'_j\gamma'_j}(\lambda)|^{2n}, \qquad (11.2.116)$$

where $\alpha' = (\alpha'_1, \ldots, \alpha'_{(l)})$ and $\gamma' = (\gamma'_1, \ldots, \gamma'_m)$ are the processes corresponding to the pair (α, γ), as given by Lemma 10.1.2.

Formulas (11.2.112) and (11.2.116) show that it is sufficient to prove the theorem for the process (α, γ), in other words, to study only the case in which the process ξ is regular. We introduce a stationary gaussian Markov process $\nu_j = \{\nu_j(t)\}, j = 1, \ldots, p$ defined by

$$\nu_j(t) = \sum_{\tau=0}^{\infty} e^{-\tau}\omega_j(t - \tau) \qquad (11.2.117)$$

if ξ is a discrete-parameter process, and by

$$\nu_j(t) = \int_0^{\infty} e^{-\tau} d_\tau \omega_j(t - \tau) \qquad (11.2.118)$$

if ξ is a continuous-parameter process, where $\omega_j(t), j = 1, \ldots, p$ is the gaussian process appearing in the decomposition (10.1.40) or (10.1.41) of the regular process α. Obviously (11.2.117) and (11.2.118) are decompositions of the form (10.1.40) and (10.1.41) for the gaussian Markov process $\nu = (\nu_1, \ldots, \nu_p)$. Since for $T > 0$ $B_{\alpha T} = B_{\omega T}$ and $B_{\nu T} = B_{\omega T}$, then $B_{\alpha T} = B_{\nu T}$. Therefore:

$$I^{(2n)}_{\hat{\alpha}_0^T \hat{\gamma}_0^T} = I^{(2n)}_{\hat{\nu}_0^T \hat{\gamma}_0^T}, \qquad (11.2.119)$$

where $\hat{\nu} = \{(\hat{\nu}_1(t), \ldots, \hat{\nu}_p(t))\}$ is the gaussian process consisting of the perpendiculars from $\nu_j(t), j = 1, \ldots, p$ onto $B_{\alpha 0} = B_{\nu 0}$,

$$\vec{TI}(\alpha, \gamma) = \mathbf{E}I(\alpha_0^T, \gamma/\alpha^0) = \mathbf{E}I(\nu_0^T, \gamma/\nu^0) = \vec{TI}(\nu, \gamma),$$

i.e.,

$$\vec{I}(\alpha, \gamma) = \vec{I}(\nu, \gamma), \qquad (11.2.120)$$

and

$$\alpha' = (\alpha'_1, \ldots, \alpha'_l), \qquad \gamma' = (\gamma'_1, \ldots, \gamma'_m),$$

are the random processes defined by Lemma 10.1.2, corresponding to the pair (α, γ) as well as the pair (ν, γ), and consequently

$$L_{\alpha\gamma} = L_{\nu\gamma}, \quad Q^{(n)}_{\alpha\gamma} = Q^{(n)}_{\nu\gamma}. \tag{11.2.121}$$

Formulas (11.2.119)–(11.2.121) show that the theorem will be proved if we can establish it for the pair (ν, γ). But for the gaussian Markov process ν.

$$I(\nu^0, \nu_T) < \infty \text{ and } \tilde{I}(\nu, \gamma) = \bar{I}(\nu, \gamma) = \vec{I}(\nu, \gamma) = L_{\nu\gamma} \tag{11.2.122}$$

for every $T > 0$. According to formula (3.6.3)

$$I(\nu_S^{S+T}, \gamma_S^{S+T}) \leqslant I(\nu_S^{S+T}, (\nu_0, \gamma)) = I(\nu_S^{S+T}, \nu_0)$$

$$+ \mathbf{E}I(\nu_S^{S+T}, \gamma/\nu^0) = I(\nu_S^{S+T}, \nu^0)$$

$$+ I(\hat{\nu}_S^{S+T}, \hat{\gamma}) \leqslant I(\nu_S^{S+T}, \nu^0) + (S + T)\vec{I}(\nu, \gamma); \; 0 < S < T.$$

Dividing every term by T and letting $T \to \infty$, we obtain, in view of (11.2.122)

$$L_{\nu\gamma} = \bar{I}(\nu, \gamma) \leqslant \lim_{T\to\infty} \frac{1}{T} I(\nu_S^{S+T}, (\nu^0, \gamma)) = \lim_{T\to\infty} \frac{1}{T}\mathbf{E}I(\nu_S^{S+T}, \gamma/\nu^0)$$

$$= \lim_{T\to\infty} \frac{1}{T} I(\hat{\nu}_S^{S+T}, \hat{\gamma}) \leqslant \vec{I}(\nu, \gamma) = L_{\nu\gamma}.$$

Using Lemmas 11.2.2 and 11.2.4, and the inequality for the absolute value of a sum, we see that

$$\overline{\lim_{T\to\infty}} \frac{1}{T} \left| I^{(2n)}_{\nu_S^{S+T}\gamma_S^{S+T}} - I^{(2n)}_{\hat{\nu}_S^{S+T}\hat{\gamma}} \right| \leqslant \overline{\lim_{T\to\infty}} \frac{1}{T}\left[\left(I^{(2n)}_{\nu_S^{S+T}(\gamma\nu^0)} - I^{(2n)}_{\nu_S^{S+T}\gamma_S^{S+T}}\right)\right.$$

$$\left. + \left(I^{(2n)}_{\nu_S^T(\gamma\nu^0)} - I^{(2n)}_{\hat{\nu}_S^{S+T}\hat{\gamma}}\right)\right] \leqslant 2ng(2n) \lim_{T\to\infty} \frac{1}{T}\,[I(\nu_S^{S+T}, (\gamma, \nu^0))$$

$$- I(\nu_S^{S+T}, \gamma_S^{S+T})) + (I(\nu_S^{S+T}, (\gamma, \nu^0)) - I(\hat{\nu}_S^{S+T}, \hat{\gamma}))] = 0$$

and

$$\overline{\lim_{T\to\infty}} \frac{1}{T} \left| I^{(2n)}_{\hat{\nu}_S^{S+T}\hat{\gamma}_S^{S+T}} - I^{(2n)}_{\hat{\nu}_S^{S+T}\hat{\gamma}} \right| \leqslant 2ng(2n) \lim_{T\to\infty} \frac{1}{T}(I(\hat{\nu}_0^{S+T}, \hat{\gamma}) - I(\hat{\nu}_S^{S+T}, \hat{\gamma}))$$

$$= 2n\, g(2n) \lim_{T\to\infty} \frac{1}{T}\mathbf{E}I(\nu_0^T, \gamma/\,\nu^0) - I(\hat{\nu}_S^{S+T}, \hat{\gamma}))$$

$$= 2n\, g(2n)(L_{\nu\gamma} - L_{\nu\gamma}) = 0.$$

Keeping in mind that Theorem 11.2.2 holds for the pair (ν, γ), we obtain from these relations that

$$\lim_{T\to\infty} \frac{1}{T+S} I^{(2n)}_{\hat{\nu}_0^{S+T}\hat{\gamma}} = \lim_{T\to\infty} \frac{1}{T} I^{(2n)}_{\hat{\nu}_0^T\hat{\gamma}} = \lim_{T\to\infty} \frac{1}{T}\, I^{(2n)}_{\nu_0^T\gamma_0^T} = g(2n)Q^{(2n)}_{\nu\gamma},$$

which proves the theorem.

COROLLARY. In the notation of the statement of the theorem, always

$$\vec{I}^{(2n)}_{\xi\eta} = \lim_{T\to\infty} \frac{1}{T} I^{(2n)}_{\hat{\xi}^{T}_{-\delta}\hat{\eta}} \leqslant g(2n) Q^{(2n)}_{\xi\eta}. \tag{11.2.123}$$

PROOF. By Corollary 3 of Lemma 10.1.5 $|r_{\xi'_j\eta'_j}(\lambda)|^2 \geqslant |r_{\alpha'_j\gamma'_j}(\lambda)|^2$ and therefore $Q^{(2n)}_{\xi\eta} \geqslant Q^{(2n)}_{\alpha\gamma}$. Since $\vec{I}(\alpha,\gamma) = L_{\alpha\gamma}$, then, as has been proved,

$$\vec{I}^{(2n)}_{\alpha\gamma} = g(2n) Q^{(2n)}_{\alpha\gamma} \leqslant g(2n) Q^{(2n)}_{\xi\eta}.$$

Comparing this relation with (11.2.112), we obtain (11.2.123).

11.3. ENTROPY STABILITY AND RATE OF CHANGE OF THE VARIANCE OF THE ENTROPY DENSITY

We introduce some notation. Let $\xi = \{(\xi_1(\cdot), \ldots, \xi_n(\cdot))\}$ and $\eta = \{(\eta_1(\cdot), \ldots, \eta_n(\cdot))\}$ be n-dimensional stationary gaussian processes, and $\xi' = \{(\xi'_1(\cdot), \ldots, \xi'_n(\cdot))\}$ and $\eta' = \{(\eta'_1(\cdot), \ldots, \eta'_n(\cdot))\}$ be the corresponding gaussian processes as defined by Lemma 10.5.1. We put

$$\vartheta^{(2n)}_{\xi\eta} = \frac{1}{2\pi} \sum_j \int \left(\frac{f_{\xi'_j\xi'_j}(\lambda)}{f_{\eta'_j\eta'_j}(\lambda)} - 1\right)^2 d\lambda, \tag{11.3.1}$$

where the limits of integration are $0, \pi$ or $0, \infty$ according to whether ξ, η are discrete-parameter processes or continuous-parameter or generalized processes. For $n = 1$ formula (11.3.1) becomes

$$\vartheta^{(2n)}_{\xi\eta} = \frac{1}{2\pi} \int \left(\frac{f_{\xi\xi}(\lambda)}{f_{\eta\eta}(\lambda)} - 1\right)^2 d\lambda. \tag{11.3.2}$$

THEOREM 11.3.1. Let $\xi = \{(\xi_1(\cdot), \ldots, \xi_n(\cdot))\}$ and $\eta = (\eta_1(\cdot), \ldots, \eta_n(\cdot))$ be n-dimensional stationary gaussian processes with absolutely continuous spectral and joint spectral functions. Then if conditions (10.5.11) and (10.5.12) are fulfilled, the random process ξ will be entropy stable with respect to the random process η. Moreover, if also

$$\bar{H}_\eta(\xi) = \lim_{T\to\infty} \frac{1}{T} H_{\eta_0^T}(\xi_0^T) = \vartheta_{\xi\eta} < \infty \tag{11.3.3}$$

then

$$\bar{D}_\eta(\xi) = \lim_{T\to\infty} \frac{1}{T} Dh_{\eta_0^T}(\xi_0^T) = \lim_{T\to\infty} \frac{1}{T} \mathbf{E}(h_{\eta_0^T}(\xi_0^T) - H_{\eta_0^T}(\xi_0^T))^2 = \ni_{\xi\eta}^{(2)} \tag{11.3.4}$$

and the distribution of the entropy density $h_{\eta_0^T}(\xi_0^T)$, *converges to a normal distribution as* $T \to \infty$, *i.e.*

$$\lim_{T\to\infty} \mathbf{P}\left\{a \leqslant \frac{h_{\eta_0^T}(\xi_0^T) - H_{\eta_0^T}(\xi_0^T)}{\sqrt{Dh_{\eta_0^T}(\xi_0^T)}} \leqslant b\right\} = \frac{1}{\sqrt{2\pi}} \int_a^b e^{-\frac{x^2}{2}} dx. \tag{11.3.5}$$

In the case where $n = 1$, conditions (10.5.11) and (10.5.12) reduce to conditions (10.5.8) and (10.5.10).

Remark. It can be shown that always

$$\varliminf_{T\to\infty} \frac{1}{T} Dh_{\eta_0^T}(\xi_0^T) = \varliminf_{T\to\infty} \frac{1}{T} \mathbf{E}(h_{\eta_0^T}(\xi_0^T) - H_{\eta_0^T}(\xi_0^T))^2 \geqslant \ni_{\xi\eta}^{(2)}. \tag{11.3.6}$$

COROLLARY. *If* $0 < \ni_{\xi\eta}, \ni_{\xi\eta}^{(2)} < \infty$, *then if conditions (10.5.11), (10.5.12) and (11.3.3) are satisfied*

$$\lim_{T\to\infty} \mathbf{P}\left\{a \leqslant \frac{h_{\eta_0^T}(\xi_0^T) - H_{\eta_0^T}(\xi_0^T)}{\sqrt{T\ni_{\xi\eta}^{(2)}}} \leqslant b\right\} = \frac{1}{\sqrt{2\pi}} \int_a^b e^{-\frac{x^2}{2}} dx. \tag{11.3.7}$$

The result of Theorem 11.3.1 can be extended to a much wider class of gaussian processes, for example, those of the form (10.5.14).

THEOREM 11.5.2. *Let* $\xi = \{\xi(t)\}$ *and* $\eta = \{\eta(t)\}$ *be one-dimensional non-generalized stationary gaussian processes, let*

$$\mathbf{E}\xi(t) = m_\xi, \mathbf{E}\eta(t) = m_\eta,$$

and let

$$\nu(t) = \xi(t) - m_\xi, \vartheta(t) = \eta(t) - m_\eta, \nu = \{\nu(t)\}, \vartheta = \{\vartheta(t)\}.$$

Then if condition (10.5.12) is fullfilled, if $\bar{H}_\vartheta(\nu) = \ni_{\nu\vartheta} = \ni_{\xi\eta}$ *and if the spectral functions of the processes* ξ η *have third derivatives which are continuous at* $\lambda = 0$, *the process* ξ *will be entropy stable with respect to the process* η,

$$\overline{D}_\eta(\xi) = \lim_{T\to\infty} \frac{1}{T} D\, h_{\eta_0^T}(\xi_0^T) = \lim_{T\to\infty} \frac{1}{T} \mathbf{E}(h_{\eta_0^T}(\xi_0^T) - H_{\eta_0^T}(\xi_0^T))^2$$

$$= \ni_{\xi\eta}^{(2)} + \frac{(m_\xi - m_\eta)^2 f_{\xi\xi}(0)}{2\pi\, f_{\eta\eta}^2(0)}, \qquad (11.3.8)$$

and the distribution of the entropy density $h_{\eta_0^T}(\xi_0^T)$ *converges to a normal distribution as* $T \to \infty$.

Example. Let $\eta(t) = \xi(t) + c$; then

$$\overline{D}_\eta(\xi) = \frac{|c|^2 f_{\xi\xi}(0)}{2\pi\, f_{\eta\eta}^2(0)}. \qquad (11.3.9)$$

Bibliography

1. Cramer, H., **Mathematical Methods of Statistics**, Princeton Univ. Press, Princeton, N.J. (1946).
2. Dobrushin, R.L., "General Formulation of Shannon's Basic Theorems of the Theory of Information," Dokl. Akad. Nauk SSSR, vol. 126, 474 (1959).
3. Dobrushin, R.L., "General Formulation of Shannon's Basic Theorems of the Theory of Information," Usp. Mat. Nauk, 14, No. 6, vol. 14, no. 6, 3-104 (1959). German translation: Arbeiten zur Informationstheorie IV, VEB Deutscher Verlag der Wissenschaften, Berlin 1963.
4. Doob, J.L., **Stochastic Processes**, John Wiley and Sons, Inc., New York (1953).
5. Feinstein, A., "A New Basic Theorem of Information Theory," Trans. I.R.E., PGIT-4, 2-22 (1954).
6. Feldman, J., "Equivalence and Perpendicularity of Gaussian Processes," Pac. Jour. Math., vol. 8, No. 4, 699-708 (1958).
7. Gelfand, I.M., "Generalized Random Processes," Dokl. Akad. Nauk SSSR, vol. 100, no. 5, 853-856 (1955).

7a. Gelfand, I.M. and N. Ya. Vilenkin, "Generalized Functions," vol. 4., "Some Applications of Harmonic Analysis," Moscow, 1961. English translation by Academic Press, New York City (in press).

8. Gelfand, I.M., A.N.Kolmogorov and A.M.Yaglom, "On the General Definitions of Quantity of Information," Dokl. Akad. Nauk, vol. 111, no. 4, 745-748 (1956).
9. Gelfand, I.M. and A.M.Yaglom, "Calculation of the Amount of Information About a Random Function Contained in Another Such Function," Usp. Mat. Nauk, vol. 12, no. 1, 3-52 (1957). English translation in American Mathematical Society Translations, Providence, R.I. Series 2, vol. 12 (1959).
10. Gnedenko, B.V. and A.N.Kolmogorov, **Limit Distributions for Sums of Independent Random Variables**, translated by K.L. Chung, Addison-Wesley Publishing Company, Inc., Reading, Mass. (1954).
11. Hajek, J., "On a Property of Arbitrary Normally Distributed Stochastic Processes," Czech. Math. Jour., vol. 8, 610-618 (1958). English translation in **Selected Translations in Mathematical Statistics and Probability,** Vol. 1, Providence, R.I., 1961.

12. Halmos, P.R., **Measure Theory**, van Nostrand Company, Inc., Princeton, N.J. (1950).
13. Hotelling, H., "Relation Between Two Sets of Variates," Biometrica 28, 321-377 (1935).
14. Ito, K., "Stationary Random Distributions," Mem. Coll. Sci. Univ. Kyoto, Ser. A, 28, 209-223 (1954).
15. Khinchin, A.I., "The Entropy Concept in Probability Theory," Usp. Mat. Nauk, vol. 8, no. 3, 3-20 (1953). English translation of this and following article under title **Mathematical Foundations of Information Theory**, by A.I.Khinchin, Dover Publications, Inc., New York (1957).
16. Khinchin, A.I., "On the Fundamental Theorems of Information Theory," Usp. Mat. Nauk, vol. 11, no. 1, 17-75 (1956). English translation: see preceding reference.
17. Kolmogorov, A.N., "Stationary Sequences in Hilbert Space," Bul. Moscow State Univ., 2, no. 6 (1941).
18. Kolmogorov, A.N., "Theory of the Transmission of Information," Proceedings of the session on scientific problems of automation, Izd. Akad. Nauk SSSR (1956).
19. Kolmogorov, A.N., A.M.Yaglom and I.M.Gelfand, "Quantity of Information and Entropy for Continuous Distributions," Proc. Third All-Union Mathematics Conference, vol. 3, Izd. Akad. Nauk SSSR (1956).
20. Kullback, S., **Information Theory and Statistics**, John Wiley and Sons, Inc. New York (1959).
21. McMillan, B., "The Basic Theorems of Information Theory," Ann. Math. Stat., vol. 24, 196-219 (1953).
22. Obukhov, A.M., "Normally Correlated Vectors," Izv. Akad. Nauk SSSR, Section on Mathematics and Natural Sciences, no. 3, 339-370 (1938).
23. Obukhov, A.M., "Correlation Theory of Vectors," Uchen. Zap. Moscow State Univ., Mathematics section, no. 45, 73-92 (1940).
24. Perez, A., "Notions generalisees d'incertitude, d'entropie et d'information du point de vue de la theorie de martingales," Transactions of the First Prague Conference on Information Theory, Statistical Decision Functions, Random Processes, Publishing House, Czech. Acad. Sci., Prague, 183-208 (1957).
25. Perez, A., "Sur la theorie de l'information dans le cas d'un alphabet abstrait," ibid., 209-244.
26. Perez, A., "Sur la convergence des incretitudes, entropies et informations echantillon (sample) vers leurs valeurs vraies," ibid., 245-252.
27. Perez, A., "Information Theory with Abstract Alphabets." **Theory of Probability and its Applications**, vol. 4, no. 1, (1959).

28. Pinsker, M.S., "Amount of Information About a Gaussian Random Process Contained in a Second Process Which is Stationarily Correlated with It," Dokl. Akad. Nauk SSSR, vol. 99, no. 2, 213-216 (1954).
29. Pinsker, M.S., "Amount of Information About a Stationary Random Process Contained in Another Stationary Process," Proc. Third All-Union Mathematics Conference, vol. 3, Izd. Akad. Nauk SSSR (1956).
30. Pinsker, M.S., "Theory of Curves in Hilbert Space Which Have Stationary n-th Increments," Izv. Akad. Nauk SSSR, Ser. Mat., 19, 319-344 (1955).
31. Pinsker, M.S., "Calculation and Estimation of the Quantity of Information, the Capacity of a Channel and the Rate of Production of Information, in Terms of the Second Moments of the Distributions," Dissertation, 1957.
32. Pinsker, M.S., "Extrapolation of Vector Random Processes and the Amount of Information Contained in One Stationary Vector Random Process Relative to Another Which is Stationarily Correlated with It," Dokl. Akad. Nauk SSSR, vol. 121, no. 1, 49-51 (1958).
33. Rosenblatt-Rot, M., "Entropy of Stochastic Processes," Dokl. Akad. Nauk SSSR, vol. 112, no. 1, 16-19 (1957).
34. Shannon, C.E., "Communication in the Presence of Noise," Proc. I.R.E., vol. 37, no. 1, 10-21 (1949).
35. Shannon, C.E., "Certain Results in Coding Theory for Noisy Channels," Inf. and Control, vol. 1, no. 1, 6-25 (1957).
36. Shannon, C.E. and W.Weaver, **The Mathematical Theory of Communication**, Univ. of Illinois Press, Urbana (1949).
37. Slepian, D., "Comments on the Detection of Gaussian Signals in Gaussian Noise," Trans. I.R.E., PGIT 4, no. 2, 65 (1958).
38. Vinokurov, V.G., "The Condition of Regularity of Random Processes," Dokl. Akad. Nauk SSSR, vol. 113, no. 5, 959-961 (1957).
39. Yaglom, A.M., **An Introduction to the Theory of Stationary Random Functions**, revised English edition, translated by R.A.Silverman, Prentice-Hall, Inc., Englewood Cliffs, N.J. (1962).
40. Zasukhin, V.N., "On the Theory of Multi-Dimensional Random Processes," Dokl. Akad. Nauk SSSR, vol. 33, 435-437 (1941).

Index